College Algebra

College Algebra

THURMAN S. PETERSON, Ph.D.

Associate Professor of Mathematics
University of Oregon

HARPER & BROTHERS PUBLISHERS

NEW YORK AND LONDON

COLLEGE ALGEBRA

Contents

Preface

This book is designed to serve as a text for college students who have had at least one year of secondary school algebra. Being intended for students with somewhat varied preparation, a complete and thorough review of elementary algebra is included in the initial chapters. This material is rigorously and concisely presented in order to provide the student with a clear understanding of the basic principles of algebra.*

Purpose. Fundamentally the objectives of the text are two-fold: first, to serve as a foundation course in algebra preparing for advanced college mathematics, and second, to serve as a terminal course in algebra for non-scientific studies. In order to serve the first purpose, all definitions, theorems, and general procedures are accurately presented with numerous illustrations of points of rigor and techniques of computation. In order to serve the second purpose, the applied value of algebra has been stressed throughout the text. In this connection a number of the advanced chapters are devoted solely to the introduction of some applied subjects. These chapters, for the most part, are independent of one another, and they may be selected in accordance with the interests of different classes.

Special Features. The fundamental principles of algebra are clearly stated in elementary terms. Numerous illustrations and illustrative examples are presented in an endeavor to make the text as independent of classroom work as possible.

Each exercise provides an abundance of carefully graded problems suitable for students of all abilities. These exercises contain adequate material for classroom discussion and testing as well as for outside preparation.

---

* A more extensive treatment of elementary and intermediate algebra will be found in the author's *Intermediate Algebra for College Students*, Harper & Brothers.

The answers to the odd-numbered problems are included in the text, and the answers to the even-numbered problems can be obtained in a separate pamphlet from the publisher on request of an instructor.

The material ordinarily included under the title of theory of equations has been divided into two chapters. The first chapter, called "Polynomials and Equations," is an independent unit in itself and contains the basic elements of the theory of equations. The second chapter, called "Theory of Equations," presents a more advanced treatment of equations, and this chapter may be omitted in a brief course.

In the chapter on determinants the subject of *eliminants* has been stressed in order to illustrate the effective use of determinants in other problems besides those of solving systems of linear equations. A discussion of second- and third-order determinants is included in the early part of the text.

In the chapter on mathematical induction several varieties of inductive problems are presented. The procedures illustrate more clearly the power and thought behind an inductive proof.

Many items of technical interest are illustrated throughout the text. Among these might be mentioned an alternate method for summing an infinite repeating decimal, a formula for the square roots of complex numbers in rectangular form, and an optional method, which is often simpler, for evaluating the constants in partial fractions.

A final chapter on statistical methods is included in the text to serve as introductory material for students whose major fields of study require an elementary knowledge of statistics.

The author wishes to take this opportunity to express his appreciation to his many friends and colleagues who have so graciously criticized and assisted in the preparation of this text. In particular, he gratefully acknowledges his indebtedness to Professor Frank E. Wood for his careful reading of the manuscript and his many suggestions and criticisms.

T. S. PETERSON

UNIVERSITY OF OREGON
May 31, 1946

College Algebra

CHAPTER 1

Fundamental Operations

1. Numbers. Of the various numbers considered in the study of arithmetic, the whole numbers 1, 2, 3, ⋯ are called the **natural numbers** or **integers**; the quotient of any two integers, such as $\frac{4}{1}$ or $\frac{5}{7}$, is called a **rational number;** and non-rational numbers, such as $\sqrt{2}$ or π, are called **irrational numbers.** These numbers, together with zero, form the **number system of arithmetic.**

If the number system of arithmetic is enlarged by including the **negative** rational and irrational numbers, we obtain what is called the **real number system.**

NOTE. These numbers are called *real* in order to distinguish them from *imaginary* and *complex* numbers, which are considered later in the book.

In algebra, as in arithmetic, the quantities with which we deal are numbers. But whereas the numbers used in arithmetic are represented by figures, each of which has a definite value, in algebra they are represented by other symbols (usually letters of the alphabet) which may have any numerical values assigned to them or whose numerical values are to be found. Such quantities are called **general** or **literal numbers.**

2. Fundamental Operations. The fundamental operations of algebra, as for arithmetic, are addition, subtraction, multiplication, and division.

I. *Addition.* The sign $+$ is used to indicate addition; the numbers added are called **addends,** and the result is called the

sum. The operation of addition is assumed to satisfy the following laws:

1. Commutative Law. *The sum of two numbers is the same in whatever order they are added. Symbolically,* $a + b = b + a$.

2. Associative Law. *The sum of three or more numbers is the same in whatever order they are grouped. Symbolically,*

$$a + (b + c) = (a + b) + c.$$

NOTE 1. The **absolute** or **numerical value** of a number x is denoted by $|x|$ and it is the value of x without regard to its sign. Thus, $|+5| = 5$ and $|-5| = 5$.

Rule of Signs. *(1) To add two numbers with like signs, add their absolute values and prefix the result with their common sign.*

(2) To add two numbers with unlike signs, subtract their absolute values and prefix the result with the sign of the number having the greater absolute value.

Illustration 1. $(-2) + (-3) = -5$, $(-7) + (+3) = -4$.

II. *Subtraction.* To subtract b from a means to find a number x such that $a = b + x$. The sign $-$ is used to indicate subtraction. Thus, $a - b = x$; a is called the **minuend,** b the **subtrahend,** and x the **difference.**

Rule of Signs. *To subtract two numbers, change the sign of the subtrahend and add to the minuend.*

Illustration 2. $(+3) - (-2) = (+3) + (+2) = +5$,
$(+4) - (+5) = (+4) + (-5) = -1$.

NOTE 2. If the difference $(a - b)$ is positive, we say that *a is greater than b* and write $a > b$; if $(a - b)$ is negative, we say that *a is less than b* and write $a < b$. In either case a is not equal to b; this is written $a \neq b$.

III. *Multiplication.* The sign $\times$ or $\cdot$ is used to indicate multiplication; the numbers multiplied are called **factors,** and the result is called the **product.**

NOTE 3. A product $a \cdot b$ is often written with no sign between; thus, $ab = a \cdot b$.

The operation of multiplication is assumed to satisfy the following laws:

1. Commutative Law. *The product of two numbers is the same in whatever order they are multiplied. Symbolically,* $ab = ba$.

2. Associative Law. *The product of three or more numbers is the same in whatever order they are grouped. Symbolically,* $a(bc) = (ab)c$.

3. Distributive Law. *The product of a number and a sum of numbers is the same as the sum of the products obtained in multiplying each number of the sum by the first number. Symbolically,* $a(b + c) = ab + ac$.

Rule of Signs. *To multiply two numbers, multiply their absolute values and prefix* $+$ *or* $-$ *according as they have like or unlike signs.*

Illustration 3. $(-2)(-3) = +6$, $(-5)(+3) = -15$.

IV. *Division.* To divide a by b means to find a number x such that $a = bx$. The sign $\div$ or $/$ is used to indicate division. Thus, $a \div b = x$; a is called the **dividend,** b the **divisor,** and x the **quotient.**

NOTE 4. If $b = 0$, no number x can be found such that $a = 0 \cdot x$. Hence, **division by zero is excluded from algebra.**

Rule of Signs. *To divide two numbers, divide their absolute values and prefix* $+$ *or* $-$ *according as they have like or unlike signs.*

Illustration 4. $(-6) \div (+2) = -3$, $(-12)/(-3) = +4$.

EXERCISE 1

Insert the proper inequality sign, $>$ or $<$, between the following:

1. 3 and 7. **2.** 5 and 0. **3.** -4 and 1. **4.** -5 and -6.

5. $\frac{1}{2}$ and $-\frac{1}{2}$. **6.** $\frac{26}{69}$ and $\frac{19}{51}$. **7.** 1.42 and $\sqrt{2}$. **8.** π and $\frac{22}{7}$.

9. Arrange the following numbers in order of increasing magnitude:

$$2, \ -2\tfrac{1}{2}, \ \tfrac{1}{2}\pi, \ -\sqrt{7}, \ 0, \text{ and } \tfrac{19}{21}.$$

10. Evaluate the absolute values: (*a*) $|-2|$, (*b*) $|+\frac{3}{4}|$, (*c*) $|-\pi|$, (*d*) $|-0.3|$.

Evaluate the following numerical expressions:

11. $(-9) + (+4)$.   **12.** $(-7) + (-2)$.   **13.** $(+5) + (-5)$.
14. $(-4) - (+3)$.   **15.** $(+2) - (-6)$.   **16.** $(-3) - (-5)$.
17. $(-2) \times (+3)$.   **18.** $(-4) \times (-3)$.   **19.** $(+5) \times (-5)$.
20. $(-6) \div (-2)$.   **21.** $(-8) \div (+2)$.   **22.** $(+9) \div (-3)$.
23. $(-2)(-3)(-4)(+5)$.   **24.** $(-2)(-3) - (-4)(-5)$.
25. $(-6)(-8)/(-4)(+3)$.   **26.** $[(-2) - (-3)] \cdot [5 - 10]$.
27. $\dfrac{(+5) - (-5)}{(-3) + (-2)}$.   **28.** $\dfrac{22 - (-14)}{-15 - (-6)}$.
29. $\dfrac{(-4)(-3)}{+6} - \dfrac{-36}{+2(-9)}$.   **30.** $\dfrac{(-1)(-18)}{11 - (+2)} + \dfrac{-6-9}{(-3)(-5)}$.

3. Powers and Exponents. A **power** of a quantity is the product obtained in multiplying the quantity by itself any number of times. Thus, $a \cdot a \cdot a \cdots$ to n factors is the **nth power of a** and is written a^n. The index n is called the **exponent** of the power and a is called the **base.**

NOTE. Observe that a^1 means a. Hence, if the exponent of a quantity is not written, it is understood to be 1.

Illustration. $-(5)^2 = -25$, $(-5)^2 = 25$, $5 \cdot 2^3 = 5 \cdot 8 = 40$.

The following rules, whose proofs are given in a later chapter, govern the use of exponents:

I. $a^m \cdot a^n = a^{m+n}$,   thus, $x^5 \cdot x^3 = x^8$.
II. If $a \neq 0$,
　　$a^m/a^n = a^{m-n}$, $m > n$;   thus, $x^7/x^4 = x^3$.
　　$a^m/a^n = 1/a^{n-m}$, $m < n$;   thus, $x^2/x^6 = 1/x^4$.
III. $(a^m)^n = a^{mn}$;   thus, $(x^2)^3 = x^6$.
IV. $(ab)^n = a^n b^n$;   thus, $(3\,x^2)^3 = 3^3 x^6 = 27\,x^6$.
V. If $b \neq 0$,
　　$(a/b)^n = a^n/b^n$;   thus, $(x^2/y^3)^4 = x^8/y^{12}$.

4. Algebraic Expressions. Any combination of numbers, numerical or general, which represents a number, is called an **algebraic expression.** If an expression consists of distinct parts connected by plus and minus signs, it is called an **algebraic sum,** and each part, with the sign preceding it, is called a **term** of the sum. If two or more terms have the same literal parts, they are called **similar** or **like terms.**

Illustration 1. In the algebraic sum $(2\,a - 3\,b + 5\,a)$, the terms are $2\,a$, $-3\,b$, and $5\,a$; and the first and last terms are similar.

An expression consisting of one term is called a **monomial,** and one consisting of two or more terms is called a **multinomial.** An expression of two terms is also called a **binomial,** and one of three terms a **trinomial.**

If two or more quantities are multiplied together to form a product, each of the quantities, or any product of them, is called a **factor** of the product. Any factor of a term is called the **coefficient** of the remaining part of the term. Thus, 3 is the numerical coefficient of $3\,ab$, and $3\,a$ is the literal coefficient of b.

An algebraic term is *integral* and *rational* in certain literal parts, if the term consists of positive integral powers of the letters multiplied by a coefficient not containing them, or if the term does not contain the letters.

Illustration 2. The terms $\frac{1}{2}\,x^2$, $-4\,x^3y^2$, and 7 are integral and rational in x and y. $5/x$ is *not* integral in x, and $2\sqrt{x}$ is *not* rational in x.

A multinomial in which each term is integral and rational is called a **polynomial.** Thus, $(6\,x^2y - 3\,xy^2z + 2\,x^2z^2 + 5)$ is a polynomial in x, y, and z. The exponent of a letter in a term is called the **degree** of the term in that letter. The sum of the exponents of all the letters in a term is called the **degree of the term,** and the **degree of a polynomial** is the same as that of the term of highest degree whose coefficient is not zero.

Illustration 3. The degree of $(5\,x^2y - 7\,x^3y^2 - 3)$ is 5, since the respective terms have the degrees 3, 5, and 0.

5. Symbols of Grouping. Parentheses ( ), brackets [ ], braces { }, and the vinculum ‾‾ are used to indicate that the terms which they contain are grouped together to form a single quantity.

Symbols of grouping may be inserted or removed according to the following rule:

Rule. (*1*) *When a grouping symbol is preceded by a plus sign, the symbol may be removed without altering the included terms.*

(*2*) *When a grouping symbol is preceded by a minus sign, the symbol may be removed if the sign of each of the included terms is changed.*

Illustration 1. $-(2x - y + 3) = -2x + y - 3$.

When one set of grouping symbols is contained within another, the innermost symbols should be removed first.

Illustration 2.
$$- [a - (2b - \overline{3a + b})] = - [a - (2b - 3a - b)]$$
$$= - [a - 2b + 3a + b] = -a + 2b - 3a - b = -4a + b.$$

EXERCISE 2

State the degree of each of the following polynomials, and give the degree of each term:

1. $4xy^2 - 3xy + 2x - 1$.   **2.** $5xyz + 2y^2 - 3xz - y$.
3. $2x - 3x^3 - x^2 + 7$.   **4.** $xy + yz + zx$.

5. In the expression $\frac{1}{3}\pi h r^2$, (*a*) what is the numerical coefficient? (*b*) What is the coefficient of h?

6. In the expression $2xy + \dfrac{3}{x} - 4x\sqrt{y}$, which terms are both integral and rational in x? in y?

Perform the indicated operations, using the rules of exponents:

7. $y^8 \cdot y^{10} \cdot y^5$.   **8.** $mn \cdot m^2n^3 \cdot m^2n$.   **9.** x^{11}/x^4.
10. a^3b/a^2b^2.   **11.** $(a^2)^4 \cdot (x^3)^3$.   **12.** $(-x^3y^4)^3$.
13. $(2x/3\,y^2)^3$.   **14.** $(mn)^2 \cdot (2\,m^2n)^3$.   **15.** $(x^2y^3)^3/(x^4y)^4$.
16. $(x^3y)^2 \cdot (x^2y^2)^3$.   **17.** $(b^3c^5)^3/(b^2c)^2$.   **18.** $(3\,p^2q)^3/(6\,pq^2)^2$.

Remove all grouping symbols and combine like terms:

19. $(4a - 3b) - (5a - b)$.   **20.** $(3x - 7) - (2x + 5)$.
21. $2x - [4 - (x - 2)]$.   **22.** $a - [a - (a - b)]$.
23. $(3m - 2n - 5) - (2m - 3n - 2)$.
24. $(a - b) - (3a - b) - (2a - 3b)$.
25. $x - [3x - (2x - \overline{3x + y})]$.
26. $(4a + 3) - \{6a - [(3a + 2) - (4a + 1)]\}$.
27. $\{[(6a + 5b) - 3b] - \overline{2a - 3b}\} - b$.

Enclose the last two terms within parentheses preceded by a minus sign; by a plus sign:

28. $a + b - c$.   **29.** $2x^2 - xy + y^2$.   **30.** $x^2 - y^2 + z^2$.

6. Addition and Subtraction. To add similar terms, we add their coefficients and take this sum as the coefficient of the common literal part. In an algebraic sum, the adding of similar terms is sometimes called **collecting terms.**

Illustration 1. Collecting terms in $(a - 5b + c + 4a + 4b - c)$, we have $(5a - b)$.

Rule for Addition. *Arrange the expressions in rows so that the like terms are in the same vertical columns; then add each column separately.*

Example 1. Find the sum of $2a - b + 5c$, $3a - 2c$, $b + c$.
Solution: Arranging according to the above rule:

$$
\begin{array}{l}
2a - b + 5c \\
3a \quad\quad - 2c \\
\quad\quad b + \quad c \\
\hline
5a \quad\quad + 4c
\end{array}
$$

NOTE 1. It is necessary that the sign $+$ precede the term $4c$ in order to indicate that it is to be added to $5a$ for the final result.

Rule for Subtraction. *Change the sign of every term in the subtrahend and add it to the other expression.*

NOTE 2. It is neither necessary nor advisable actually to change the signs of the terms in the subtrahend; the operation of changing signs should be performed *mentally.*

Example 2. Subtract $3x^2 - 7xy + 5y^2$ from $4x^2 - 3y^2$.
Solution: Arranging in vertical order, we have

$$
\begin{array}{l}
4x^2 \quad\quad - 3y^2 \\
3x^2 - 7xy + 5y^2 \\
\hline
x^2 + 7xy - 8y^2
\end{array}
$$

EXERCISE 3

Add:

1. $14x^2 - 10x - 1$
$5x^2 + 3x - 5$
$-x^2 - 2x - 3$

2. $6m - 5n - 3p$
$-4m + n + 6p$
$-7m + 4n - 4p$

3. $\frac{1}{2}x^2 + xy - \frac{2}{3}y^2$
$-\frac{1}{4}x^2 - \frac{1}{5}xy + \frac{1}{3}y^2$

4. $-\frac{1}{6}x + \frac{2}{3}y - z$
$\frac{1}{3}x - \frac{5}{6}y - \frac{1}{2}z$

5. $2.1x - 1.3y + 6.7$
$-3.2x + 1.6y - 4.8$

6. $-3.2a - 6.9b + c$
$1.9a - 2.1b - 3.6c$

   7. $2\,a - 3\,b + c$, $c - a - b$, and $4\,b + 2\,a - 5\,c$.

   8. $\frac{1}{3}\,x + \frac{1}{2}\,y - z$, $x + \frac{1}{3}\,z$, $-\frac{1}{3}\,y - \frac{1}{2}\,z$, and $\frac{1}{2}\,x + y - z$.

   9. $2\,x^2 - 3$, $\frac{1}{3} - \frac{1}{2}\,x^2 - \frac{1}{2}\,y^2$, $\frac{4}{5} - \frac{2}{3}\,x^2$, and $2\,y^2 + \frac{1}{3}$.

   10. $3.67\,b - 6.66\,a - 2.48\,c$, $9.01\,a - 4.76\,b + 5.55\,c$, and $2.81\,b - 3.07\,c - 4.19\,a$.

Subtract the second polynomial from the first:

11. $5\,x - 2\,y$; $4\,x - 7\,y$.   **12.** $-6\,a^2 + b^2$; $4\,a^2 - 3\,b^2$.

13. $4\,a^2 + 2\,a$; $-3\,a^2 + a$.   **14.** $-7\,y^2 + 6$; $-2\,y^2 + 6$.

   15. $4\,x^4 - 3\,x^3 - 2\,x + 1$; $3\,x^4 - x^3 - x^2$.

   16. $-x^3 - x^2 + 7\,x - 9$; $6\,x^2 + 7\,x - 8$.

   17. $\frac{1}{2}\,a + \frac{1}{3}\,b - \frac{1}{6}$; $\frac{1}{3}\,a - \frac{1}{2}\,b - \frac{2}{3}$.

   18. $\frac{3}{4}\,x - \frac{1}{2}\,y + \frac{1}{3}\,z$; $\frac{1}{3}\,x + \frac{1}{4}\,y - \frac{1}{2}\,z$.

   19. $2.5\,a - 6.3\,b - 9.1\,c$; $3.4\,a + 2.6\,b - 7.5\,c$.

   20. $-6.21\,p^2 + 3.27\,pq - 5.95\,q^2$; $9.27\,p^2 - 6.93\,q^2$.

   21. From $(6\,x^2 - 3\,x - 7)$ take the sum of $(x^3 + x + 1)$ and $(x - 3\,x^2 + 2)$.

   22. What expression must be subtracted from $(4\,a - 3\,b + 2\,c)$ so as to leave $(2\,a - 5\,b + c)$?

   23. Find the sum of $(2\,x - 5\,y + z)$ and $(3\,y - x)$, and subtract the result from $(z - 4\,y)$.

   24. Subtract $(5\,x^2 - 2\,x + 1)$ from unity, and add $(3\,x^2 - 2\,x)$.

   25. Increase $(2\,ab - 3\,ac + 4\,bc)$ by $(2\,ac - ab)$, then subtract $(ab + ac - bc)$ from this result.

   26. What must be added to $(5\,x^2 - 3)$ to obtain zero?

   27. What expression added to $(3\,a - 4\,c + b)$ gives the same result as that obtained in taking $(b + 2\,c - 3\,a)$ from $(2\,a - 4\,b + c)$?

   28. Subtract $(x^2 - xy)$ from zero, and add the difference to the sum of $(3\,x^2 - 5\,y^2)$ and $(xy - x^2 - y^2)$.

   29. Increase $(2\,x^2 + 3\,x - 1)$ by the excess of $(5 - 2\,x)$ over $(3 - x^2)$.

   30. What quantity is $(3\,a + 5\,b - c)$ greater than the sum of $(a - b)$ and $(c - 4\,a - 3\,b)$?

7. Multiplication. In accordance with the *distributive law for multiplication* the product of a monomial and a multinomial is found by multiplying each term of the multinomial by the monomial.

Illustration. $3\,a(4\,a^2 - 6\,ab + b) = 12\,a^3 - 18\,a^2b + 3\,ab$.

Rule for Multiplication. *The product of two multinomials is the algebraic sum of all the partial products obtained in multiplying each term of one multinomial by each term of the other.*

Example. Multiply $(3 x^2 - x - 2)$ by $(3 x - 4)$.

Solution: Arranging vertically, we have

$$
\begin{array}{ll}
 \quad 3 x^2 - x - 2 & \textbf{(multiplicand)} \\
 \qquad\quad 3 x - 4 & \textbf{(multiplier)} \\
\end{array}
$$

Multiplying by $3 x$: $9 x^3 - 3 x^2 - 6 x$

Multiplying by $- 4$: $- 12 x^2 + 4 x + 8$

Adding: $9 x^3 - 15 x^2 - 2 x + 8$ **(product)**

Check: Let $x = 2$, then multiplicand $= 8$, multiplier $= 2$, and the product should equal 16. Setting $x = 2$ in the product, we obtain

product $= 9(2)^3 - 15(2)^2 - 2(2) + 8 = 72 - 60 - 4 + 8 = 16.$

EXERCISE 4

Multiply and collect like terms:

1. $2 x(3 x - 5)$.   **2.** $- y(2 - y - y^2)$.   **3.** $3 a(2 x - 5 y)$.

4. $(x - 2)(x + 4)$.   **5.** $(2 x + 3)(x - 5)$.   **6.** $(4 x - 3)(3 x + 2)$.

7. $(3 x - 4)^2$.   **8.** $(x - 2 y + 3)^2$.   **9.** $(2 a - b - c)^2$.

10. $(a - 3)(3 a^2 - 2 a + 7)$.   **11.** $(x - y)(x^2 + xy + y^2)$.

12. $(2 x - y)(4 x^2 - xy - 7 y^2)$.   **13.** $(6 a + 7 b)(3 a^2 - 2 ab + b^2)$.

14. $(x + y + 1)(2 x - y - 3)$.   **15.** $(x^2 + 2 x - 1)(x^3 - x - 2)$.

16. $(2 x - 1)(x + 3)(x - 5)$.   **17.** $(3 a - 1)(2 a + 3)(a - 4)$.

18. $(x^n - 2)(3 x^{2n} - x^n - 2)$.   **19.** $(x + a)(x^k - ax^{k-1} + a^k)$.

20. $(6 x^3 - 3 x^2 y - 4 xy^2 - y^3)(3 x^2 - 2 xy + 5 y^2)$

8. Division. The operation of division is the inverse of multiplication. Hence, to divide a multinomial by a monomial, divide each term of the multinomial by the monomial and combine results.

Illustration. $\dfrac{6 x^3 - 4 x^2 - 2 x}{- 2 x} = - 3 x^2 + 2 x + 1.$

Rule for Division. *To divide one **polynomial** by another,*

(1) Arrange the terms of the dividend and divisor according to descending powers of some common letter;

(2) Divide the first term of the dividend by the first term of the divisor to obtain the first term of the quotient;

(3) *Multiply the divisor by the term of the quotient obtained in step* (2) *and subtract this product from the dividend to obtain a new dividend;*

(4) *Repeat steps* (2) *and* (3) *until a remainder is obtained which is either zero or is of lower degree than the divisor.*

Example. Divide $(x^3 - 2 x^2 - 7)$ by $(x^2 + 2 x - 3)$.

Solution:

$$
\begin{array}{r}
x - 4 \qquad\qquad \text{(quotient)} \\
\text{(divisor)} \quad x^2 + 2 x - 3 \overline{\smash{\big)}\, x^3 - 2 x^2 \qquad - 7} \quad \text{(dividend)} \\
\underline{x^3 + 2 x^2 - 3 x} \\
- 4 x^2 + 3 x - 7 \\
\underline{- 4 x^2 - 8 x + 12} \\
11 x - 19 \quad \text{(remainder)}
\end{array}
$$

Hence, $\qquad \dfrac{x^3 - 2 x^2 - 7}{x^2 + 2 x - 3} = x - 4 + \dfrac{11 x - 19}{x^2 + 2 x - 3}.$

A problem in division may be checked, either numerically or algebraically, by using the fundamental relation

dividend = quotient × divisor + remainder.

EXERCISE 5

Find the following quotients:

1. $(4 xyz - 8 x^2z) \div (- 4 xz)$.

2. $(9 m^2n^3 - 21 m^3n^2) \div 3 m^2n^2$.

3. $\dfrac{\frac{1}{3} a^4b^3 - \frac{2}{3} a^3b^4 - \frac{1}{2} a^2b^2}{\frac{1}{6} a^2b^2}$.

4. $\dfrac{1.62 x^5 - 3.2 x^4 - 5.02 x^3}{- 0.2 x^3}$.

5. $(6 x^2 + 11 x + 3) \div (3 x + 1)$.

6. $(9 a^2 + 24 a + 16) \div (3 a + 4)$.

7. $(3 y^2 + 7 y - 7) \div (3 y - 2)$.

8. $(6 x^2 - x - 2) \div (2 x + 1)$.

9. $(5 x^2 - 6 x - 2) \div (x - 1)$.

10. $(8 a^3 + b^3) \div (2 a + b)$.

11. $(a^3 - 5 a^2 - 4 a + 2) \div (a + 1)$.

12. $(53 x^2 - 30 x + 15 x^3 - 8) \div (3 x - 2)$.

13. $(x^3 - x^4 + 7 x - 5) \div (x - 2)$.

14. $(9 x^4 + 37 x^2 + 4 - 6 x^3 - 24 x) \div (3 x - 1)$.

15. $(4 x^3 - 4 x^2 - 9 x + 5) \div (2 x^2 - x - 5)$.

16. $(4 y^3 - 6 - 13 y) \div (2 y^2 - 2 - 3 y)$.

17. $(a^4 + 2 a^3 + 4 a - 4) \div (a^2 + 2)$.

18. $(x^4 - 9 x^2 + 5 x - 4) \div (x^2 - 3 x + 1)$.

19. $(x^{3n} - 2 x^{2n} - 14 x^n - 5) \div (x^n - 5)$.

20. $(6 a^{3n} + 7 a^{2n} - 4 a^n - 4) \div (3 a^n + 2)$.

CHAPTER 2

Products and Factors

9. Factoring. When an algebraic expression is the product of two or more quantities, each of these quantities is called a **factor** of the expression, and the determination of these factors is called the **factoring** of the expression.

Unless otherwise stated, we shall limit the process to the factoring of polynomials with rational coefficients and to the determination of similar factors. Such factors will be called **prime factors** if they cannot be factored further without violating the above restrictions.

10. Product Formulas. Certain products occur more frequently than others in mathematics; and in order to facilitate both multiplication and factoring, it is recommended that the following list of products be memorized:

   I. $a(x + y) = ax + ay.$
   II. $(a + b)(a - b) = a^2 - b^2.$
  III. $(a + b)^2 = a^2 + 2\,ab + b^2.$
  IV. $(a - b)^2 = a^2 - 2\,ab + b^2.$
   V. $(x + a)(x + b) = x^2 + (a + b)x + ab.$
  VI. $(ax + b)(cx + d) = acx^2 + (ad + bc)x + bd.$
 VII. $(a + b)(a^2 - ab + b^2) = a^3 + b^3.$
VIII. $(a - b)(a^2 + ab + b^2) = a^3 - b^3.$
  IX. $(a + b + c)^2 = a^2 + b^2 + c^2 + 2\,ab + 2\,ac + 2\,bc.$

Find the following products by inspection:

1. $2 a(3 x - 4 a)$.
2. $- 3 x^2(2 x - 7)$.
3. $4 m(x - y + 2 z)$.
4. $x(3 x^2 - x - 2)$.
5. $(x + 4)(x - 4)$.
6. $(2 x + 5 y)(2 x - 5 y)$.
7. $(ab - 2 c)(ab + 2 c)$.
8. $(5 m - n)(5 m + n)$.
9. $(5 - 2 xy)^2$.
10. $(3 x + 4)^2$.
11. $(3 ax - 5 y)^2$.
12. $(3 - 2 a^2)^2$.
13. $(x - 8)(8 - x)$.
14. $(x + 5)(x - 3)$.
15. $(x^2 + 10)(x^2 - 12)$.
16. $(2 a - b)(2 a - 3 b)$.
17. $(3 y - 1)(2 y + 1)$.
18. $(2 - 3 x)(5 - x)$.
19. $(3 p - 5)(5 - 3 p)$.
20. $(5 x - 4)(3 x + 2)$.
21. $(x - 2)(x^2 + 2 x + 4)$.
22. $(2 x + 3)(4 x^2 - 6 x + 9)$.
23. $(3 y + 1)(9 y^2 - 3 y + 1)$.
24. $(4 y^2 - 1)(16 y^4 + 4 y^2 + 1)$.
25. $(x + y - z)^2$.
26. $(2 x - 3 y + z)^2$.
27. $(2 p - q - 3 r)^2$.
28. $(3 a + b - 4 c)^2$.

Find the following products, using the product formulas. For example, $[(a + b) - 2] [(a + b) + 2] = (a + b)^2 - 4 = a^2 + 2 ab + b^2 - 4$.

29. $[(a + b) - 3][(a + b) + 3]$.
30. $[(a - x) - 2][(a - x) + 3]$.
31. $[(x - y) - 5][(x - y) - 2]$.
32. $[(u + v) - 3][(u + v) + 4]$.
33. $[(x - 2 y) + 2]^2$.
34. $[(2 a + b) - x]^2$.
35. $(2 a + b - 2)(2 a + b + 2)$.
36. $(x - 3 y + z)(x - 3 y - 2 z)$.
37. $(p + 2 q + r)(p + 2 q - r)$.
38. $(2 a - x + y)(2 a - x - 3 y)$.
39. $(a + b + c)(a + b - c)$.
40. $(2 x - y - z)(2 x - 2 y - z)$.

11. Factoring by Inspection. The product formulas of the preceding article become factor formulas when read from right to left. The group may be summarized in the following elementary factor forms:

I. *Common monomial factors.*

II. *Differences of two squares.*

III. *Trinomials.*

IV. *Sums and differences of two cubes.*

Illustration 1. $3 a^4b - 3 a^3b^2 + 6 a^2b^2 = 3 a^2b(a^2 - ab + 2 b)$.
Illustration 2. $4 x^2 - 9 y^2 = (2 x + 3 y)(2 x - 3 y)$.
Illustration 3. $8 x^3 - 27 = (2 x - 3)(4 x^2 + 6 x + 9)$.

In the factoring of trinomials by inspection it is helpful to note the following:

1. If the third term of the trinomial is *positive*, then the second terms of its factors both have the *same sign*.

2. If the third term of the trinomial is *negative*, then the second terms of its factors have *opposite sign*.

Example. Factor $5 x^2 + 7 x - 6$.

Solution: Write $(5 x \quad 2)(x \quad 3)$ for a first trial. Since 2 and 3 must have opposite signs, the *difference* between the inner and the outer products must be $7 x$. However, since $(5 \cdot 3) - (2 \cdot 1) = 13$, this combination fails.

Next try $(5 x \quad 3)(x \quad 2)$. Since $(5 \cdot 2) - (3 \cdot 1) = 7$, these factors will be correct if we insert signs so that the *positive* will predominate.

Thus, $5 x^2 + 7 x - 6 = (5 x - 3)(x + 2)$.

NOTE. In all problems of factoring, remove monomial factors before attempting any other method of factoring. Contrary to the general rule, monomial factors are not usually expressed in factored form. Thus, we write $6 x^2$ and not $2 \cdot 3 \cdot x \cdot x$.

EXERCISE 7

Factor:

1. $5 ab^2 + 25 a^2b$.
2. $9 x^2y^3 + 3 x^2y^2$.
3. $a^4b^5 + a^6b^3 - a^5b^4$.
4. $6 m^2n^3 - 9 m^4n - 3 m^2n$.
5. $a(a - x) + x(a - x)$.
6. $a(2 a - b) - 3 b(2 a - b)$.
7. $100 - 81 x^2$.
8. $0.81 a^2 - 0.49 b^2$.
9. $\frac{4}{9} a^2 - \frac{1}{4}$.
10. $(x + y)^2 - 9$.
11. $x^2 - x - 42$.
12. $35 - 2 c - c^2$.
13. $20 + 8 x - x^2$.
14. $x^2y^2 - 17 xy + 42$.
15. $4 a^2 + 8 a + 3$.
16. $25 a^2 + 10 ab - 3 b^2$.
17. $50 x^2 - 15 x - 104$.
18. $20 m^2 + 11 mn - 45 n^2$.
19. $a^3x^3 + 1$.
20. $27 a^3 - b^3$.
21. $\frac{1}{8} p^3 - 125$.
22. $x^4 + xy^3$.
23. $4 a^4 - 4 a^2$.
24. $3 ax^3 - 18 ax^2 - 21 ax$.
25. $a^2x^4 - a^5x$.
26. $9 a^2x^2 - 49 x^2$.
27. $(x^2 + y^2)^2 - 4 x^2y^2$.
28. $(x^2 + 6)^2 - 25 x^2$.
29. $9(x + y)^2 - (2 x - y)^2$.
30. $a^6 - 64 x^6$.
31. $(a + b)^2 + a + b$.
32. $x^2(2 x + 1) - (4 x^2 - 1)$.
33. $ax^4 - ay^4$.
34. $8 y^6 - 65 y^3 + 8$.
35. $x^4 - 7 x^2y^2 + 12 y^4$.
36. $(x + 5)^2 - (x + 5) - 12$.
37. $x^2 - (3 x^2 - 2)^2$.
38. $a^3 + (a + 1)^3$.
39. $(x^2 - y^2) + x(x + y)$.
40. $a^{12} - a^4x^8$.

12. Factoring by Grouping. Although an algebraic expression may not fall directly into one of the elementary factor forms, it is sometimes possible, by proper grouping, to reduce it to one of those forms. The procedure is illustrated in the following examples.

Example 1. Factor $x^2 - ax + bx - ab$.

Solution: Grouping the first two terms and the last two terms, we have

$$\begin{aligned} x^2 - ax + bx - ab &= (x^2 - ax) + (bx - ab) \\ &= x(x - a) + b(x - a) \\ &= (x - a)(x + b). \end{aligned}$$

Example 2. Factor $a^2 - b^2 + 2bc - c^2$.

Solution: Grouping the last three terms, we have

$$\begin{aligned} a^2 - b^2 + 2bc - c^2 &= a^2 - (b^2 - 2bc + c^2) \\ &= a^2 - (b - c)^2 \\ &= (a + b - c)(a - b + c). \end{aligned}$$

EXERCISE 8

Factor:

1. $ma + mb - na - nb$.
2. $x^3 - 5x^2 + 2x - 10$.
3. $3p^3 + 9p^2 + p + 3$.
4. $a^3 - a^2x + ax^2 - x^3$.
5. $ac + d - c - ad$.
6. $abc - bc + a - 1$.
7. $3a^3 - 9a^2b - 2ab^2 + 6b^3$.
8. $4m^3 - 8m^2 - m + 2$.
9. $x^2 + 2xy + y^2 - 1$.
10. $a^2 - b^2 - 2a + 2b$.
11. $a^2 + ac - ab - bc$.
12. $x^4 - x^2 - 4x - 4$.
13. $a^2 + 2ab + b^2 + a + b$.
14. $c^2 - 6cd + 9d^2 - 4$.
15. $9a^2 - 4x^2 + 4xy - y^2$.
16. $ax^2 - ay^2 + bx^2 - by^2$.
17. $x^3 + y^3 - x - y$.
18. $a^3 - b^3 + a^2 - b^2$.
19. $ab(x^2 + 1) + x(a^2 + b^2)$.
20. $x^7 + x^4 - 16x^3 - 16$.

13. Special Forms of Factoring.

One useful method of factoring is stated in the following theorem, whose proof is given in Article 107.

Factor Theorem. *If a polynomial in x with rational coefficients equals zero when a rational number a is substituted for x, then $(x - a)$ is a factor of the polynomial.*

Example 1. Factor $x^3 - x - 6$.

Solution: By trial we find that this expression reduces to zero when 2 is substituted for x. Hence, by the above theorem $(x - 2)$ is a factor. Dividing the given expression by $(x - 2)$, we obtain the quotient $(x^2 + 2x + 3)$. Thus, in factored form, we have

$$x^3 - x - 6 = (x - 2)(x^2 + 2x + 3).$$

NOTE 1. If the highest power of x has a coefficient $+1$ or -1 and the other coefficients are integers, then the only rational values which can make the polynomial zero are integral factors of the constant term. Thus, in Example 1, we test ± 1, ± 2, ± 3, and ± 6. If none of these make the polynomial zero, then it cannot be factored by means of the factor theorem.

Some trinomials of the form $(x^4 + ax^2y^2 + y^4)$ can be written as the difference of two squares.

Example 2. Factor $x^4 + x^2y^2 + y^4$.
Solution: Adding and subtracting x^2y^2, we have

$$x^4 + 2\,x^2y^2 + y^4 - x^2y^2 = (x^2 + y^2)^2 - x^2y^2$$
$$= (x^2 + y^2 + xy)(x^2 + y^2 - xy).$$

If n is a positive odd integer, then $(x^n + y^n)$ has the factor $(x + y)$. This follows from the factor theorem since the substitution of $-y$ for x makes the expression zero.

Similarly $(x^n - y^n)$ has the factor $(x - y)$ for all positive integral values of n, and if n is even it also has the factor $(x + y)$.

Example 3. Factor $x^7 + y^7$.
Solution: Since the power is odd, we have the factor $(x + y)$. By division we obtain the other factor. Thus,

$$x^7 + y^7 = (x + y)(x^6 - x^5y + x^4y^2 - x^3y^3 + x^2y^4 - xy^5 + y^6).$$

NOTE 2. If n is a positive even integer, then a binomial of the form $(x^n - y^n)$ should *first* be factored as a difference of two squares. Thus, $x^6 - y^6 = (x^3 + y^3)(x^3 - y^3)$.

EXERCISE 9

Express each of the following as a product of two factors:

1. $x^3 + 2\,x^2 - 1$.
2. $x^3 + x^2 + x - 3$.
3. $x^3 + 2\,x^2 - 7\,x - 8$.
4. $x^5 + 2\,x^3 - 2\,x + 1$.

Express each of the following as a product of three factors:

5. $x^3 + 6\,x^2 + 11\,x + 6$.
6. $x^3 + 4\,x^2 + x - 6$.
7. $x^4 - 3\,x^3 + 6\,x - 4$.
8. $x^5 + x^2 - x - 1$.

Factor:

9. $x^3 - 3\,x^2 + 4\,x - 4$.
10. $x^3 - 3\,x - 2$.
11. $x^3 - 2\,x^2 - 9$.
12. $x^3 - 5\,x^2 + 8\,x - 4$.
13. $x^4 - 2\,x^3 + x^2 - 4$.
14. $x^4 - x^3 + 4\,x - 16$.
15. $x^4 - 11\,x^2 + 18\,x - 8$.
16. $x^3 - 2\,x^2y + 3\,y^2$.
17. $x^3 - 7\,x^2y + 11\,xy^2 - 5\,y^3$.
18. $x^4 + 5\,x^3 + 5\,x^2 - 5\,x - 6$.
19. $x^5 + x^4 - x^2 - 7\,x + 6$.
20. $x^5 - 10\,x^2 + 15\,x - 6$.

Factor as a difference of two squares:

21. $x^4 + 2 x^2 + 9$.   **22.** $4 a^4 + 3 a^2b^2 + b^4$.

23. $x^4 - 7 x^2y^2 + y^4$.   **24.** $25 x^4 - 9 x^2y^2 + 16 y^4$.

25. $9 y^4 - y^2 + 16$.   **26.** $9 m^4 - 4 m^2n^2 + 4 n^4$.

Factor:

27. $x^5 + y^5$.   **28.** $a^6 - 64$.   **29.** $a^4 - x^4$.   **30.** $x^9 - y^9$.

31. $x^8 - 81 a^4$.   **32.** $32 x^5 - 1$.   **33.** $a^7 + b^7$.   **34.** $4 x^4 + y^4$.

14. Highest Common Factor and Lowest Common Multiple. A factor of two or more expressions, which has the greatest possible number of prime factors, is called their **highest common factor (H.C.F.)**.

A quantity which has another expression as a factor is called a **multiple** of that expression. A multiple of two or more expressions, which has the smallest possible number of prime factors, is called their **lowest common multiple (L.C.M.)**.

To find the H.C.F. and the L.C.M. of two or more expressions, resolve each expression into its prime factors, then

(1) The H.C.F. *is the product obtained in taking each common prime factor to the lowest power appearing in any of the expressions.*

(2) The L.C.M. *is the product obtained in taking each prime factor to the highest power appearing in any of the expressions.*

Illustration. For $8 x^5y^3$ and $2 x^3y^4z^2$, the H.C.F. is $2 x^3y^3$ and the L.C.M. is $8 x^5y^4z^2$.

    Example. Find the H.C.F. and L.C.M. of (x^2-y^2), $(x^2+2 xy+y^2)$, and $(x^3 + y^3)$.

Solution:
$$x^2 - y^2 = (x + y)(x - y)$$
$$x^2 + 2 xy + y^2 = (x + y)^2$$
$$x^3 + y^3 = (x + y)(x^2 - xy + y^2).$$

Hence,   H.C.F. $= (x + y)$,

and   L.C.M. $= (x + y)^2(x - y)(x^2 - xy + y^2)$.

EXERCISE 10

Find the H.C.F. and L.C.M. of the following expressions, and express each result in factored form:

1. 9, 15, 75.   **2.** 12, 24, 60.   **3.** 52, 78, 338.

4. $6 x^2y^3z^4, 9 x^3yz^2$.   **5.** $12 a^3c^2, 52 ab^2c$.

6. $2 m^2n, 8 mn^3, 6 m^2n^2$.   **7.** $3 x^2, 6 xy, 12 ay^2$.

8. $4 a^2x, 6 ay^2, 9 axy$.   **9.** $7 ab^2, 21 a^2b, 56 ab$.

10. $x^2 - 4, x^2 - x - 2, x^2 - 4x + 4$.
11. $x^2 + 4x + 4, x^2 - 2x - 8, x^3 + 8$.
12. $2a^2 - 2a, 4a^4 - 4a^2, 8a^3 - 8a^2 - 16a$.
13. $x^2 - 2x - 3, x^2 - x - 6, x^2 + 3x + 2$.
14. $x^3 - 3x^2 + x - 3, 9 - x^2, x^3 - 27$.
15. $a^8 - b^8, a^4 - b^4, a^2 - b^2, a - b$.

CHAPTER 3

Fractions

15. Definitions. The indicated quotient of two algebraic expressions is called an **algebraic fraction,** or merely a **fraction.** The dividend is called the **numerator,** the divisor is called the **denominator,** and the numerator and denominator are called the **terms of the fraction.**

Since division by zero has no meaning, it is apparent that a fraction has no meaning when the denominator is zero. Hence, in the discussion and problems which follow, it is assumed that no denominators are zero.

NOTE. The fraction $1/a$ is called the **reciprocal** of the number a, and subsequently it is shown that the reciprocal of a/b is b/a.

16. Reduction of Fractions. The rules governing the operations on algebraic fractions are the same as those used in arithmetic. These rules are based on the definition of a fraction and the following fundamental principle:

Rule 1. *The value of a fraction is not changed if both the numerator and denominator are multiplied, or divided, by the same number (zero excluded).*

If we divide the numerator and denominator of a fraction by their *highest common factor*, the equivalent fraction obtained is said to be **reduced to lowest terms.**

Example. Reduce $\dfrac{4\,x^2 - 9\,y^2}{2\,x^2 - xy - 6\,y^2}$ to lowest terms.

Solution:

$$\frac{4\,x^2 - 9\,y^2}{2\,x^2 - xy - 6\,y^2} = \frac{(2\,x + 3\,y)(2\,x - 3\,y)}{(x - 2\,y)(2\,x + 3\,y)} = \frac{2\,x - 3\,y}{x - 2\,y}.$$

Note. Eliminating a factor from the numerator and denominator of a fraction by division is called **canceling** the factor.

17. The Signs of a Fraction. A fraction may have three signs associated with it: the sign of the numerator, the sign of the denominator, and the sign of the fraction itself. By Rule 1 and the law of signs in multiplication, it follows that *any two of these signs may be changed without changing the value of the fraction.*

Illustration 1. $\dfrac{a}{b} = -\dfrac{-a}{b} = -\dfrac{a}{-b} = \dfrac{-a}{-b}.$

In general, the following rule applies:

Rule 2. *If an **odd,** or **even,** number of factors in the terms of a fraction have their signs changed, then the sign of the fraction is changed or is not changed, respectively.*

Illustration 2. $\dfrac{(x - 2)}{(x-1)(x-3)} = \dfrac{(x - 2)}{(1-x)(3-x)} = -\dfrac{(2 - x)}{(1-x)(3-x)}.$

EXERCISE 11

Find the reciprocal of each of the following:

1. 7. **2.** $2\frac{1}{4}$. **3.** 0.625. **4.** $\frac{3}{4}\,a$. **5.** $a - b$.

For what values of x are the following fractions undefined?

6. $\dfrac{x}{x - 1}.$ **7.** $\dfrac{a - 2\,x}{a^2 - x^2}.$ **8.** $\dfrac{x - 2}{x^2 + x - 6}.$

In each of the following equalities, find the missing term:

9. $\dfrac{4}{7} = \dfrac{?}{28}.$ **10.** $\dfrac{-a^2}{2} = \dfrac{?}{-8\,a^2}.$ **11.** $\dfrac{3\,xy}{2\,a} = \dfrac{9\,ax^2y}{?}.$

12. $\dfrac{a}{2\,b} = \dfrac{2\,a(a - b)}{?}.$ **13.** $\dfrac{4\,a^2}{5\,b} = \dfrac{52\,a^3b^2}{?}.$ **14.** $-\dfrac{-2}{4\,a^2} = \dfrac{a^2}{?}.$

15. $\dfrac{a + 3}{a - 2} = \dfrac{a^2 - 9}{?}.$ **16.** $\dfrac{1}{x - y} = \dfrac{?}{y - x}.$ **17.** $\dfrac{1}{x + y} = \dfrac{?}{y + x}.$

18. $\dfrac{2x - a}{3x + a} = \dfrac{?}{9ax + 3a^2}.$ **19.** $\dfrac{2\,x - 1}{a} = \dfrac{1 - 4\,x^2}{?}.$ **20.** $\dfrac{a - x}{b - x} = \dfrac{?}{x^2 - b^2}.$

Reduce to lowest terms:

21. $\dfrac{32\,x^3y^2z}{56\,x^2y^2z^2}.$ **22.** $\dfrac{-51\,abcx^3}{-85\,a^3bcx}.$ **23.** $\dfrac{38\,bx^5y^4}{95\,ax^3y^7}.$

24. $\dfrac{ax + bx}{a^2 - b^2}.$ **25.** $\dfrac{ax}{a^2x^2 - ax}.$ **26.** $\dfrac{2\,ab + 2\,b}{a^2 - 1}.$

27. $\dfrac{3\,x^2 - 6\,xy}{4\,xy^2 - 2\,x^2y}.$ **28.** $\dfrac{a^2 - 4}{a^3 - 8}.$ **29.** $\dfrac{2\,x^2 - 5\,x + 3}{2\,x^2 - x - 3}.$

30. $\dfrac{q^2 - p^2}{(p - q)^2}.$ **31.** $\dfrac{a^2x^2 - ax}{a^2x^2 - 1}.$ **32.** $\dfrac{6 + x - 2\,x^2}{3\,x^2 - 8\,x + 4}.$

33. $\dfrac{3\,x^4 + 9\,x^3y + 6\,x^2y^2}{x^4 + x^3y - 2\,x^2y^2}.$ **34.** $\dfrac{18\,p^2 + 3\,pq - 10\,q^2}{21\,p^2 - 26\,pq + 8\,q^2}.$

35. $\dfrac{2\,x^3 + 2\,x^2 - 3\,x - 3}{2\,x^3 - 2\,x^2 - 3\,x + 3}.$ **36.** $\dfrac{x^2 + 4\,xy + 4\,y^2 - a^2}{a^2 - ax - 2\,ay}.$

37. $\dfrac{a^2 + b^2 - c^2 + 2\,ab}{a^2 - b^2 + c^2 + 2\,ac}.$ **38.** $\dfrac{a^2 + 2\,ab}{a + 2\,b + a^2 - 4\,b^2}.$

39. $\dfrac{x^3 - 7\,x + 6}{x^3 + x^2 - 10\,x + 8}.$ **40.** $\dfrac{x^3 - y^3}{x^4 + x^2y^2 + y^4}.$

18. Addition and Subtraction of Fractions. In order to add or subtract two or more fractions, it is first necessary to express the fractions in equivalent forms having the same denominator. For this denominator we usually use the lowest common multiple of the given denominators. This expression is called the **lowest common denominator** (**L.C.D.**) of the fractions.

Rule 3. *To obtain fractions with the same* L.C.D., *multiply the terms of each fraction by the quotient obtained in dividing the* L.C.D. *by the denominator of that fraction.*

Illustration 1. The L.C.D. of $\dfrac{a}{3\,xy}, \dfrac{b}{6\,xz},$ and $\dfrac{c}{2\,yz}$ is $6\,xyz$. Hence, the equivalent fractions are $\dfrac{2\,az}{6\,xyz}, \dfrac{by}{6\,xyz},$ and $\dfrac{3\,cx}{6\,xyz}.$

Rule 4. *To add or subtract fractions,* (1) *express them as equivalent fractions with the same* L.C.D., *then* (2) *add or subtract the numerators and retain the common denominator.*

Example. Combine $\dfrac{1}{x} - \dfrac{2}{2\,x - 1} + \dfrac{4}{4\,x^2 - 1}.$

Solution: The L.C.D. is $x(2x - 1)(2x + 1)$; hence,

$$\frac{1}{x} - \frac{2}{2x - 1} + \frac{4}{4x^2 - 1} = \frac{(4x^2 - 1) - 2x(2x + 1) + 4x}{x(2x - 1)(2x + 1)}$$
$$= \frac{4x^2 - 1 - 4x^2 - 2x + 4x}{x(2x - 1)(2x + 1)}$$
$$= \frac{2x - 1}{x(2x - 1)(2x + 1)} = \frac{1}{x(2x + 1)}.$$

Check: When $x = 2$, we have

$$\frac{1}{x} - \frac{2}{2x - 1} + \frac{4}{4x^2 - 1} = \frac{1}{2} - \frac{2}{3} + \frac{4}{15} = \frac{3}{30} = \frac{1}{10},$$

and

$$\frac{1}{x(2x + 1)} = \frac{1}{2(5)} = \frac{1}{10}.$$

In numerical checking, avoid those values of the variable for which a fraction is undefined.

NOTE. In combining fractions, be particularly careful not to discard the denominator.

Occasionally a problem may be simplified by changing the signs of certain factors.

Illustration 2. $\dfrac{2 + x}{x - 1} + \dfrac{x - 3}{1 - x} = \dfrac{2 + x}{x - 1} + \dfrac{3 - x}{x - 1} = \dfrac{5}{x - 1}.$

EXERCISE 12

Combine and simplify:

1. $\dfrac{4x + 3}{4} - \dfrac{2x + 5}{5} - \dfrac{3x - 7}{6}.$

2. $\dfrac{2x + 1}{5} - \dfrac{2x - 1}{7} - \dfrac{x - 3}{10}.$

3. $\dfrac{x - y}{xy} + \dfrac{y - z}{yz} + \dfrac{z - x}{xz}.$

4. $\dfrac{3a + 4b}{ab} - \dfrac{a - 5c}{ac} - \dfrac{9}{a}.$

5. $\dfrac{2x - a}{ax} + \dfrac{x - 2b}{bx} + \dfrac{3}{x}.$

6. $\dfrac{x + a}{ax} - \dfrac{a + 1}{a} + \dfrac{2x - 1}{x}.$

7. $\dfrac{3}{2y + 3} + \dfrac{2}{3y - 2}.$

8. $\dfrac{a}{x + a} - \dfrac{b}{x + b}.$

9. $\dfrac{3x - 2}{x + 1} - \dfrac{x - 3}{2x + 2} + \dfrac{x}{x - 1}.$

10. $\dfrac{2x + 5}{2x - 4} - \dfrac{x - 1}{2x + 1} - \dfrac{2x - 1}{4x + 2}.$

11. $\dfrac{1}{x + 1} - \dfrac{2}{x + 2} + \dfrac{1}{x + 3}.$

12. $\dfrac{xy}{16x^2 - y^2} + \dfrac{x}{4x + y}.$

13. $\dfrac{4}{x^2 - 4} - \dfrac{3}{x^2 - x - 2}.$

14. $\dfrac{3}{y + 1} + \dfrac{4}{y - 1} - \dfrac{7y}{y^2 - 1}.$

15. $\dfrac{1}{a+b} - \dfrac{1}{a-b} + \dfrac{2\,a}{a^2-b^2}.$

16. $\dfrac{a^2-b^2}{ab} - \dfrac{ab-b^2}{ab-a^2}.$

17. $\dfrac{a-x}{x^2-a^2} - \dfrac{b-x}{x^2-b^2}.$

18. $\dfrac{7}{x^2-3\,x-10} + \dfrac{5}{6+x-x^2}.$

19. $\dfrac{2}{6-3\,x} + \dfrac{5}{x-2} - \dfrac{3}{4-2\,x}.$

20. $\dfrac{4}{4\,m^2-1} - \dfrac{5}{6\,m^2+m-1}.$

21. $\dfrac{3}{2+a-6\,a^2} - \dfrac{1}{1+a-2\,a^2}.$

22. $\dfrac{x+1}{2\,x+1} - \dfrac{x-1}{2\,x-1} - \dfrac{1}{2\,x}.$

23. $\dfrac{3}{2\,x^2+x-1} - \dfrac{2}{2-3\,x-2\,x^2}.$

24. $\dfrac{x+1}{x+2} - \dfrac{x-2}{x+1} + \dfrac{6}{x^2-1}.$

25. $\dfrac{xy}{x^2y^2-xy} + \dfrac{xy}{x^2y^2+xy}.$

26. $\dfrac{m}{1+m} - \dfrac{m}{1-m} - \dfrac{m^2}{m^2-1}.$

27. $\dfrac{x}{x^2+5\,x+6} + \dfrac{4}{x^2+6\,x+8} - \dfrac{2}{x^2+7\,x+12}.$

28. $\dfrac{4}{x^2-6\,x+5} + \dfrac{3\,x}{x^2+x-2} + \dfrac{11}{x^2-3\,x-10}.$

29. $\dfrac{x^2-3}{x^3+2\,x^2-3\,x-6} - \dfrac{x^2-2}{x^3+2\,x^2-2\,x-4}.$

30. $\dfrac{a}{(a-b)(a-c)} + \dfrac{b}{(b-c)(b-a)} + \dfrac{c}{(c-a)(c-b)}.$

19. Multiplication and Division of Fractions.

Rule 5. *To multiply two or more fractions, multiply the numerators to obtain the numerator of the product, and multiply the denominators to obtain the denominator of the product.*

Example 1. Find $\dfrac{x^2+y^2}{a^2+2\,ab} \cdot \dfrac{a^2-4\,b^2}{x^3+xy^2}.$

Solution:

$$\frac{x^2+y^2}{a^2+2\,ab} \cdot \frac{a^2-4\,b^2}{x^3+xy^2} = \frac{(x^2+y^2)}{a(a+2\,b)} \cdot \frac{(a+2\,b)(a-2\,b)}{x(x^2+y^2)} = \frac{a-2\,b}{ax}.$$

Rule 6. *To divide one fraction by another, multiply the fraction by the inverse of the divisor.*

Illustration. $\frac{5}{8} \div \frac{3}{4} = \frac{5}{8} \times \frac{4}{3} = \frac{5}{6}.$

Example 2. Find $\dfrac{ax^2-ay^2}{x^2-xy-2\,y^2} \div \dfrac{x^2-xy}{x^2-2\,xy}.$

Solution:

$$\frac{ax^2-ay^2}{x^2-xy-2\,y^2} \div \frac{x^2-xy}{x^2-2\,xy} = \frac{ax^2-ay^2}{x^2-xy-2\,y^2} \cdot \frac{x^2-2\,xy}{x^2-xy}$$
$$= \frac{a(x+y)(x-y)}{(x+y)(x-2\,y)} \cdot \frac{x(x-2\,y)}{x(x-y)} = a.$$

EXERCISE 13

Perform the indicated operations and simplify:

1. $\dfrac{14\,a^3b^2}{9\,x^2y^2} \cdot \dfrac{6\,x^3y}{35\,a^2b^4}$.

2. $\dfrac{15\,a^4x^3}{4\,b^2y} \div \dfrac{5\,a^3x^4}{8\,by^2}$.

3. $\dfrac{72\,m^3n^4}{25\,p^2q^3} \div \dfrac{18\,m^2n^5}{35\,p^4q}$.

4. $\dfrac{x+1}{x} \cdot \dfrac{x^2}{x^2+x}$.

5. $\dfrac{(a-1)^2}{x} \div \dfrac{a^2-1}{ax}$.

6. $\dfrac{c}{c+d} \cdot \dfrac{c^2-d^2}{2\,c}$.

7. $\dfrac{3\,ax^2-9\,ax}{10\,x^2+5\,x} \cdot \dfrac{2\,x^3+x^2}{a^2x-3\,a^2}$.

8. $\dfrac{x^2y^3-xy^4}{x^4y^3+x^3y^4} \cdot \dfrac{x^3y^3+x^2y^4}{x^3y-x^2y^2}$.

9. $\dfrac{m^4-n^4}{m^4-m^2n^2} \div \dfrac{m^2+n^2}{m^3+m^2n}$.

10. $\dfrac{a^2b+ab^2}{a^3-a^2b} \div \dfrac{ab+b^2}{ab-b^2}$.

11. $\dfrac{ax-a}{bx-3\,b} \div \dfrac{cx-c}{dx-3\,d}$.

12. $\dfrac{x^2-4\,x+3}{42\,x^2} \cdot \dfrac{7\,x^2-7\,x}{x^2-2\,x+1}$.

13. $\dfrac{a^2+5\,a+6}{a^2-1} \cdot \dfrac{3+2\,a-a^2}{a^2-9}$.

14. $\dfrac{2\,b+1}{2\,b+2} \cdot \dfrac{2\,b^2-b-3}{4\,b^2-4\,b-3}$.

15. $\dfrac{xy+3\,y}{x^3-1} \div \dfrac{x+3}{x^2+x+1}$.

16. $\dfrac{a^2-x^2}{ax-2\,x^2} \div \dfrac{a^2-2\,ax+x^2}{2\,a^2-4\,ax}$.

17. $\dfrac{4\,a^2-6\,ax}{4\,a^2-16\,x^2} \div \dfrac{4\,a^2-9\,x^2}{4\,a^2-8\,ax}$.

18. $\dfrac{x^3+x^2-20\,x}{24-2\,x-x^2} \div \dfrac{x^2+5\,x}{ax+6\,a}$.

19. $\dfrac{a^2-b^2}{a^2b^2} \cdot \dfrac{a^4}{a+b} \cdot \dfrac{b^2}{ab-a^2}$.

20. $\dfrac{1-x^2}{4\,x^2} \cdot \dfrac{3\,ax}{2-2\,x} \cdot \dfrac{8}{ax+a}$.

21. $\dfrac{a^2+ax}{3\,ax+2\,x^2} \cdot \dfrac{2\,ax-x^2}{ax+x^2} \div \dfrac{4\,a^2-2\,ax}{9\,a+6\,x}$.

22. $\dfrac{2\,ax+x^2}{3\,a^2-ax} \cdot \dfrac{6\,a+2\,x}{6\,a-12\,x} \div \dfrac{2\,a^2+ax}{ax^2-2\,x^3}$.

23. $\dfrac{4\,x^2-9}{4\,x-4} \cdot \dfrac{4\,x-7}{2\,x^2-x-3} \div \dfrac{2\,x+3}{4\,x^2-4}$.

24. $\dfrac{x^2-x-20}{x^2-25} \cdot \dfrac{x^2-x-2}{x^2+2\,x-8} \div \dfrac{x+1}{x^2+5\,x}$.

25. $\dfrac{x^4-y^4}{4\,x^2-8\,xy+3\,y^2} \cdot \dfrac{2\,x-y}{x^2-xy} \div \dfrac{x^2+y^2}{2\,x^2-3\,xy}$.

26. $\dfrac{x^3+x^2+x+1}{2\,x^2-5\,x+3} \cdot \dfrac{2\,x^2-3\,x}{x^2-1} \div \dfrac{x^2+1}{x-1}$.

27. $\dfrac{x^3+2\,x^2-x-2}{x^2-4} \cdot \dfrac{x^2+x+1}{2\,x+2} \div \dfrac{x^3-1}{x-2}$.

28. $\left[\dfrac{a^4-b^4}{a^2-2\,ab+b^2} \div \dfrac{a^2+ab}{a-b}\right] \cdot \dfrac{a^5-a^3b^2}{a^2b+b^3} \div \left(\dfrac{a}{b}-\dfrac{b}{a}\right)$.

29. $\dfrac{1-x^2}{(1+xy)^2-(x+y)^2} \div \dfrac{1}{2}\left(\dfrac{1}{1-y}+\dfrac{1}{1+y}\right)$.

30. $\dfrac{6\,x^2y^2}{(a+b)} \div \left\{\dfrac{3(a-b)x}{7(c+d)} \div \left[\dfrac{4(c-d)}{21\,xy^2} \div \dfrac{c^2-d^2}{4(a^2-b^2)}\right]\right\}$.

20. Mixed Expressions. An algebraic expression which is partly integral and partly fractional is called a **mixed expression.**

Illustration 1. $\left(1 + \dfrac{1}{x}\right)$ and $\left(\dfrac{x^2}{x - y} - x\right)$ are mixed expressions.

Before applying the operations of algebra to such expressions, it is usually advisable to reduce them to single fractions.

Illustration 2. In reducing $\left(x - \dfrac{x}{1 + x}\right)$ to a fraction, we write the denominator of the integral part as 1 and combine as usual. Thus,

$$\frac{x}{1} - \frac{x}{1 + x} = \frac{x(1 + x) - x}{1 + x} = \frac{x + x^2 - x}{1 + x} = \frac{x^2}{1 + x}.$$

21. Complex Fractions. A fraction having one or more other fractions in its numerator, denominator, or in both, is called a **complex fraction.**

Complex fractions are usually simplified as follows:

1. Reduce the numerator and the denominator to single fractions.

2. Invert the denominator and multiply by the numerator.

Example. Simplify: $\dfrac{\dfrac{a}{b} - \dfrac{b}{a}}{\dfrac{1}{a} + \dfrac{1}{b}}.$

Solution:

$$\frac{\dfrac{a}{b} - \dfrac{b}{a}}{\dfrac{1}{a} + \dfrac{1}{b}} = \frac{\dfrac{a^2 - b^2}{ab}}{\dfrac{b + a}{ab}} = \frac{(a + b)(a - b)}{ab} \cdot \frac{ab}{(a + b)} = a - b.$$

NOTE. Many complex fractions may be partially simplified readily by multiplying the numerator and denominator by some common factor. Thus, in the preceding example, if we multiply the numerator and the denominator by ab, we obtain $\dfrac{a^2 - b^2}{b + a}$, which reduces to the answer $(a - b)$.

EXERCISE 14

Reduce the following to single fractions:

1. $4 - \dfrac{3}{x + 2}.$ 2. $\dfrac{a^2}{a - b} - a.$ 3. $\dfrac{x^2 - 9}{x + 4} - x - 7.$

Perform the indicated operation and simplify:

4. $\left(\dfrac{x}{y} - \dfrac{y}{x}\right)\left(x - \dfrac{x^2}{x+y}\right).$

5. $\left(x - \dfrac{1}{x}\right) \div \left(x + \dfrac{1}{x} - 2\right).$

6. $\left(p^2 - \dfrac{1}{p^2}\right) \div \left(p + \dfrac{1}{p}\right).$

7. $\left(\dfrac{x^2 + y^2}{x} - 2y\right)\left(1 + \dfrac{y}{x-y}\right).$

8. $\left(x - \dfrac{2}{x+1}\right)\left(x + \dfrac{1}{x+2}\right).$

9. $\left(a^2 - \dfrac{1}{a}\right) \div \left(a + \dfrac{1}{a+1}\right).$

Simplify:

10. $\dfrac{x-1}{x - \dfrac{1}{x}}.$

11. $\dfrac{x - \dfrac{1}{y}}{\dfrac{1}{x} - y}.$

12. $\dfrac{\dfrac{1}{a^2} - \dfrac{1}{b^2}}{\dfrac{1}{a} - \dfrac{1}{b}}.$

13. $\dfrac{\dfrac{1}{x} + \dfrac{1}{y}}{1 + \dfrac{x}{y}}.$

14. $\dfrac{a - \dfrac{c^2}{b}}{\dfrac{ab}{c} - c}.$

15. $\dfrac{8m - \dfrac{1}{m^2}}{4 - \dfrac{1}{m^2}}.$

16. $1 - \dfrac{1}{1 - \dfrac{1}{x}}.$

17. $\dfrac{x}{1 - \dfrac{1-x}{1+x}}.$

18. $\dfrac{\dfrac{a}{1+a} - \dfrac{1-a}{a}}{\dfrac{a}{1+a} + \dfrac{1-a}{a}}.$

19. $\dfrac{y + \dfrac{xy}{y-x}}{\dfrac{x^2}{x^2 - y^2} - 1}.$

20. $\dfrac{\dfrac{a+x}{a-x} - \dfrac{a-x}{a+x}}{\dfrac{a}{a-x} - \dfrac{a}{a+x}}.$

21. $\dfrac{1}{x^2 - \dfrac{x^3 - 1}{x + \dfrac{1}{x+1}}}.$

22. $\dfrac{\dfrac{x-a}{x-b} - \dfrac{x-b}{x-a}}{\dfrac{1}{x-a} - \dfrac{1}{x-b}}.$

23. $\dfrac{\dfrac{a+b}{1-ab} - b}{1 + \dfrac{b(a+b)}{1-ab}}.$

24. $\dfrac{\left(a + \dfrac{1}{a}\right)^2 - 1}{\left(a - \dfrac{1}{a^2}\right)\left(a - 1 + \dfrac{1}{a}\right)}.$

25. $\dfrac{x + \dfrac{y^2(x+y)}{x^2 - y^2}}{1 - \dfrac{y(x-y)}{x^2}}.$

26. $\dfrac{2 - \dfrac{x-8}{x^2 - 2x - 3}}{\dfrac{12x + 1}{x+3} - \dfrac{6x - 17}{x-3}}.$

27. $\dfrac{1 - \dfrac{a^2 - b^2 - c^2}{2bc}}{1 - \dfrac{a^2 + b^2 - c^2}{2ab}}.$

28. $\dfrac{p - q - \dfrac{2p(p-q)}{p+q}}{\dfrac{p^2 + q^2}{pq + q^2} - 1}.$

29. $\dfrac{x + \dfrac{16x - 27}{x^2 - 16}}{x - 1 + \dfrac{13}{x+4}}.$

30. If $x = \dfrac{ab}{a+b}$, evaluate $\dfrac{x + 2a}{x - 2b} - \dfrac{x - 2a}{x + 2b} - \dfrac{4ab}{x^2 - 4b^2}.$

CHAPTER 4

Equations

22. Equations and Identities. A statement of equality between two algebraic expressions is called an **equation,** and the expressions are called the **members** or **sides** of the equation. An equation is called an **identical equation,** or an **identity,** if its members are equal for all permissible values of the symbols involved; otherwise it is called a **conditional equation,** or simply an **equation.**

Illustration 1. $x^2 - a^2 = (x + a)(x - a)$ is an identity, whereas $x - 3 = 2$ is a conditional equation whose members are equal only when $x = 5$.

NOTE. The symbol $\equiv$, read *identically equals*, is frequently used to emphasize that an equation is an identity.

Those quantities whose values are restricted by a conditional equation are called the **unknowns,** and they are usually represented by the letters toward the end of the alphabet. If a set of values for the unknowns reduces a given equation to an identity, these values are said to **satisfy the equation** and they are called a **solution** of the equation. For an equation in one unknown, the solution is also called a **root** of the equation.

Illustration 2. $x = 3$ is a root of $x^2 - 9 = 0$, and $x = 3$, $y = -1$ is a solution of $x + y = 2$.

To **solve** an equation means to find all of its solutions. In this chapter we shall limit the discussion to the solution of equations in one unknown.

23. Equivalent Equations. Two equations having the same solutions are said to be **equivalent equations.** Thus, $x - 4 = 0$ and $3x = 12$ are equivalent equations, each having the single root $x = 4$, whereas $x = 4$ and $x^2 = 4x$ are *not* equivalent since the latter equation also has the root $x = 0$.

In solving an equation it is usually necessary to transform the equation by applying some algebraic operation to its members. A new equation obtained in this manner is called a **derived equation,** and it may or may not be equivalent to the original equation.

The following operations always give equivalent equations:

1. Increasing or decreasing both members by the same quantity.

2. Multiplying or dividing both members by the same quantity, provided that this quantity is not zero and does not contain the unknown.

The above operations justify the **rule of transposition.**

Any term may be moved from one member of an equation to the other, provided that its algebraic sign is changed.

NOTE 1. If both members of an equation are multiplied by an expression containing the unknown or if they are both raised to the same integral power, the derived equation may have roots not contained in the original equation. These are called **extraneous roots,** and the derived equation is said to be **redundant** with respect to the original equation. If the solving of an equation necessitates either of these operations, the extraneous roots should be eliminated by checking in the original equation.

Illustration 1. Multiplying both members of the equation $\frac{1}{x} = \frac{1}{x(x+1)}$ by the L.C.D. $x(x+1)$, we obtain the derived equation $x + 1 = 1$, which has the root $x = 0$. When $x = 0$, the members of the original equation are undefined. Hence this root is extraneous, and the original equation has no roots.

NOTE 2. If both members of an equation are divided by an expression containing the unknown, the derived equation may have fewer roots than the original equation; and if it does, it is called **defective** with respect to the original equation.

Illustration 2. The equation $x(x-1) = 2(x-1)$ has the roots $x = 1$ and $x = 2$. If both members are divided by $(x-1)$, we obtain the defective equation $x = 2$.

24. Linear Equations in One Unknown. An equation of the form

$$ax + b = 0, \quad a \neq 0$$

is known as an **integral rational equation of the first degree** in x, or simply as a **linear equation** in x.

In solving equations which are reducible to linear equations, the following procedure is suggested:

1. Clear of fractions (if any occur in the equation).

2. Remove parentheses (if any occur in the equation).

3. Transpose terms so that all and only terms containing the unknown are on one side of the equation.

4. Divide both members by the coefficient of the unknown.

5. Check results, if extraneous roots are possible.

Note. A fractional equation is **cleared of fractions** by multiplying both members by the L.C.D. of the fractions.

Example 1. Solve $1 - \dfrac{3x + 5}{6} = \dfrac{1}{x} - \dfrac{x}{2}$.

Solution: To clear of fractions, we multiply by $6x$; thus,

$$6x - x(3x + 5) = 6 - 3x^2.$$

Eliminating parentheses and transposing, we have

$$6x - 3x^2 - 5x + 3x^2 = 6; \text{ hence } x = 6.$$

Check: Setting $x = 6$ in the original equation, we have

$$1 - \frac{18 + 5}{6} = \frac{1}{6} - \frac{6}{2}, \quad \text{or} \quad -\frac{17}{6} = -\frac{17}{6}.$$

Example 2. Solve for x: $(x - a)^2 = (x - b)^2$.
Solution: Eliminating parentheses, we have

$$x^2 - 2ax + a^2 = x^2 - 2bx + b^2;$$

transposing, $\qquad 2bx - 2ax = b^2 - a^2;$

factoring, $\qquad 2(b - a)x = (b - a)(b + a);$

dividing, $\qquad x = \frac{1}{2}(a + b).$

EXERCISE 15

Solve each of the following equations, and check the root:

1. $2x - 2 = 7x + 18.$
2. $2(4x - 3) = 5(x - 3).$
3. $2(3x - 2) = 7(x - 1) - 5.$
4. $x - 3(5x + 2) = 3 - 10x.$
5. $\frac{1}{2}(3x - 1) = \frac{1}{3}(x - 2) + 6.$
6. $\frac{2}{3}(3x + 5) + 1 = \frac{1}{2}(x - \frac{1}{3}).$
7. $0.3(x + 1.6) = 2.3(x - 0.4).$
8. $x - 0.2(2 - x) = 1.31.$
9. $15(62x + 7) = 38(24x + 3).$
10. $(x - 5)^2 = (x + 7)^2.$

11. $(x + 5)(x - 1) = (x + 3)(x - 2) + 13.$

12. $x(x - 3) - 2x^2 = 3 - x(x + 2).$

13. $(2x + 3)^2 - x(4x - 1) = 3x - 11.$

14. $(x - 2)(x + 3)(x - 4) = x^2(x - 3) + 4.$

15. $(x + 1)(x + 2)(x + 3) = (x - 3)(x + 4)(x + 5) + 84.$

16. $\dfrac{2(x + 3)}{3} + \dfrac{16}{15} = \dfrac{4(2x + 5)}{5}.$

17. $x - \dfrac{x+1}{3} + \dfrac{x+3}{5} = \dfrac{3x-2}{3}.$

18. $\dfrac{5}{2x} + \dfrac{1}{3} = \dfrac{1}{x} + \dfrac{11}{6}.$

19. $\dfrac{5x + 1}{5} - \dfrac{2\frac{4}{5}}{x + 2} = \dfrac{2x - 1}{2}.$

20. $\dfrac{2x - 3}{3x} = \dfrac{x + 1}{x - 1} - \dfrac{1}{3}.$

21. $\dfrac{3x + 4}{6x - 5} = \dfrac{2x + 5}{4x - 1}.$

22. $\dfrac{3}{2x - 1} + \dfrac{7}{2 - 4x} = \dfrac{1}{6}.$

23. $\dfrac{3x - 1}{x - 3} - \dfrac{x + 5}{x + 2} = 2.$

24. $\dfrac{5}{x - 1} + \dfrac{2}{x - 3} = \dfrac{7}{x - 2}.$

25. $\dfrac{2}{x + 1} + \dfrac{1}{x - 1} = \dfrac{2x + 1}{x^2 - 1}.$

26. $\dfrac{3}{x - 2} - \dfrac{1}{x + 2} = \dfrac{4}{x^2 - 4}.$

27. $\dfrac{x + 6}{2x^2 + 5x} = \dfrac{x + 1}{2x^2 + x - 10}.$

28. $\dfrac{9}{2x^2 - x - 1} + \dfrac{2}{2x^2 - 9x - 5} = \dfrac{3}{x^2 - 6x + 5}.$

29. $\dfrac{x + 4}{x^2 + 3x + 2} - \dfrac{x + 3}{2 + x - x^2} = \dfrac{2x - 3}{x^2 - 4}.$

30. $\dfrac{1}{x} - \dfrac{1}{x + 5} = \dfrac{1}{x - 1} - \dfrac{1}{x + 4}.$

Solve each of the following equations for x:

31. $3(2x - 3a) + 2(3x - a) = a.$

32. $\frac{1}{2}x - \frac{1}{3}a = \frac{1}{4}x - \frac{1}{5}b.$

33. $a + 2 = 2(x + 4) - a(x + 2).$

34. $m(m - x) + 2mn = n(x - n).$

35. $(x + a)(x + b) = x(x + c).$

36. $x(x - a) + a = x(x - b) + b.$

37. $\dfrac{x - a}{2a + 5b} = \dfrac{x - b}{3a + 4b}.$

38. $\dfrac{1}{x} + \dfrac{1}{x - a} = \dfrac{2}{x + a}.$

39. $\dfrac{p + q}{x + 1} = \dfrac{p - q}{x - 1}.$

40. $\dfrac{x + c}{x - d} - \dfrac{x - c}{x + d} = \dfrac{c^2 - d^2}{x^2 - d^2}.$

Solve each of the following formulas for the letter indicated:

41. $V = \frac{1}{4}\pi d^2 h$, for h.

42. $F = \frac{9}{5}C + 32$, for C.

43. $l = a + (n - 1)d$, for n.

44. $s = v + \frac{1}{2}a(2n - 1)$, for n.

45. $(P - p)(V - v) = K$, for p.

46. $F = M(a - a') + F'$, for a.

47. $\dfrac{e}{E} = \dfrac{r}{R + r}$, for r.

48. $\dfrac{P - P_1}{P - P_2} = k$, for P.

49. $E = I\left(R + \dfrac{r}{n}\right)$, for n.

50. $S = \dfrac{a - rl}{1 - r}$, for r.

25. Symbolic Representations. In solving algebraic problems which are given in the form of written statements, it is first necessary to translate these statements into algebraic symbolism. To do this it is essential to have a clear and exact understanding of the terms and phrases used to describe common situations and events.

When in doubt as to the exact meaning of any statement involving letters, it is suggested that suitable numbers be chosen for the letters, and the meaning of the statement investigated with respect to these numbers.

Illustration 1. By how much does x exceed a? Since 15 exceeds 12 by 3, or $(15 - 12)$, it is clear that x exceeds a by $(x - a)$.

In algebra, percentages should always be reduced to their equivalent numerical values. Thus, $7\% = 0.07$ or $\frac{7}{100}$, and $r\% = 0.01\,r$ or $\frac{r}{100}$.

Illustration 2. What number is 25% more than h? Since $25\% = \frac{1}{4}$, we wish to increase h by $\frac{1}{4}$ of h; this is $h + \frac{1}{4}\,h$ or $\frac{5}{4}\,h$.

In arithmetic a two-figure integer such as 48 indicates the sum of 4 tens and 8 ones; that is, $48 = 4 \times 10 + 8$. When letters are used to represent digits the latter representation must be used. Thus, an integer whose hundreds' digit is a, whose tens' digit is b, and whose units' digit is c, is represented by $(100\,a + 10\,b + c)$.

Note 1. The even integers are 2, 4, 6, 8, etc., and the odd integers are 1, 3, 5, 7, etc.

Denominate numbers should be expressed in the same units before any algebraic operations are applied. Thus, the perimeter of a rectangle whose dimensions are x feet and y yards is either $(2\,x + 6\,y)$ feet or $(\frac{2}{3}\,x + 2\,y)$ yards.

Note 2. The **perimeter** of a polygon is the sum of the lengths of its sides.

EXERCISE 16

Express in algebraic symbols:

1. What is the next even integer after $2\,n$?
2. What is the largest odd integer which is less than $(2\,n + 1)$?
3. What number is 20% larger than x?

4. How many days are there in w weeks and d days?

5. What is the length of a rectangle whose perimeter is P, if the width is 4?

6. What is the average of a and b?

7. How many cents are there in q quarters and d dimes?

8. What is the area of a rectangle in square feet, if its length is x yards and its width is y feet?

9. What number exceeds y by 4 less than x?

10. A boy is h years old, and five years hence his age will be half that of his father. How old is the father now?

11. A has the same amount of money as B. They bet five dollars and B loses. If after the bet B has x dollars, how much does A have?

12. Traveling at a rate of r feet per second, how many miles does one go in t hours?

13. How many pints of alcohol are contained in g gallons of a solution which is 25% alcohol?

14. How many men are required to do in a hours what b men do in ac hours?

15. If a man can make x boxes in h hours, how many can he make in m minutes?

16. What is the simple interest on a dollars for a years at a per cent?

17. What is the number whose tens' digit is x and whose units' digit is $(2x + 1)$?

18. How long is the diagonal of a rectangle whose dimensions are a and b?

19. The annual interest on x dollars is y dollars. What is the annual interest on a dollars at a rate 1% greater?

20. What is the altitude of an isosceles triangle whose base is b and whose perimeter is $2P$?

26. Stated Problems. A written or verbal statement expressing a condition or conditions of equality which exist among one or more unknown quantities is called a **stated problem.**

The following procedure is suggested for the solution of such problems, a single unknown being used:

1. Represent one of the unknown quantities by some symbol such as x.

2. Write the algebraic representations of the other unknown quantities in terms of the unknown, x.

3. From a condition of the problem, form an equation involving the unknown quantities.

4. Solve the resulting equation for x, and find the other unknowns by substituting in step 2.

5. Check the solution by determining whether or not it satisfies the conditions of the written statement of the problem.

Example 1. A tank can be filled by one pipe in 30 minutes and emptied by another in 50 minutes. If both pipes are open, how long will it take to fill the tank?

Analysis: Let x minutes be the time required to fill the tank.

In one minute the first pipe fills $\frac{1}{30}$ of the tank and the second pipe empties $\frac{1}{50}$. Hence, in x minutes the first fills $\frac{x}{30}$ of the tank and the second empties $\frac{x}{50}$.

Since the tank is filled in x minutes, the difference of the fractional parts filled and emptied must equal 1; thus,

Solution:
$$\frac{x}{30} - \frac{x}{50} = 1; \quad 5x - 3x = 150; \quad x = 75.$$

Answer: It will take 1 hour and 15 minutes to fill the tank.

Check: In 75 minutes, the first pipe provides enough to fill $\frac{75}{30}$, or $2\frac{1}{2}$ tanks, while the second pipe drains $\frac{75}{50}$, or $1\frac{1}{2}$ tankfuls.

The analysis of a stated problem is often clearer if the facts of the problem are written in tabulated form.*

Example 2. How much of an 85% solution of acid should be added to 32 ounces of a 45% solution in order to obtain a 60% solution?

Analysis: Let x = the number of ounces of 85% solution added; then

Amt. of Sol. $\times$ Percentage = Amt. of Acid

Strong solution .	x	0.85	$0.85\,x$
Weak solution . .	32	0.45	14.4
Mixture	$x + 32$	0.60	$0.60(x + 32)$

Solution:
$$0.85x + 14.4 = 0.60(x + 32),$$
$$0.25x = 4.8,$$
$$x = 19.2.$$

*For a more detailed study of stated problems, see Peterson's *Intermediate Algebra for College Students*, Harper & Brothers.

Answer: 19.2 ounces of 85% solution should be added.

Check: 19.2 oz. at 85% = 16.32 oz. acid
                   32   oz. at 45% = 14.40 oz. acid
                   _____
                                    30.72 oz. acid.
Or,   51.2 oz. at 60% = 30.72 oz. acid.

EXERCISE 17

1. Find three consecutive even integers such that if the smallest, the second, and the largest are divided by 5, 10, and 15 respectively, the sum of the quotients is 10.

2. A boy ran to a store at the rate of 5 miles per hour and he walked back at the rate of 4 miles per hour. If it took 9 minutes for the round trip, how far away is the store?

3. A confectioner buys some candy bars at two for a nickel and sells them three for a dime. If he makes $2.50, how many candy bars did he buy?

4. A is twice as old as B and in three years will be three times as old as C, who is five years younger than B. Find their ages.

5. How much of an alloy which is 25% copper should be added to 250 pounds of an alloy which is 65% copper in order to obtain an alloy which is 50% copper?

6. In a two-figure number the tens' digit is 1 more than the units' digit, and the number itself is seven times the sum of the digits. Find the number.

7. The width of a rectangle is $\frac{5}{7}$ of the length. If both dimensions are increased 2 feet, the area is increased by 52 square feet. Find the dimensions of the rectangle.

8. A man has $1500 more invested at 4% than he has invested at 5%. If his annual income from these two investments is $348, how much does he have invested at each rate?

9. A can do a job in 45 minutes and with the help of B he can do it in 20 minutes. How long would it take B alone to do the job?

10. A bag contains white balls and black balls. Eight more than half the number of balls are black balls, and six more than half the number of black balls are white balls. How many white balls and black balls does the bag contain?

11. A boy's age is one year more than one-fifth of his father's age, and in four years his age will be one year less than one-third of his father's age. How old is the boy?

12. One solution contains 6 parts alcohol to 3 parts water and another contains 3 parts alcohol to 7 parts water. How much of each should be taken in order to obtain 110 ounces of a solution which is half alcohol and half water?

13. The sum of the digits of a two-figure number is 10. The number itself equals the sum of six times the tens' digit and seven times the units' digit. Find the number.

14. If each side of a square were decreased 4 inches, the decrease in area would be the same as the increase in area would have been if the sides had been increased 2 inches. Find the area of the square.

15. A man has $10,000 to invest. He invests $4000 at 6% and $3500 at 4%. At what rate should he invest the remainder in order to have a yearly income of $500?

16. One pipe can fill a tank in 2 hours, a second pipe in 3 hours, and a third pipe in 6 hours. How long would it take the three pipes together to fill the tank?

17. A dealer buys some horses at $100 each, and through disease he loses 10% of them. By selling the remainder at $125 each, he makes $4000 on the transaction. How many horses did he buy?

18. A motorist drove at an average rate of 45 miles per hour outside the city limits and 20 miles per hour inside the city limits. If a trip of 25 miles took him 50 minutes, how much of it was within the city limits?

19. A man can do a piece of work in 6 days and his older son can do it in 10 days. The man and his older son work together for 2 days, and then the man and his younger son finish the job in 2 days. How long would it take the younger son alone to do the work?

20. A man has $7500 invested, part at $3\frac{1}{2}$% and the remainder at 5%. If the amounts invested at each rate had been interchanged, the yearly interest would have been increased by $7.50. Find the amount invested at each rate.

21. The denominator of a certain fraction is 2 more than the numerator. If the numerator is increased by 9 and the denominator is increased by 3, the resulting fraction equals the reciprocal of the original fraction. What is the fraction?

22. A woman has 35 cents more than she needs to purchase 50 Christmas cards. If she should purchase cards each of which costs one cent more, she would have 15 cents more than enough to purchase 45 cards. How much money has she?

23. At 7 A.M. a fast train traveling 60 miles per hour leaves Los Angeles for San Francisco, a distance of 400 miles. At 9 A.M. a train traveling 40 miles per hour leaves San Francisco for Los Angeles. At what time will these two trains pass each other?

24. A man being asked his age replied, "If you take one year from my present age the result will be three times my son's age, and three years ago my age was twice what his will be in five years." Find his age.

25. In a three-figure number the tens' digit is the same as the units' digit, and the hundreds' digit is 3 less than the units' digit. If the number itself is equal to sixteen times the sum of the digits, what is the number?

26. A grocer has 20 pounds of walnuts worth 40 cents a pound and 10 pounds of Brazil nuts worth 50 cents a pound. How many pounds of almonds at 20 cents a pound must he mix with these in order to have a mixture of the three nuts which he can sell for 35 cents a pound?

27. The altitude of a triangle is 3 more than one-half the base, and its area is 30 less than the area of a square having the altitude for a side. Find the area of the triangle.

28. The number of months in the age of a man on his birthday in 1924 was exactly a third of the number denoting the year in which he was born. In what year was he born?

29. A chemist mixes a pints of an $m\%$ acid solution with b pints of an $n\%$ acid solution. What is the percentage strength of the mixture?

30. At what times between five and six o'clock will the hands of a clock be at right angles to each other?

31. Show that a symmetric number of four digits is always a multiple of 11. NOTE: A symmetric number is a number which is identically the same as the number with its digits reversed.

32. In a certain factory some of the workmen receive $2.50 a day, others more. The total paid in wages each day is $1000. An assessment made for charity to raise $475 requires $1.00 from each man receiving $2.50 a day, and half a day's pay from every man receiving more. How many men receive $2.50 a day?

33. Eighteen years ago A was three times as old as B. A is now three times as old as B was, when A was as old as B is now. Find their present ages.

34. A cyclist rode one-third of a trip at 10 miles per hour, one-third at 9 miles per hour, and the remainder at 8 miles per hour. If he had ridden half the distance at 10 miles per hour and the other half at 8 miles per hour, he would have been one minute longer on the way. What distance did he ride?

CHAPTER 5

Functions and Graphs

27. Constants and Variables. A general number is called a **constant** if it is assumed that its value does not change in the course of a problem. Constants are of two kinds: (1) **absolute constants,** such as 8, $\frac{1}{3}$, − 4, and π, each of which has the same value in any problem; and (2) **arbitrary constants,** each of which retains its value without change throughout a problem, but which may change from one problem to another.

A general number which may assume different values in the course of a problem is called a **variable.** It may happen, however, that a variable does not change its value. For example, during a certain period of time we should expect the temperature to vary, but it is entirely possible that it may remain the same. Although the temperature in this case remains constant, we should consider it a variable since initially we had no way of knowing that it would remain constant.

Illustration. The formula $V = \frac{1}{3}\pi r^2 h$ gives the volume of a right circular cone having a height h and a circular base of radius r. In this formula, $\frac{1}{3}$ and π are absolute constants, and V, h, and r are variables. If we were interested only in such cones having a fixed base, then r would be an arbitrary constant and V and h would be considered variables.

28. Functions. By means of the formula $A = \pi r^2$, we can find the area A of a circle when we know its radius r. This

36

dependence of the variable A on the variable r is expressed mathematically by saying that A is a **function** of r.

If a variable y depends on a variable x in such a way that when x assumes a value we can obtain at least one value for y, then y is said to be a function of x.

Since the implication of this definition is that y depends on x, we call x the **independent variable** and y the **dependent variable,** or **function.**

The definition of a function does not state explicitly how we find the value of the function when we know the value of the independent variable; it merely asserts that it can be found. In general, these functional values are determined in one of two ways: either (1) from an equation or formula, or (2) from a statistically determined table of values.

Illustration 1. The expression $(x^2 + 2x - 3)$ is a function of x. If $x = -5$, the value of the function is $(25 - 10 - 3)$ or 12.

Illustration 2. The following table based on data compiled by the United States government gives the average heights of boys according to their age:

Age, years	1	2	3	4	5	6	7	8	9	10	11	12	13	14	15	16
Height, inches	29.4	33.8	37.1	39.5	41.6	43.8	45.7	47.8	49.7	51.7	53.3	55.1	57.2	59.9	62.3	65.0

This table has been made by making a great many measurements and averaging them. Since we can find the value of H, the average height, when we know A, the age, it follows that H is a function of A. Observe, however, that there is no formula for H in terms of A.

29. Functional Notation. Functions of a single variable are often represented by symbols such as $f(x)$, $g(r)$, $\phi(z)$, and so on. The letter in parentheses indicates the independent variable and the prefixed letter indicates a given relationship. The symbol $f(x)$ is read "*the f-function of x*" or, briefly, "*f of x.*" The value of $f(x)$ when $x = a$ is denoted by $f(a)$.

Illustration 1. If $F(x) = x^2 + 4$, then $F(-2) = (-2)^2 + 4 = 8$, $F(a) = a^2 + 4$, and $F(x + y) = (x + y)^2 + 4$.

A function depending on two or more independent variables is represented symbolically in a similar manner. Thus, a function of two variables x and y is written as $f(x, y)$ and is read "f of x and y." The value of $f(x, y)$ when $x = a$ and $y = b$ is denoted by $f(a, b)$.

Illustration 2. If $\psi(s, t) = st - 2t + 1$, then $\psi(2, 1) = (2)(1) - 2(1) + 1 = 1$, $\psi(a, -2) = -2a + 5$, and $\psi(x + y, b) = b(x + y) - 2b + 1$.

An equation such as $y = f(x)$ is said to define y as an **explicit function** of x. If, however, two variables x and y are related by an equation such as $F(x, y) = 0$, then each of the variables is said to be an **implicit function** of the other. When an equation of the form $y = f(x)$ is solved for x in terms of y, as $x = \phi(y)$, the function $\phi(y)$ is called the **inverse function** of $f(x)$.

Illustration 3. The equation $2x - 3y - 5 = 0$ gives x and y implicitly. Solving for each variable, we obtain the explicit function $x = \frac{1}{2}(3y + 5)$, and its inverse $y = \frac{1}{3}(2x - 5)$.

Example. If $f(x) = \dfrac{1 + x}{1 - x}$, show that $f(1 - x) + f(1 + x) = -2$.

Solution: Substituting $(1 - x)$ and $(1 + x)$ for x respectively, we have

$$f(1 - x) = \frac{1 + (1 - x)}{1 - (1 - x)} = \frac{2 - x}{x},$$

$$f(1 + x) = \frac{1 + (1 + x)}{1 - (1 + x)} = \frac{2 + x}{- x}.$$

Hence, $f(1 - x) + f(1 + x) = \dfrac{2 - x}{x} - \dfrac{2 + x}{x} = \dfrac{-2x}{x} = -2$.

EXERCISE 18

1. If $f(x) = 2x - 1$, find $f(2)$, $f(0)$, $f(-1)$ $f(\frac{3}{4})$, and $f(-\frac{1}{2})$.
2. If $g(y) = y^2 - 3y$, find $g(-1)$, $g(0)$, $g(3)$, $g(\frac{2}{3})$, and $g(-\frac{2}{5})$.
3. If $F(r) = r/(1 + r)$, find $F(2)$, $F(-5)$, $F(0)$, $F(\frac{3}{2})$, and $F(-\frac{2}{3})$.
4. If $\phi(x) = x^3 - 2x - 3$, find $\phi(-3)$, $\phi(2a)$, and $\phi(y + 1)$.
5. If $\psi(z) = \dfrac{2z - 3}{1 - z}$, find $\psi(2)$, $\psi\left(\dfrac{1}{a}\right)$, and $\psi(2x + 1)$.
6. If $F(x, y) = 2x - 3y$, find $F(5, 4)$, $F(\frac{1}{2}, -\frac{2}{3})$, and $F(a, -2)$.
7. If $R(a, b) = \dfrac{a + 1}{b + 1}$, find $R(5, -3)$, $R(\frac{1}{5}, \frac{1}{2})$, and $R(a - 1, 4)$.
8. If $\phi(m, n) = m^2 - n^2$, find $\phi(4, -3)$, $\phi(\frac{1}{3}, \frac{1}{6})$, and $\phi(a+b, a-b)$.
9. If $f(x, y, z) = 2x - 5y - z$, find $f(2, -3, 1)$, $f(-3, 0, \frac{1}{2})$, and $f(x, 1, -4)$.
10. If $g(x, y, z) = x^2 + yz$, find $g(-1, 0, 3)$, $g(3a, -2a, a)$, and $g(y, z, x)$.

11. If $f(x) = x^2 - 3x + 1$, find $f(x + h) - f(x)$.

12. If $G(y) = 1/(y + 1)$, find $G(y + h) - G(y)$.

13. If $\phi(x) = x^2/(1 + x)$, find $x^3\phi(1/x) - \phi(x)$.

14. If $h(z) = z/(1 - z)$, show that $\frac{1}{2}[h(z) + h(-z)] = h(z^2)$.

15. If $g(x) = x(x + 1)(x + 2)$, show that $xg(x + 1) - (x + 1)g(x)$ $= 2 g(x)$.

16. If $f(x) = x^2 - 1$ and $g(x) = 2x + 1$, find $f[g(x)]$ and $g[f(x)]$.

17. If $F(x, y) = \dfrac{x - y}{x + y}$, find $F\left(\dfrac{1}{x}, \dfrac{1}{y}\right) + F(x, y)$.

18. If $F(x, y) = x^3 + 4xy^2 + y^3$, show that $F(ax, ay) = a^3F(x, y)$.

19. If $xy + 3x - 4y + 2 = 0$, determine y as a function of x.

20. If $y = \dfrac{3x - 2}{5 - x}$, find the inverse function.

30. Statistical Graphs. When statistical data showing the functional relationship between two variables are given by means of a table of values, it is not always easy to understand the significance of the data as a whole. To aid us in this respect, we may picture the data by making a drawing that represents the numbers in the table. Such a drawing is called a **graph.**

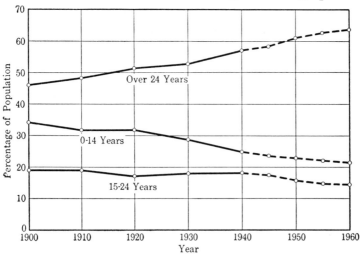

FIGURE 1.

Figure 1 shows a graphic portrayal of the United States population by age groups, with estimates for the future, made by the United States Bureau of the Census.

U. S. Population in Percentage, by Age Groups

Year	1900	1910	1920	1930	1940	1945	1950	1955	1960
0–14 years	34.4	32.1	31.8	29.4	25.1	23.6*	23.1*	22.4*	21.6*
15–24 years	19.6	19.7	17.7	18.3	18.2	17.6*	15.9*	14.8*	14.7*
Over 24 years	46.0	48.2	50.5	52.4	56.7	58.8*	61.1*	62.8*	63.7*

* Estimate.

Rules for Making Statistical Graphs

1. On a sheet of ruled paper draw two lines, called axes, at right angles to each other.

2. Mark off equal divisions on each axis, and number them in succession. A suitable scale should be chosen on each axis in order that the graph will be large and yet remain on the paper.

3. Each pair of values in the table determines a point on the paper. Plot these values and connect the succession of points thus obtained by straight lines.

NOTE. If one of the varying quantities increases or decreases by uniform amounts, it should in general be represented on the horizontal axis.

EXERCISE 19

1. The following table gives the motor vehicle registrations in the United States to the nearest million. Graph the registrations as a function of the time.

Year	1929	'30	'31	'32	'33	'34	'35	'36	'37	'38	'39	'40	'41	'42
Registra-tions	24	26	27	26	24	24	25	26	29	30	30	31	33	33

2. The wholesale price index on foods in the United States is indicated in the following table. The index number 100 is chosen to

represent the average prices in 1929. Graph the numbers with respect to time.

Year	1929	'30	'31	'32	'33	'34	'35	'36	'37	'38	'39	'40	'41	'42
Index no.	100	91	75	61	60	71	84	82	86	79	77	79	87	99

3. The federal income tax receipts for the state of Oregon are given in the following table in millions of dollars. Graph these figures with respect to time.

Year	1929	'30	'31	'32	'33	'34	'35	'36	'37	'38	'39	'40	'41	'42	'43
Receipts	5.9	5.4	4.1	2.4	1.5	1.7	2.6	3.7	5.9	7.5	6.4	6.5	12.1	33.6	79.1

4. The following table gives the average weights of boys according to their age. Graph the weight as a function of the age.

Age, years	1	2	3	4	5	6	7	8	9	10	11	12	13	14	15	16
Weight, pounds	21.9	27.1	32.2	35.9	41.1	45.2	49.1	53.9	59.2	65.3	70.2	76.9	84.4	94.9	107.1	121.0

5. Using the data in Illustration 2, page 37, graph the average height of boys as a function of their age.

6. The birth rate and death rate in the United States per 1000 population are given in the following table. Graph each with respect to time on the same chart.

Year	1929	'30	'31	'32	'33	'34	'35	'36	'37	'38	'39	'40
Birth rate	18.9	18.6	18.0	17.4	16.5	17.1	16.9	16.7	17.1	17.6	17.3	17.9
Death rate	11.9	11.3	11.1	10.9	10.7	11.0	10.9	11.5	11.3	10.6	10.6	10.8

7. The monthly precipitation in inches for Seattle, New Orleans, and Denver is given in the following table. Graph each with respect to time on the same chart and compare.

Month	Jan.	Feb.	Mar.	Apr.	May	June	July	Aug.	Sept.	Oct.	Nov.	Dec.
Seattle	4.9	3.9	3.0	2.4	1.9	1.3	0.6	0.7	1.8	2.8	5.0	5.6
New Orleans	4.3	4.2	4.7	5.2	4.6	5.9	6.4	5.8	5.0	3.3	3.1	4.8
Denver	0.4	0.5	1.0	2.1	2.2	1.4	1.7	1.4	1.0	1.0	0.6	0.7

8. The monthly mean temperatures in Fahrenheit for New York, Chicago, and Los Angeles are given in the following table. Graph each with respect to time on the same chart and compare.

Month	Jan.	Feb.	Mar.	Apr.	May	June	July	Aug.	Sept.	Oct.	Nov.	Dec.
New York	31	31	38	49	61	69	74	73	67	56	44	35
Chicago	24	26	35	47	58	67	72	72	65	54	40	29
Los Angeles	55	56	58	59	62	66	70	71	69	65	61	57

31. Rectangular Coordinates. In somewhat the same manner as we have pictured statistical data, it is possible also to picture mathematical formulas and equations. To do this we form what is called a **system of rectangular coordinates.** First draw a horizontal straight line XX' and a vertical straight line YY'. These lines divide the plane into four parts called **quadrants** which are numbered as shown in Figure 2. The line XX' is called the **x-axis,** YY' is called the **y-axis,** and together they are called the **coordinate axes.** Their point of intersection O is called the **origin.**

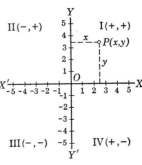

FIGURE 2.

The position of any point in the plane may be described by giving its distances from these two axes. To measure such distances, we arbitrarily choose some unit of length, and agree that horizontal distances measured to the *right* of the y-axis shall be *positive*, and those to the *left* shall be *negative*. Similarly, vertical distances measured *upward* from the x-axis are *positive* and those measured *downward* are *negative*.

Let P be any point of the plane whose horizontal distance from the y-axis is x and whose vertical distance from the x-axis is y. Then x is called the **abscissa** or **x-coordinate** of the point P, and y is called the **ordinate** or **y-coordinate** of the point P. Together these values are called the **rectangular coordinates** of the point P and we write them in the form (x, y). The position of a point is determined if its coordinates are known.

Conversely, if the position of a point is known, its coordinates can be found by measuring its distances from the two axes. The process of locating points when their coordinates are given is called the **plotting** of the points.

Example. Draw a line connecting the points $A(-2, 3)$ and $B(1, -1)$, and find its length.

Solution: In the notation used for representing points, remember that the first number given is the x-coordinate, and that the algebraic signs indicate directions.

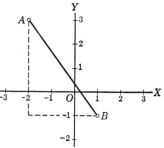

FIGURE 3.

Starting at the origin, to plot the point $(-2, 3)$ we move to the left two units and then up three units. To plot $(1, -1)$ we move one unit to the right of the origin and then down one unit.

After connecting these two points with a straight line, we may draw a horizontal and a vertical line as shown in Figure 3. Since the triangle thus formed is a right triangle, we can find the length of the hypotenuse using the following geometric theorem:

Theorem of Pythagoras. *In any right triangle the square on the hypotenuse is equal to the sum of the squares on the other two sides.*

Since the sides of the above triangle are evidently 3 and 4, we have

$$AB = \sqrt{3^2 + 4^2} = 5.$$

EXERCISE 20

1. On ruled paper, locate the points whose coordinates are as follows: $A(-1, 2)$, $B(4, 3)$, $C(0, -4)$, $D(-4, -2)$, $E(2\frac{1}{2}, 0)$, $F(-2, -3\frac{1}{2})$.

2. In Figure 4, what are the coordinates of the points A, B, C, D, E, and F?

3. Plot the points $A(2, 5)$, $B(2, 1)$, $C(-3, -3)$, $D(4, -3)$. How long are the line segments AB and CD?

4. (a) Plot the points: $A(-1, 5)$, $B(7, 5)$, $C(7, -1)$, $D(-1, -1)$. (b) What kind of a figure is $ABCD$? (c) Draw the diagonals AC and BD, and find the coordinates of their point of intersection.

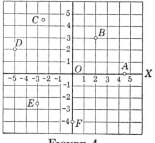

FIGURE 4.

5. Plot the points: $A(-6, 7)$, $B(2, -3)$, $C(0, 8)$, $D(-3, -1)$. What is the point of intersection of AB and CD?

6. Plot the points: $A(-5-3)$, $B(-2, 1)$, $C(0, -3)$, $D(2, 3)$. Extending AB and CD, find their point of intersection.

7. Find the distance between the points $(-7, 3)$ and $(5, -2)$.

8. Three vertices of a rectangle are at $(2, 5)$, $(-3, 5)$, and $(2, -1)$. Find the coordinates of the fourth vertex.

9. Plot the points $A(-4, -3)$, $B(1, -3)$, $C(-1\frac{1}{2}, 3)$. (a) What kind of triangle is ABC? (b) Find the lengths of its sides.

10. Plot the points: $A(-7, 0)$, $B(3, 0)$, $C(-2, 5)$. (a) Is ABC a right triangle? Why? (b) Find the lengths of its sides.

11. Plot the points: $A(-5, -4)$, $B(4, -4)$, $C(4, 2)$, $D(1, 5)$. What is the area of the quadrilateral $ABCD$?

12. Find the sides of the triangle formed by the points $A(-9, -9)$, $B(7, 3)$, and $C(-2, 15)$. Using the Pythagorean theorem, determine whether or not ABC is a right triangle.

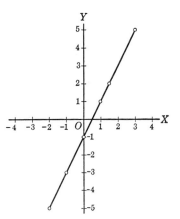

FIGURE 5.

32. Graphs of Functions. The pictorial representation of a function is called the **graph** or **locus** of the function, and the means by which it is obtained is called the **graphing** or **plotting** of the function.

Example 1. Plot the graph of the function $(2x - 1)$.

Solution: Let $y = 2x - 1$; then choose different values for x and compute the corresponding values of y as shown in the table.

When $x =$	0	1	3	$\frac{3}{2}$	-1	-2
then $y =$	-1	1	5	2	-3	-5

If we plot these pairs of values on a rectangular coordinate system and draw a smooth curve through them, we obtain a straight line, as indicated in Figure 5.

NOTE 1. The graph of any equation of the form $ax + by + c = 0$, which is of the first degree in x and y, is a straight line. For this reason such equations are usually called *linear equations*.

NOTE 2. Since a line is completely determined when two distinct points are known, only two table entries are needed in graphing a linear equation. In general, the points where the line crosses the coordinate axes are the easiest to obtain. These are called the **intercepts** on the axes.

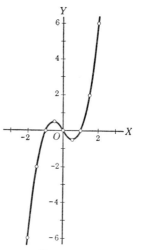

The principles underlying the graphing of any functions are the same. In summarized form, they are:

1. Select arbitrary values of the independent variable.

2. Compute the corresponding values of the function and arrange in tabular form.

3. Plot the pairs of values thus obtained, and connect the succession of points with a smooth curve.

Example 2. Graph the function $(x^3 - x)$.

FIGURE 6.

Solution: Let $y = x^3 - x$; then by substitution we find the following pairs of corresponding values of x and y:

When $x =$	-2	$-\frac{3}{2}$	-1	$-\frac{1}{2}$	0	$\frac{1}{2}$	1	$\frac{3}{2}$	2
then $y =$	-6	$-\frac{15}{8}$	0	$\frac{3}{8}$	0	$-\frac{3}{8}$	0	$\frac{15}{8}$	6

Plotting these values, we obtain the graph shown in Figure 6. There is no set rule to indicate what arbitrary values of x to select in setting up a table of points. Observe in this instance that it was essential to choose fractional values of x. If the four points having fractional abscissa are suppressed, the remaining five points do not clearly depict the nature of the curve. In general, *when in doubt as to the character of the curve in any interval, plot points in that interval to locate the curve definitely.*

EXERCISE 21

Graph each of the following functions:

1. $3x - 2$.   **2.** $5 - 2x$.   **3.** $\frac{1}{2}x + 3$.
4. $\frac{1}{2}x^2$.   **5.** $x - x^2$.   **6.** $x^2 + 4x - 5$.
7. $x^3 - x^2$.   **8.** $x^3 - 3x^2 + 2x$.   **9.** $4x - x^3$.

Graph each of the following equations:

10. $2x + 3y = 9.$ **11.** $2y + 7 = 0.$ **12.** $x + y = 0.$

13. $x^2 + 2y = 6.$ **14.** $y = 4x^2 - 8x - 5.$ **15.** $y = 6 + x - x^2.$

16. $y = x^3 - 2x^2 + x.$ **17.** $x^3 + y = 1.$ **18.** $x^4 = y + x^2.$

19. Plot the graphs of $y = x + b$, for $b = -3, 0, 3$, on the same coordinate system. What have these lines in common?

20. Plot the graphs of $y = mx + 2$, for $m = -2, 0, 2$, on the same coordinate system. What have these lines in common?

21. Plot the graphs of the function $(x^2 + 5x + a)$, for $a = -6, 0, 6$, on the same coordinate system.

22. Plot the graphs of the function $(ax - x^2)$, for $a = -2, 0, 2$, on the same coordinate system.

23. Plot the graph of the function $(3 - 4x - 4x^2)$, and from the graph determine the maximum value which the function can have.

24. Plot the graph of the function $(20x^2 + 40x + 27)$, and from the graph determine the minimum value which the function can have.

CHAPTER 6

Systems of Linear Equations

33. Linear Equations in Two Unknowns. An equation of
the form

$$ax + by + c = 0 \qquad (1)$$

where *a*, *b*, and *c* are constants is called a **general linear
equation in *x* and *y*.**

If x and y have values which satisfy (1), this pair of values is
called a **solution** of the equation. An equation such as (1) by
itself has an unlimited number of solutions, and consequently
it is said to be **indeterminate.**

Two or more equations of the form of (1) are said to comprise
a system of linear equations in two unknowns. If a pair
of corresponding values of x and y satisfy each equation, the
system is said to have the solution (x, y) and the equations of the
system are said to be **consistent;** they are also called **simul-
taneous equations.** If no such values exist, the system has no
solution and the equations are said to be **inconsistent.**

**34. Graphic Solution of Systems of Two Equations in
Two Unknowns.** The graphic method is summarized as follows:

*1. The graphs of the equations are plotted on the same coordinate
system.*

*2. The coordinates of any point of intersection of the graphs
form a solution of the system.*

47

Example 1. Solve graphically: $\begin{cases} x - y = 1, & (L_1) \\ 2x + y = 5, & (L_2) \end{cases}$

Solution: Plotting each of the two lines separately on the same coordinate system, we see that the lines intersect at the point where $x = 2$ and $y = 1$. These values constitute the only solution of the given
system of equations.

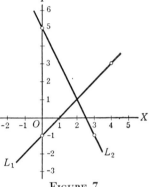

Note. In general, a graphic solution
of a system of equations gives only
approximate results.

When we plot the graphs of two
linear equations in two unknowns
on the same coordinate system, we
find that the two lines drawn
either (1) intersect in a single point,
(2) are identical, or (3) are parallel.
Corresponding to these three situ-

Figure 7.

ations, the equations of the system are said to be (1) **consistent**
and **independent**, (2) **consistent** and **dependent**, or (3) **inconsistent**.

EXERCISE 22

Graph and classify the following systems of equations. If they are
consistent and independent, find the solution.

1. $\begin{cases} 2x + y = -5, \\ x - 2y = 0. \end{cases}$
2. $\begin{cases} y = 2x + 4, \\ x = 1 - y. \end{cases}$
3. $\begin{cases} 3x + 5 = y, \\ x + 2y = 3. \end{cases}$

4. $\begin{cases} x = 2y - 1, \\ 4y = 2x + 2. \end{cases}$
5. $\begin{cases} 2x + 4y = 5, \\ 3x + 6y = 10. \end{cases}$
6. $\begin{cases} 3x + y = 1, \\ 2y + 7 = 0. \end{cases}$

7. $\begin{cases} 2x - y = 5, \\ 2x + y = 7. \end{cases}$
8. $\begin{cases} 4x - y = 3, \\ 2x + 1 = \frac{1}{2}y. \end{cases}$
9. $\begin{cases} \frac{1}{4}x + y = -5, \\ x - \frac{1}{3}y = 6. \end{cases}$

10. $\begin{cases} 3x - y = 3, \\ \frac{1}{2}x + \frac{1}{3}y = 2. \end{cases}$
11. $\begin{cases} y = 0.3x - 0.2, \\ 1.5x = y - 2. \end{cases}$
12. $\begin{cases} x = \frac{2}{3}y + 2, \\ y = \frac{3}{2}x - 3. \end{cases}$

13. $\begin{cases} x + y = 1, \\ 7x + 5 = 3y. \end{cases}$
14. $\begin{cases} x + y = 0, \\ 5x - 4y = 10. \end{cases}$
15. $\begin{cases} 5x + 2y = 4, \\ 5x - 2y = 2. \end{cases}$

**35. Algebraic Solution of Systems of Two Linear Equa-
tions in Two Unknowns.** If the equations of a system are
satisfied by the same values of the variables, any equation
formed by combining them will also be satisfied by these values.
To solve a system algebraically, we wish to obtain a derived
equation which contains only one of the unknowns.

The process by which we cause either of the unknowns to be eliminated is called *elimination*. This may be done in various ways, but the following two methods are particularly useful:

I. Rule for Elimination by Addition or Subtraction. *Multiply each equation, when necessary, by positive numbers to make the coefficients of one unknown numerically the same. Then add or subtract the resulting equations to eliminate that unknown.*

II. Rule for Elimination by Substitution. *In either of the equations, solve for one of the unknowns in terms of the other and substitute this expression in the second equation.*

Example. Solve algebraically:
$$\begin{cases} 5\,x + 4\,y = 8, & (1) \\ 3\,x - 2\,y = 7. & (2) \end{cases}$$

Solution by addition and subtraction:

Multiply (2) by 2: $\qquad 6\,x - 4\,y = 14.$ $\qquad\qquad$ (3)
Rewrite (1): $\qquad\qquad 5\,x + 4\,y = 8.$ $\qquad\qquad$ (4)
Add (3) and (4): $\qquad\qquad 11\,x = 22,$ or $x = 2.$
Substitute $x = 2$ in (1): $5(2) + 4\,y = 8,$ or $y = -\frac{1}{2}.$

Solution by substitution:

Solve (2) for x: $\qquad\qquad\qquad\qquad x = \frac{1}{3}(2\,y + 7).$ $\quad$ (5)
Substitute (5) in (1): $\qquad 5 \cdot \frac{1}{3}(2\,y + 7) + 4\,y = 8.$ $\quad$ (6)
Solve (6) for y: $\qquad 10\,y + 35 + 12\,y = 24,$ or $y = -\frac{1}{2}.$
Substitute $y = -\frac{1}{2}$ in (2): $\qquad 3\,x - 2(-\frac{1}{2}) = 7,$ or $x = 2.$

Check: Substituting $x = 2$ and $y = -\frac{1}{2}$ in the given equations, we have

$$5(2) + 4(-\tfrac{1}{2}) = 8, \quad \text{and} \quad 3(2) - 2(-\tfrac{1}{2}) = 7,$$
$$10 - 2 = 8, \qquad\qquad\qquad 6 + 1 = 7,$$
$$8 = 8, \qquad\qquad\qquad\qquad 7 = 7.$$

Note. When both unknowns are eliminated simultaneously, the equations of the system are *consistent* and *dependent* if a numerical identity is obtained, or *inconsistent* if a numerical inequality is obtained.

EXERCISE 23

Eliminate by addition and subtraction, solve and check:

1. $\begin{cases} x + 2\,y = 10, \\ x - 2\,y = -6. \end{cases}$ $\qquad$ 2. $\begin{cases} 5\,x + 2\,y = 6, \\ 3\,x + 4\,y = 12. \end{cases}$ $\qquad$ 3. $\begin{cases} 3\,x - 5\,y = 13, \\ 6\,x + 7\,y = -8. \end{cases}$

4. $\begin{cases} 7\,x - 2\,y = 4, \\ 9\,x - 3\,y = 3. \end{cases}$ $\qquad$ 5. $\begin{cases} 8\,x - 6\,y = 9, \\ 12\,x + 4\,y = 7. \end{cases}$ $\qquad$ 6. $\begin{cases} 6\,x - 5\,y = 23, \\ 9\,x + 7\,y = 20. \end{cases}$

Eliminate by substitution, solve and check:

7. $\begin{cases} y = 3x - 5, \\ x + 4y = 6. \end{cases}$
8. $\begin{cases} y = 2x + 3, \\ x = 2y - 3. \end{cases}$
9. $\begin{cases} 3x + 2y = 5, \\ x = \frac{1}{2}(3y + 12). \end{cases}$

10. $\begin{cases} 2x + 3y = 9, \\ 3x + 2y = 11. \end{cases}$
11. $\begin{cases} 5x + 3y = 7, \\ 9x - y = 3. \end{cases}$
12. $\begin{cases} 2x - 7y = 5, \\ 5x + 2y = 6. \end{cases}$

Solve the following systems of equations by any method:

13. $\begin{cases} 20x + 23y = 11, \\ 14x - 13y = 95. \end{cases}$
14. $\begin{cases} 17x - 13y = 7, \\ 19x - 11y = 29. \end{cases}$
15. $\begin{cases} 29x + 17y = 22, \\ 58x + 31y = 35. \end{cases}$

16. $\begin{cases} 11x + 5y = 53, \\ 31x - 14y = 37. \end{cases}$
17. $\begin{cases} 21x + 13y = 55, \\ 42x - 11y = 73. \end{cases}$
18. $\begin{cases} 49x - 43y = 71, \\ 23x - 21y = 17. \end{cases}$

Considering $1/x$ and $1/y$ as unknowns, solve the following systems of equations for x and y:

19. $\begin{cases} \dfrac{2}{x} - \dfrac{1}{y} = 3, \\ \dfrac{3}{x} - \dfrac{2}{y} = 1. \end{cases}$
20. $\begin{cases} \dfrac{3}{x} + \dfrac{5}{y} = 10, \\ \dfrac{5}{x} - \dfrac{3}{y} = -23. \end{cases}$
21. $\begin{cases} \dfrac{5}{3x} + \dfrac{3}{5y} = \dfrac{8}{15}, \\ \dfrac{7}{4x} + \dfrac{6}{5y} = \dfrac{3}{4}. \end{cases}$

Solve the following systems of equations:

22. $\begin{cases} \frac{1}{5}x + \frac{2}{3}y = 20, \\ \frac{3}{4}x - \frac{1}{6}y = 11. \end{cases}$
23. $\begin{cases} \dfrac{x-1}{3} + y = 6, \\ 5x - 3y = 5. \end{cases}$
24. $\begin{cases} \dfrac{x+1}{y-3} = 2, \\ \frac{1}{3}x + y = 6. \end{cases}$

25. $\begin{cases} 5(x+3) + 9(y+1) = 5, \\ 3(2x+1) - 7(y-3) = 19. \end{cases}$
26. $\begin{cases} 6(3x-1) + 3(y+5) = 16, \\ 3(x+2) - 4(3y-1) = 7. \end{cases}$

27. $\begin{cases} (x+3)(y+1) = (x+2)(y+2), \\ \frac{1}{2}x + \frac{1}{3}y = 2. \end{cases}$
28. $\dfrac{2x-1}{9} = \dfrac{2y-7}{5} = \dfrac{2x-y}{4}.$

29. $\begin{cases} \dfrac{1}{x+1} + \dfrac{1}{y+1} = 0, \\ \dfrac{1}{2x+1} + \dfrac{1}{y} = 0. \end{cases}$
30. $\begin{cases} \dfrac{x-1}{x} = \dfrac{y}{y+2}, \\ \dfrac{x+3}{x} = \dfrac{y}{y-2}. \end{cases}$

Solve for x and y:

31. $\begin{cases} 4x - y = c - 9d, \\ 3x + 2y = 9c - 4d. \end{cases}$
32. $\begin{cases} 2mx - 3ny = 2, \\ 3mx + 2ny = 16. \end{cases}$

33. $\begin{cases} ax + 2by = 3c, \\ 2ax - by = 11c. \end{cases}$
34. $\begin{cases} x + 3y = 7ab, \\ 2x - y = 7. \end{cases}$

35. $\begin{cases} ax + by = 2a^2 - 2b^2, \\ x - y = a + b. \end{cases}$
36. $\begin{cases} ax - by = a^2 + b^2, \\ bx + ay = a^2 + b^2. \end{cases}$

36. Systems of Three Linear Equations in Three Unknowns.
The solution of three linear equations in three unknowns may be reduced to the solution of two linear equations

in two unknowns by eliminating the same unknown from any two pairs of the given equations. These two equations can then be solved for two of the unknowns, and the remaining unknown can be found by substitution in any one of the given equations.

NOTE 1. A system of n linear equations in n unknowns may be solved in the same manner by reducing the system to $(n-1)$ linear equations in $(n-1)$ unknowns and by repeating this process as long as necessary.

Example. Solve:
$$\begin{cases} 3x - y - 2z = 9, & (1) \\ 2x + y + z = 7, & (2) \\ x + 2y + 3z = 4. & (3) \end{cases}$$

First solution: Suppose that we choose to eliminate y.

Add (1) and (2):	$5x - z = 16.$	(4)
Multiply (1) by 2:	$6x - 2y - 4z = 18.$	(5)
Add (3) and (5):	$7x - z = 22.$	(6)
Subtract (4) from (6):	$2x = 6,$ or $x = 3.$	
Substitute $x = 3$ in (6):	$7(3) - z = 22,$ or $z = -1.$	
Substitute $x = 3, z = -1$ in (2):	$2(3) + y + (-1) = 7,$ or $y = 2.$	

Second solution: Suppose again that we choose to eliminate y.

Solve (2) for y:
$$y = 7 - 2x - z. \qquad (7)$$
Substitute in (1): $3x - (7 - 2x - z) - 2z = 9,$
$$5x - z = 16. \qquad (8)$$
Substitute in (3): $x + 2(7 - 2x - z) + 3z = 4,$
$$-3x + z = -10. \qquad (9)$$

By adding we obtain $x = 3$. Hence, as before, $z = -1$ and $y = 2$.

Check: Substituting $x = 3$, $y = 2$, and $z = -1$ in the given equations gives:

$$3(3) - (2) - 2(-1) = 9, \qquad 2(3) + (2) + (-1) = 7,$$
$$9 - 2 + 2 = 9, \qquad\qquad 6 + 2 - 1 = 7,$$
$$9 = 9. \qquad\qquad\qquad 7 = 7.$$

and
$$(3) + 2(2) + 3(-1) = 4,$$
$$3 + 4 - 3 = 4,$$
$$4 = 4.$$

NOTE 2. Usually a system of three linear equations in three unknowns has a single solution. The cases in which such systems have no solutions or an unlimited number of solutions are considered in Chapter 21.

Solve the following systems of equations:

1. $\begin{cases} x - 2y + z = 3, \\ 2x + y - z = 7, \\ 3x - y + 2z = 6. \end{cases}$
2. $\begin{cases} 2x + y - 2z = 3, \\ 3x - 2y + 3z = 9, \\ z = x + y. \end{cases}$

3. $\begin{cases} 2x + y - 3z = 1, \\ x - y + 2z = 1, \\ x + 3y - z = 6. \end{cases}$
4. $\begin{cases} 4x + y - 2z = 2, \\ x - 2y + z = 5, \\ 2x - y - 3z = 4. \end{cases}$

5. $\begin{cases} 3x - y - 3z = 1, \\ x - 3y + z = 1, \\ 5x - 4z = 8. \end{cases}$
6. $\begin{cases} x - 2y + z = 7, \\ 2x + 3z = 4, \\ y + 2z = 1. \end{cases}$

7. $\begin{cases} 2x - y + 3z = 4, \\ x + 3y + 3z = -2, \\ 3x + 2y - 6z = 6. \end{cases}$
8. $\begin{cases} 3x + 2y - z = 2, \\ x - y - 9z = 1, \\ 4x + 3y + 3z = 0. \end{cases}$

9. $\begin{cases} \frac{1}{2}x + \frac{1}{3}y + \frac{1}{4}z = 3, \\ \frac{1}{3}x - \frac{5}{6}y + \frac{1}{2}z = \frac{1}{6}, \\ \frac{3}{4}x + \frac{2}{3}y - \frac{5}{8}z = 1. \end{cases}$
10. $\begin{cases} x + \frac{1}{2}y + \frac{1}{3}z = \frac{1}{6}, \\ y + \frac{1}{2}z + \frac{1}{3}x = \frac{4}{3}, \\ z + \frac{1}{2}x + \frac{1}{3}y = -\frac{7}{12}. \end{cases}$

11. $\begin{cases} \dfrac{1}{x} - \dfrac{1}{y} - \dfrac{1}{z} = 0, \\ \dfrac{3}{x} + \dfrac{1}{y} + \dfrac{3}{z} = 1, \\ \dfrac{2}{x} + \dfrac{1}{y} + \dfrac{1}{z} = 1. \end{cases}$
12. $\begin{cases} x + y + \dfrac{1}{z} = 3, \\ 2x - y + \dfrac{1}{z} = 4, \\ x - y - \dfrac{2}{z} = 4. \end{cases}$

13. $\begin{cases} \frac{1}{2}(x + 2) - \frac{1}{3}(y + 3) = 2, \\ \frac{1}{4}(y - 1) + \frac{1}{3}(z + 4) = 2, \\ \frac{1}{2}(z + 1) - \frac{1}{3}(x + 1) = 2. \end{cases}$
14. $\begin{cases} (x - 1)(z - 2) = xz - y, \\ (y - 2)(z + 1) = z(y - 1), \\ (x + 2)(y - 1) = xy + 2. \end{cases}$

15. $\begin{cases} 2x - y - z = -3, \\ 2x - 2y + z = a, \\ x + 3y - 3z = a - 3. \end{cases}$
16. $\begin{cases} x + ay + z = a + 2, \\ x - a^2y + z = 1, \\ ax - a^3y + cz = c. \end{cases}$

17. $\begin{cases} x - 2y + z - 3w = 1, \\ 2x + y - 2z - w = 9, \\ x - y - 3z + 2w = 16, \\ 4x - 3y + 7z = -3. \end{cases}$
18. $\begin{cases} x - 2y + z = 8, \\ y - 2z + w = -12, \\ z - 2w + x = 12, \\ x + y + z + w = 2. \end{cases}$

37. Solution of Two Linear Equations in Two Unknowns by Determinants. Consider the system of equations

$$\begin{cases} a_1x + b_1y = k_1, \\ a_2x + b_2y = k_2. \end{cases} \quad \begin{array}{c} (1) \\ (2) \end{array}$$

Multiplying (1) by b_2, (2) by b_1, and subtracting, we have

$$(a_1b_2 - a_2b_1)x = k_1b_2 - k_2b_1.$$

Multiplying (1) by a_2, (2) by a_1, and subtracting, we have

$$(a_1b_2 - a_2b_1)y = a_1k_2 - a_2k_1.$$

Thus, if $a_1b_2 - a_2b_1 \neq 0$, the general solution of the original system of equations is given by

$$x = \frac{k_1b_2 - k_2b_1}{a_1b_2 - a_2b_1}, \quad y = \frac{a_1k_2 - a_2k_1}{a_1b_2 - a_2b_1}. \tag{3}$$

This result is more easily remembered by representing the expression $(a_1b_2 - a_2b_1)$ by the symbol

$$\begin{vmatrix} a_1 & b_1 \\ a_2 & b_2 \end{vmatrix},$$

which is called a **determinant.** Since this array has two columns and two rows it is called a **determinant of the second order.** The numbers a_1, a_2, b_1, and b_2 are called the **elements** of the determinant, and the elements a_1 and b_2 form its **principal diagonal.** The expression $(a_1b_2 - a_2b_1)$ is called the **expansion** of the determinant, and the products a_1b_2 and a_2b_1 are called the **terms** of the determinant.

Illustration. $\begin{vmatrix} 2 & -5 \\ 4 & -3 \end{vmatrix} = (2)(-3) - (4)(-5) = -6 + 20 = 14.$

By the above definition of a determinant, it is apparent that the solution (3) may be written in the form

$$x = \frac{\begin{vmatrix} k_1 & b_1 \\ k_2 & b_2 \end{vmatrix}}{\begin{vmatrix} a_1 & b_1 \\ a_2 & b_2 \end{vmatrix}}, \quad y = \frac{\begin{vmatrix} a_1 & k_1 \\ a_2 & k_2 \end{vmatrix}}{\begin{vmatrix} a_1 & b_1 \\ a_2 & b_2 \end{vmatrix}} \tag{4}$$

provided that the determinant in the denominators is not zero.

For linear equations written in the form of (1) and (2), we observe the following in the solution (4):

1. The determinants in the denominators are the same, and their elements are the coefficients of the unknowns.

2. The determinant in the numerator, for any unknown, is the same as that in the denominator **except that** *the coefficients of this unknown are replaced by the constant terms.*

Example. Solve by determinants: $\begin{cases} 5x + 4y = 8, \\ 3x - 2y = 7. \end{cases}$

Solution: The equations are written in the required form; hence

$$x = \frac{\begin{vmatrix} 8 & 4 \\ 7 & -2 \end{vmatrix}}{\begin{vmatrix} 5 & 4 \\ 3 & -2 \end{vmatrix}} = \frac{-16 - 28}{-10 - 12} = \frac{-44}{-22} = 2,$$

$$y = \frac{\begin{vmatrix} 5 & 8 \\ 3 & 7 \end{vmatrix}}{-22} = \frac{35 - 24}{-22} = \frac{11}{-22} = -\frac{1}{2}.$$

NOTE. If the determinant in the denominator of (4) is zero, the given equations are either dependent or inconsistent.

EXERCISE 25

1–18. Solve Problems 1 to 18 in Exercise 23, using determinants.

38. Determinants of the Third Order. The symbol

$$\begin{vmatrix} a_1 & b_1 & c_1 \\ a_2 & b_2 & c_2 \\ a_3 & b_3 & c_3 \end{vmatrix}$$

is called a **determinant of the third order** and it is defined to represent the algebraic sum

$$a_1 b_2 c_3 + a_3 b_1 c_2 + a_2 b_3 c_1 - a_3 b_2 c_1 - a_1 b_3 c_2 - a_2 b_1 c_3. \quad (1)$$

The numbers a_1, a_2, a_3, b_1, and so on, are called the **elements** of the determinant, and the elements a_1, b_2, and c_3 form its **principal diagonal**. The expression (1) is called the **expansion**

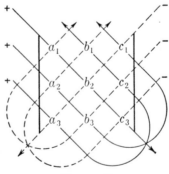

FIGURE 8.

of the determinant, and the products $a_1b_2c_3$, $a_3b_1c_2$, and so on, are called the **terms** of the determinant.

The schematic diagram shown in Figure 8 may be used as an aid to remembering the expansion of a third-order determinant. The positive terms of (1) are the three diagonal products obtained in moving in the direction of the principal diagonal, and the three negative terms of (1) are the diagonal products obtained in following the direction of the other diagonal.

Illustration. $\begin{vmatrix} 2 & 4 & -1 \\ 1 & -2 & 3 \\ 3 & 1 & 2 \end{vmatrix} = (-8) + (-1) + (36) \\ - (6) - (6) - (8) = 7.$

NOTE. If the first two columns of the determinant are repeated at the right, the diagram shown in Figure 9 may also be used.

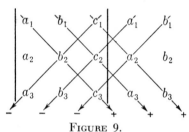

FIGURE 9.

EXERCISE 26

Find the value of each of the following determinants:

1. $\begin{vmatrix} 3 & -2 & 3 \\ 2 & 4 & -1 \\ 1 & -1 & 2 \end{vmatrix}$.

2. $\begin{vmatrix} 5 & 1 & 4 \\ -2 & 2 & 3 \\ 3 & -2 & 1 \end{vmatrix}$.

3. $\begin{vmatrix} 0 & 3 & 1 \\ 6 & 2 & -1 \\ -4 & 5 & 2 \end{vmatrix}$.

4. $\begin{vmatrix} -1 & 2 & 3 \\ 2 & -1 & 2 \\ 3 & 2 & -1 \end{vmatrix}$.

5. $\begin{vmatrix} 4 & -3 & 2 \\ 1 & 5 & 6 \\ 5 & 0 & -1 \end{vmatrix}$.

6. $\begin{vmatrix} 1 & 4 & 7 \\ 2 & 5 & 8 \\ 3 & 6 & 9 \end{vmatrix}$.

Expand the following determinants:

7. $\begin{vmatrix} 1 & a & -b \\ -a & 1 & c \\ b & -c & 1 \end{vmatrix}$.

8. $\begin{vmatrix} 1 & 1 & 1 \\ 1 & 1+a & 1 \\ 1 & 1 & 1+b \end{vmatrix}$.

Solve each of the following equations:

9. $\begin{vmatrix} x+1 & 4 & 3 \\ x-3 & 1 & -1 \\ x+2 & -2 & 4 \end{vmatrix} = 0.$

10. $\begin{vmatrix} x-1 & 3 & 1 \\ 2 & x & -2 \\ x-2 & 2 & 1 \end{vmatrix} = 0.$

39. Solution of Three Linear Equations in Three Unknowns by Determinants.

Applying the methods of elimination to the following system of linear equations

$$\begin{cases} a_1x + b_1y + c_1z = k_1, \\ a_2x + b_2y + c_2z = k_2, \\ a_3x + b_3y + c_3z = k_3, \end{cases} \tag{1}$$

we obtain

$$x = \frac{k_1b_2c_3 + k_3b_1c_2 + k_2b_3c_1 - k_3b_2c_1 - k_1b_3c_2 - k_2b_1c_3}{a_1b_2c_3 + a_3b_1c_2 + a_2b_3c_1 - a_3b_2c_1 - a_1b_3c_2 - a_2b_1c_3},$$

$$y = \frac{a_1k_2c_3 + a_3k_1c_2 + a_2k_3c_1 - a_3k_2c_1 - a_1k_3c_2 - a_2k_1c_3}{a_1b_2c_3 + a_3b_1c_2 + a_2b_3c_1 - a_3b_2c_1 - a_1b_3c_2 - a_2b_1c_3},$$

$$z = \frac{a_1b_2k_3 + a_3b_1k_2 + a_2b_3k_1 - a_3b_2k_1 - a_1b_3k_2 - a_2b_1k_3}{a_1b_2c_3 + a_3b_1c_2 + a_2b_3c_1 - a_3b_2c_1 - a_1b_3c_2 - a_2b_1c_3},$$

provided that the denominators are not zero.

By the definition of a third-order determinant, it is apparent that the above solution may be written in the form

$$x = \frac{\begin{vmatrix} k_1 & b_1 & c_1 \\ k_2 & b_2 & c_2 \\ k_3 & b_3 & c_3 \end{vmatrix}}{\begin{vmatrix} a_1 & b_1 & c_1 \\ a_2 & b_2 & c_2 \\ a_3 & b_3 & c_3 \end{vmatrix}}, \quad y = \frac{\begin{vmatrix} a_1 & k_1 & c_1 \\ a_2 & k_2 & c_2 \\ a_3 & k_3 & c_3 \end{vmatrix}}{\begin{vmatrix} a_1 & b_1 & c_1 \\ a_2 & b_2 & c_2 \\ a_3 & b_3 & c_3 \end{vmatrix}}, \quad z = \frac{\begin{vmatrix} a_1 & b_1 & k_1 \\ a_2 & b_2 & k_2 \\ a_3 & b_3 & k_3 \end{vmatrix}}{\begin{vmatrix} a_1 & b_1 & c_1 \\ a_2 & b_2 & c_2 \\ a_3 & b_3 & c_3 \end{vmatrix}}, \tag{2}$$

provided that the determinant in the denominators is not zero.

For linear equations written in the form of (1), we observe the following in the solution (2):

1. The determinants in the denominators are the same, and their elements are the coefficients of the unknowns.

2. The determinant in the numerator, for any unknown, is the same as that in the denominator **except that** *the coefficients of this unknown are replaced by the constant terms.*

Example. Solve by determinants: $\begin{cases} 3x - y - 2z = 9, \\ 2x + y + z = 7, \\ x + 2y + 3z = 4. \end{cases}$

Solution: The equations are written in the required form; hence

$$x = \frac{\begin{vmatrix} 9 & -1 & -2 \\ 7 & 1 & 1 \\ 4 & 2 & 3 \end{vmatrix}}{\begin{vmatrix} 3 & -1 & -2 \\ 2 & 1 & 1 \\ 1 & 2 & 3 \end{vmatrix}} = \frac{(27)+(-28)+(-4)-(-8)-(18)-(-21)}{(9)+(-8)+(-1)-(-2)-(6)-(-6)}$$
$$= \frac{6}{2} = 3.$$

$$y = \tfrac{1}{2} \begin{vmatrix} 3 & 9 & -2 \\ 2 & 7 & 1 \\ 1 & 4 & 3 \end{vmatrix} = \tfrac{1}{2}[(63)+(-16)+(9)-(-14)-(12)-(54)]$$
$$= \tfrac{1}{2}[4] = 2.$$

$$z = \tfrac{1}{2} \begin{vmatrix} 3 & -1 & 9 \\ 2 & 1 & 7 \\ 1 & 2 & 4 \end{vmatrix} = \tfrac{1}{2}[(12)+(36)+(-7)-(9)-(42)-(-8)]$$
$$= \tfrac{1}{2}[-2] = -1.$$

NOTE. If the determinant in the denominators of (2) is zero, the given equations are either dependent or inconsistent.

EXERCISE 27

1–10. Solve Problems 1 to 10 in Exercise 24 by determinants.

40. Problems Leading to Systems of Equations. In order to obtain a single solution to a system of linear equations, as we have seen, it is essential to have as many equations as there are unknowns. Consequently in the solution of stated problems using n unknowns the statement should contain n *independent conditions* from which the necessary equations may be obtained.

Example 1. A man can row downstream 3 miles in 20 minutes, but it takes him an hour to return. How fast can he row in still water, and what is the rate of the current?

Analysis: If x miles per hour represents his rate of rowing in still water and y miles per hour represents the rate of the stream, then $(x + y)$ is his rate downstream and $(x - y)$ is his rate upstream.

Hence, from the formula *Rate* $\times$ *Time* = *Distance*, we have

$$\begin{cases} \tfrac{1}{3}(x + y) = 3, \\ x - y = 3. \end{cases}$$

Solution: Clearing of fractions, we have

$$\begin{cases} x + y = 9, \\ x - y = 3. \end{cases}$$

Solving, we obtain $x = 6$ and $y = 3$.

Answer: He can row 6 miles per hour in still water, and the rate of the current is 3 miles per hour.

Example 2. If the numerator and denominator of a fraction are each decreased by 1, it equals $\frac{1}{2}$; but if they are each increased by 1, it equals $\frac{4}{7}$. What is the fraction?

Analysis: Let x represent the numerator of the fraction, and y the denominator. Then from the statement we have

$$\frac{x-1}{y-1} = \frac{1}{2} \quad \text{and} \quad \frac{x+1}{y+1} = \frac{4}{7}.$$

Solution: Clearing of fractions and transposing, we obtain

$$\begin{cases} 2x - y = 1, \\ 7x - 4y = -3. \end{cases}$$

Solving these equations, we obtain $x = 7$ and $y = 13$.

Answer: The fraction is $\frac{7}{13}$.

Example 3. A certain number of three digits is equal to 28 times the sum of its digits. If the tens' digit and the units' digit are interchanged, the number is increased by 18; and if all three digits are reversed, the number is increased by 198. Find the number.

Analysis: Let x be the hundreds' digit, y the tens' digit, and z the units' digit. Then the conditions of the problem may be written in the form

$$\begin{cases} 100x + 10y + z = 28(x + y + z), \\ 100x + 10z + y = 100x + 10y + z + 18, \\ 100z + 10y + x = 100x + 10y + z + 198. \end{cases}$$

Solution: Collecting like terms and simplifying, we obtain

$$\begin{cases} 8x - 2y - 3z = 0, \\ -y + z = 2, \\ -x + z = 2. \end{cases}$$

Solving, we obtain $x = 2$, $y = 2$, and $z = 4$.

Answer: The number is 224.

EXERCISE 28

1. Find two numbers such that twice the larger exceeds three times the smaller by 1, and three times the larger exceeds their sum by 7.

2. Seven bats and six balls cost $12.05, and five bats and ten balls cost $11.75. What is the price of each bat and each ball?

3. A crew can row 1 mile down a stream in 6 minutes and 1 mile up the same stream in 10 minutes. What is the rate of the stream?

4. A man has a pile of coins consisting of dimes and quarters and worth $6.70. He observes that if the dimes were quarters and

the quarters were dimes, he would have $1.65 more. How many of each coin has he?

5. *A* and *B*, starting at the same time from two points 22 miles apart, walk toward each other and meet in 2 hours and 45 minutes. If *A* had walked twice as fast, they would have met in 2 hours. At what rate did *B* walk?

6. A man owns two stores. In 1944 one store earned 10% of the investment in it and the other lost 5%, netting a gain of $4750. In 1945 the first store earned 8% and the second earned 6%, netting a gain of $9300. What is the value of each store?

7. *A*'s age next year will be twice what *B*'s age was 8 years ago, and *B*'s age next year will be twice what *A*'s age was 11 years ago. Find their present ages.

8. A motorboat traveling at full speed against a current goes 10 miles per hour, and traveling at half speed with the current it goes 8 miles per hour. What is the rate of the current?

9. Four pounds of Grade *A* tea mixed with 5 pounds of Grade *B* tea is worth 25 cents a pound, and 7 pounds of Grade *A* mixed with 2 pounds of Grade *B* is worth 28 cents a pound. What is the price of each grade per pound?

10. The wages of 10 men and 7 boys amount to $68.75. If 3 men together receive 80 cents more than 4 boys, what are the wages of each man and each boy?

11. A number between 10 and 100 is four times the sum of its digits. If the number is doubled and then decreased by 9, the result will be the number with its digits reversed. Find the number.

12. If *A* works for 8 days and *B* for 15 days they can complete a certain job, or if *A* works for 12 days and *B* for 10 days they can complete the same job. How long would it take each working alone to do the job?

13. An airplane flying from Los Angeles to San Francisco against a wind traveling 15 miles per hour makes the trip in $2\frac{1}{2}$ hours. On the return, with the aid of a tail wind blowing 25 miles per hour, the plane makes the trip in 2 hours. What is the air distance between the two cities?

14. The sum of the perimeters of two squares of different sizes is 112 inches. If two sides of the squares are placed together, the outside perimeter of the figure formed is 90 inches. Find the size of each square.

15. A man has two sons, one 3 years older than the other. Two years ago the father's age was three times the sum of his boys' ages, and next year his age will be twice the sum of their ages. Find the present ages of all three.

16. Find a fraction which reduces to $\frac{1}{2}$ if 10 is added to its denominator, and which reduces to $\frac{3}{4}$ if 1 is added to its numerator.

17. Three pounds of tea and seven pounds of coffee cost $4.30. If the price of tea should increase 10% and that of coffee should decrease 10%, the cost of the above quantities would be $4.17. Find the price of each per pound.

18. It takes A 4 hours longer than B to walk 30 miles, but if he doubles his pace he takes 1 hour less than B. Find their rates of walking.

19. A man has $9000 invested, part at 4%, part at 5%, and the remainder in a business enterprise. One year the business lost 2% and the man's net income was $205. The next year the business paid 10% and he received altogether $565. Find how much he has invested in the business enterprise.

20. A chemist had a solution of 60% acid. He added some distilled water, reducing the concentration to 40%. He then added 1 quart more water, reducing the concentration to 30%. How much of the 30% solution did he then have?

21. The perimeter of a rectangle is 60 feet. If the length is decreased 1 foot and the width is increased 1 foot, the area of the rectangle will be increased by 3 square feet. Find the dimensions of the rectangle.

22. A number consists of three digits, the middle one being zero. If the hundreds' digit is halved and the other two digits are interchanged, the number is decreased by 137; and if the digits of the original number are reversed, the number obtained is greater by 297. Find the number.

23. A hiker walks a certain distance. If he had walked 1 mile per hour faster, he would have taken five-sixths as much time; and if he had walked 1 mile per hour slower, he would have taken 3 hours longer. What distance did he walk?

24. A club purchased a boat, each member paying an equal share. If there had been 3 more members, each would have paid a dollar less; but if there had been 2 less, each would have paid a dollar more. How many members are there?

25. A tank is equipped with a pipe which drains it continuously. If a pipe filling the tank is turned on full force, it fills the tank in 3 hours. If the pipe is turned on only half speed, it takes 12 hours to fill the tank. How long does it take the drain to empty a full tank?

26. If the length of a rectangle is decreased 1 foot and the width is increased 2 feet, the area is increased by 17 square feet; but if the width is decreased 1 foot and the length is increased 2 feet, the area is decreased by 1 square foot. What are the dimensions of the rectangle?

27. A passenger boat takes 4 hours and a freighter takes $5\frac{1}{2}$ hours to make the trip from A to B by way of a canal which is 12 miles long. Outside the canal the passenger boat travels 24 miles per hour and the freighter travels 18 miles per hour. Inside the canal the rate of the freighter is two-thirds that of the passenger boat. Find the distance from A to B by way of the canal.

28. On an inclined railway the fare is 75 cents for the upward trip and 25 cents for the downward trip. One day a certain number of passengers rode up; some of them rode down, while the rest walked. The receipts of the railway were $155. The next day three times as many passengers rode up as on the first day. All of these either walked or rode down during the day, but there were 120 more who walked than on the previous day. The receipts for the second day were $445. How many passengers rode up the first day?

29. A woman paid $10 for 2 yards of white, 3 yards of blue, and 1 yard of red material. Later she needed more material and paid $3 for $\frac{1}{3}$ yard of white, $\frac{1}{2}$ yard of blue, and $\frac{1}{2}$ yard of red. Find the price of the red material, and show that it was more expensive than either of the other materials.

30. The combined weight of the baggage of two airplane passengers is 120 pounds. One passenger pays $1.00 and the other $2.00 for excess above the weight allowed without charge. If all the baggage had belonged to one person, he would have had to pay $4.50. How many pounds of baggage was each person allowed to carry without charge?

CHAPTER 7

Exponents and Radicals

41. Laws of Exponents. If n is any positive integer and a is any number, we define the expression a^n to mean the product of n factors each of which is equal to a; thus

$$a^n = a \cdot a \cdot a \cdots a(n \text{ factors}).$$

The symbol a^n is read "the nth power of a" or simply "a to the nth." The number a is called the **base** and n the **exponent** of the power.

In the statement of the following **laws of exponents,** we shall limit our proofs to those cases in which the exponents are positive integers. These laws are valid, however, for a more general class of exponents which are defined later in this chapter.

Note 1. When literal exponents occur in the following discussion, it is assumed that they are positive and integral.

Law I. $a^m \cdot a^n = a^{m+n}$.

Proof:
$$a^m \cdot a^n = (a \cdot a \cdot a \cdots \text{ to } m \text{ factors})(a \cdot a \cdot a \cdots \text{ to } n \text{ factors})$$
$$= a \cdot a \cdot a \cdots \text{ to } (m + n) \text{ factors}$$
$$= a^{m+n}.$$

Illustration 1. $x^5 \cdot x^3 = x^8$; $b^k \cdot b^{k+3} = b^{2k+3}$.

Law II. (1) $\dfrac{a^m}{a^n} = a^{m-n}$, **if** $m > n$ **and** $a \neq 0$.

(2) $\dfrac{a^m}{a^n} = 1$, if $m = n$ and $a \neq 0$.

(3) $\dfrac{a^m}{a^n} = \dfrac{1}{a^{n-m}}$, if $m < n$ and $a \neq 0$.

Proof: (1) $\dfrac{a^m}{a^n} = \dfrac{a \cdot a \cdot a \cdots \text{to } m \text{ factors}}{a \cdot a \cdot a \cdots \text{to } n \text{ factors}}$

$$= \dfrac{a \cdot a \cdot a \cdots \text{to } (m - n) \text{ factors}}{1}$$

$$= a^{m-n}.$$

The proofs of (2) and (3) are left to the student.

Illustration 2. $\dfrac{3^7}{3^5} = 3^2; \ \dfrac{y^k}{y^k} = 1; \ \dfrac{x^2}{x^6} = \dfrac{1}{x^4}.$

Law III. $(a^m)^n = a^{mn}.$

Proof: $(a^m)^n = a^m \cdot a^m \cdot a^m \cdots \text{to } n \text{ factors}$

$$= a^{m+m+m+\cdots \text{ to } n \text{ terms}}$$

$$= a^{mn}.$$

Illustration 3. $(x^4)^3 = x^{12}; \ (2^{k-1})^k = 2^{k^2-k}.$

Law IV. $(ab)^n = a^n b^n.$

Proof: $(ab)^n = (ab) \cdot (ab) \cdot (ab) \cdots \text{to } n \text{ factors}$

$$= (a \cdot a \cdot a \cdots \text{to } n \text{ factors})(b \cdot b \cdot b \cdots \text{to } n \text{ factors})$$

$$= a^n b^n.$$

Illustration 4. $(x^k y^2)^4 = (x^k)^4 (y^2)^4 = x^{4k} y^8;$
$(-4 a^2 b)^3 = (-4)^3 (a^2)^3 (b)^3 = -64 a^6 b^3.$

Law V. $\left(\dfrac{a}{b}\right)^n = \dfrac{a^n}{b^n}$, if $b \neq 0$.

Proof: $\left(\dfrac{a}{b}\right)^n = \left(\dfrac{a}{b}\right) \cdot \left(\dfrac{a}{b}\right) \cdot \left(\dfrac{a}{b}\right) \cdots \text{to } n \text{ factors}$

$$= \dfrac{a \cdot a \cdot a \cdots \text{to } n \text{ factors}}{b \cdot b \cdot b \cdots \text{to } n \text{ factors}}$$

$$= \dfrac{a^n}{b^n}.$$

Illustration 5. $\left(\dfrac{2 x^k}{y^3}\right)^3 = \dfrac{(2)^3 (x^k)^3}{(y^3)^3} = \dfrac{8 x^{3k}}{y^9}.$

NOTE 2. Observe, especially, that an exponent indicates the power to be taken of that quantity and only that quantity to which it is attached.

Thus, $-(x^3)^2$ means $-(x^3)(x^3) = -x^6$, whereas $(-x^3)^2$ means $(-x^3)(-x^3) = x^6.$

EXERCISE 29

Perform the indicated operations, using the laws of exponents:

1. x^3x^4.   **2.** m^2m^6.   **3.** $y^8y^3y^5$.   **4.** $a^2x^3 \cdot a^3x^4$.   **5.** $3^3 \cdot 3^5$.

6. $\dfrac{x^5}{x^2}$.   **7.** $\dfrac{z^5}{z^8}$.   **8.** $\dfrac{a^2b^2}{ab^2}$.   **9.** $\dfrac{xy^2}{x^3y^3}$.   **10.** $\dfrac{abc^5}{ab^2c^3}$.

11. $(a^5)^5$.   **12.** $(-m^2)^3$.   **13.** $-(b^8)^2$.

14. $(2\,x)^4$.   **15.** $(-3\,a^2)^2$.   **16.** $(ax^2)^3$.

17. $(a^2b^3c)^2$.   **18.** $(-x^5y^4)^3$.   **19.** $(2\,ab^2)^3$.

20. $(3\,ax^2y^3)^3$.   **21.** $\left(\dfrac{a}{x^2}\right)^4$.   **22.** $\left(\dfrac{5}{p}\right)^3$.

23. $\left(-\dfrac{x}{2}\right)^2$.   **24.** $\left(\dfrac{2\,x}{3\,y^2}\right)^3$.   **25.** $\left(\dfrac{ab^3}{2\,x^2}\right)^5$.

26. $a^{k-2}a^2$.   **27.** $2^m \cdot 2^{6-m}$.   **28.** $x^{p(p-1)}x^p$.

29. $\dfrac{x^{k+3}}{x^{k-1}}$.   **30.** $\dfrac{y^{ax+b}}{y^{ax+c}}$.   **31.** $\dfrac{a^{n^2-1}}{a^{n-1}}$.

32. $(-2\,a^pb^q)^2$.   **33.** $(a^2b^{x-1})^x$.   **34.** $-(3\,x^m)^{m-1}$.

35. $\left(\dfrac{2\,a}{x^2}\right)^m$.   **36.** $\left(\dfrac{a^mb}{c^p}\right)^m$.   **37.** $\left(\dfrac{xy^{n-1}}{z^2}\right)^2$.

Perform the indicated operations and simplify:

38. $(ax^2)^2(ax^3)^3$.   **39.** $(mn^2)^2(2\,m^2n)^4$.

40. $(2\,a^2b^3)^2(-ab^3)^5$.   **41.** $\dfrac{(3\,p^2q)^3}{(6\,pq^2)^2}$.

42. $\dfrac{(xy^2)^3(x^2y^3)^2}{(x^5y)^2}$.   **43.** $\left(\dfrac{2\,a^2}{x}\right)^3\left(\dfrac{x^2}{2\,a}\right)^4$.

44. $\dfrac{(6\,a^5b^3)^4}{(3\,ab^2)^3(2\,a^2b)^5}$.   **45.** $\left(\dfrac{a^2b}{x}\right)^4\left(\dfrac{a}{b^2x^3}\right)^2\left(\dfrac{x^2}{a^2}\right)^5$.

46. $\left(\dfrac{2\,a}{3\,c}\right)^2\left(\dfrac{6\,c}{b^2}\right)^3\left(\dfrac{b^3}{4\,a}\right)^2$.   **47.** $\dfrac{a^{2m+n}a^n}{a^{m+2n}}$.

48. $\dfrac{(b^{x+1})^{x+1}}{(b^{x+2})^x}$.   **49.** $\left(\dfrac{a^2}{b^n}\right)^n\left(\dfrac{b^{n^2}}{a^n}\right)^2$.

50. $\dfrac{3^k \cdot 9^{k+1}}{3^{3k+1}}$.   **51.** $\dfrac{(x^{b+1})^ax^{a+b}}{(x^{a+1})^b}$.

42. Roots. *If* n *is a positive integer and* $r^n = a$, *then* r *is called an* nth root *of* a.

Illustration 1. 3 and (-3) are *square roots* of 9, since $3^2 = 9$ and $(-3)^2 = 9$; (-2) is a *cube root* of (-8), since $(-2)^3 = -8$.

This illustration indicates that a number may have more than one nth root; in Article 103 it is shown that every number a, except zero, has exactly n distinct nth roots. If n is odd and a is real, exactly one of the n roots is real. If n is even and a is positive, exactly two of the n roots are real; they are numerically equal but of opposite sign. If n is even and a is negative, none of the n roots are real.

The **principal nth root of a real number** a is denoted by the symbol $\sqrt{a}$ and is defined as (a) the positive nth root of a, if a is positive, or (b) the negative nth root of a, if a is negative and n is odd.

NOTE. When a is negative and n is even, the symbol $\sqrt[n]{a}$ represents a new type of number called an *imaginary number*. These numbers are discussed in Article 51 and Chapter 14. For the present we shall assume that literal expressions are such that imaginary numbers do not occur.

Illustration 2. The principal roots $\sqrt{4}$, $\sqrt[3]{8}$, $\sqrt[4]{16}$, and $\sqrt[5]{32}$ each equal 2, whereas $\sqrt[3]{-8}$ and $\sqrt[5]{-32}$ each equal -2, and $\sqrt{-4}$ and $\sqrt[4]{-16}$ represent imaginary numbers.

EXERCISE 30

Give the square roots of each of the following numbers:

1. 25. **2.** 49. **3.** 64. **4.** 81. **5.** a^2.
6. b^4. **7.** x^4y^2. **8.** $36\,m^2$. **9.** $16\,a^4$. **10.** $121\,x^{10}$.

Give the real cube root of each of the following numbers:

11. 8. **12.** -27. **13.** -64. **14.** 125. **15.** a^3.
16. $-c^9$. **17.** $64\,x^3y^6$. **18.** $1000\,m^{12}$. **19.** $-a^{27}$. **20.** $\frac{8}{27}\,x^6$.

If letters represent positive numbers, give the principal roots as indicated.

21. $\sqrt{144}$. **22.** $-\sqrt{400}$. **23.** $\sqrt[3]{27}$. **24.** $\sqrt[4]{16}$.
25. $\sqrt[3]{-216}$. **26.** $\sqrt[5]{243}$. **27.** $-\sqrt[5]{-32}$. **28.** $-\sqrt[3]{\frac{1}{8}}$.
29. $\sqrt[3]{64\,m^3n^3}$. **30.** $\sqrt[4]{81\,a^8}$. **31.** $\sqrt[5]{a^{10}b^{15}}$. **32.** $\sqrt[6]{(-x)^6}$.

If letters represent positive numbers, evaluate and combine:

33. $\sqrt{169} + \sqrt[3]{343}$. **34.** $\sqrt[4]{16} + \sqrt[3]{-27}$. **35.** $\sqrt[3]{64\,a^3} - \sqrt[5]{a^5}$.
36. $\sqrt[9]{a^9} + \sqrt{9\,a^2}$. **37.** $\sqrt[3]{-8} + \sqrt{225}$. **38.** $\sqrt[4]{81} - \sqrt[5]{-1}$.
39. $\sqrt{a^4} - \sqrt[3]{-8\,a^6}$. **40.** $\sqrt[4]{625\,x^4} - \sqrt[7]{x^7}$. **41.** $\sqrt[4]{\frac{16}{81}} - \sqrt{\frac{1}{4}}$.

43. Fractional Exponents. The number a^n has been defined when n is a positive integer, and such numbers have been shown to satisfy the laws of exponents as given in Article 41. We wish, if possible, to find a meaning for the symbol a^n, when n has fractional, zero, or negative values, such that these new expressions will satisfy the same laws of exponents.

For example, if $a^{\frac{1}{2}}$ is to satisfy the first law of exponents, we must have

$$a^{\frac{1}{2}} \cdot a^{\frac{1}{2}} = a^{\frac{1}{2}+\frac{1}{2}} = a^1 = a,$$

that is, $a^{\frac{1}{2}}$ must be a square root of a. Similar reasoning shows that $a^{\frac{1}{3}}$ must be a cube root of a, $a^{\frac{3}{2}}$ must be a square root of a^3, and so on. Consequently if m and n are positive integers, **we define $a^{\frac{m}{n}}$ to represent the principal nth root of a^m, symbolically** *

$$a^{\frac{m}{n}} = \sqrt[n]{a^m} = \left(\sqrt[n]{a}\right)^m.$$

Illustration. $\quad 2\,x^{\frac{1}{5}} = 2\sqrt[5]{x}; \quad 16^{\frac{3}{4}} = (\sqrt[4]{16})^3 = (2)^3 = 8;$
$$(-8)^{\frac{1}{3}} = \sqrt[3]{-8} = -2.$$

44. Zero Exponent. If zero as an exponent is to satisfy the first law of exponents, then

$$a^0 \cdot a^n = a^{0+n} = a^n.$$

Thus, $a^0 = a^n/a^n = 1$, if $a \neq 0$. Hence, **the exponent zero is defined by the equation**

$$a^0 = 1, \text{ if } a \neq 0.$$

Illustration. $4^0 = 1; \quad (2\,x^2)^0 = 1; \quad 5\,x^0 = 5 \cdot 1 = 5.$

45. Negative Exponents. If the first law of exponents is to hold for negative exponents, then

$$a^n \cdot a^{-n} = a^{n-n} = a^0 = 1.$$

Hence, if n is a positive rational number, **a negative exponent is defined by the equation**

$$a^{-n} = \frac{1}{a^n}, \text{ if } a \neq 0.$$

Illustration 1. $x^{-1} = \frac{1}{x}; \quad 2^{-3} = \frac{1}{2^3} = \frac{1}{8}; \quad 9^{-\frac{1}{2}} = \frac{1}{9^{\frac{1}{2}}} = \frac{1}{3}.$

* These operations are reversible if a is positive whenever n is even. Without this restriction we would have such contradictions as the following:
$$1 = \sqrt{+1} = \sqrt{(-1)^2} \overset{?}{=} (\sqrt{-1})^2 = -1.$$

It follows from the above definition that any factor of the numerator of a fraction may be changed to the denominator, or vice versa, if the sign of its exponent is changed.

Illustration 2. $\dfrac{ax^{-2}}{by^{-3}} = \dfrac{a \cdot \dfrac{1}{x^2}}{b \cdot \dfrac{1}{y^3}} = \dfrac{\dfrac{a}{x^2}}{\dfrac{b}{y^3}} = \dfrac{a}{x^2} \cdot \dfrac{y^3}{b} = \dfrac{ay^3}{bx^2}.$

NOTE. In applying the above operation, it is necessary to distinguish carefully between *factors* and *terms*. Thus, $\dfrac{1}{a^{-1} + b^{-1}}$ does *not* reduce to $a + b$, but becomes $1 \big/ \left(\dfrac{1}{a} + \dfrac{1}{b}\right)$ or $\dfrac{ab}{a + b}$.

We have proved that a^n satisfies the laws of exponents when n is a positive integer. With the above definitions and with all possibilities being considered separately, it can be shown that a^n will also satisfy the same laws of exponents when n is any rational number.*

Example 1. Using the laws of exponents, find (1) $x^{\frac{1}{2}} \cdot x^{-\frac{1}{4}}$; (2) $(2\,x^{\frac{2}{3}})^6$; and (3) $\left(\dfrac{ax^{-2}}{y^3}\right)^{-2}$.

Solution: (1) $x^{\frac{1}{2}} \cdot x^{-\frac{1}{4}} = x^{\frac{1}{2} + (-\frac{1}{4})} = x^{\frac{1}{4}}$,

(2) $(2\,x^{\frac{2}{3}})^6 = 2^6 x^{\frac{2}{3} \cdot 6} = 64\,x^4$,

(3) $\left(\dfrac{ax^{-2}}{y^3}\right)^{-2} = \dfrac{a^{-2}x^4}{y^{-6}} = \dfrac{x^4 y^6}{a^2}.$

Example 2. Expand $(x^{\frac{2}{3}} + y^{-\frac{2}{3}})^2$.

Solution: $(x^{\frac{2}{3}} + y^{-\frac{2}{3}})^2 = (x^{\frac{2}{3}})^2 + 2(x^{\frac{2}{3}})(y^{-\frac{2}{3}}) + (y^{-\frac{2}{3}})^2$

$= x^{\frac{4}{3}} + 2\,x^{\frac{2}{3}}y^{-\frac{2}{3}} + y^{-\frac{4}{3}}.$

Example 3. Express $\dfrac{ab^{-1} - a^{-1}b}{a^{-1} + b^{-1}}$ in simplest form with positive exponents.

Solution:

$$\dfrac{ab^{-1} - a^{-1}b}{a^{-1} + b^{-1}} = \dfrac{\dfrac{a}{b} - \dfrac{b}{a}}{\dfrac{1}{a} + \dfrac{1}{b}} = \dfrac{\dfrac{a^2 - b^2}{ab}}{\dfrac{a + b}{ab}}$$

$$= \dfrac{(a - b)(a + b)}{ab} \cdot \dfrac{ab}{(a + b)} = a - b.$$

* For an exception, see Article 42, NOTE.

EXERCISE 31

Find the value of each of the following:

1. $25^{\frac{1}{2}}$.   **2.** $(-8)^{\frac{1}{3}}$.   **3.** $16^{\frac{1}{4}}$.   **4.** 3^0.

5. 4^{-1}.   **6.** $(\frac{1}{8})^{\frac{2}{3}}$.   **7.** $(-1)^{\frac{3}{5}}$.   **8.** $9^{\frac{3}{2}}$.

9. $(\frac{2}{3})^{-2}$.   **10.** $(-1)^0$.   **11.** $8^{-\frac{2}{3}}$.   **12.** $(0.16)^{\frac{1}{2}}$.

13. $(0.125)^{\frac{2}{3}}$.   **14.** $(\frac{1}{32})^{-\frac{2}{5}}$.   **15.** $(-27)^{\frac{4}{3}}$.   **16.** $3\,x^0$.

17. $\sqrt[3]{-8^{-2}}$.   **18.** $\sqrt[6]{64^{-1}}$.   **19.** $\sqrt[5]{-7^0}$.   **20.** $\sqrt{9^{-3}}$.

21. $2^{-57} \cdot 2^{59}$.   **22.** $4^{-\frac{1}{2}} \cdot (\frac{1}{2})^{-4}$.   **23.** $8^{\frac{2}{3}} \cdot (4\,x)^0$.   **24.** $27^{-\frac{2}{3}} \cdot 9^{\frac{3}{2}}$.

25. $(0.25)^{-\frac{1}{2}} \cdot (-\frac{1}{2})^0$.   **26.** $2^0 + 2^{-1} + 2^{-2}$.

27. $4^{-\frac{3}{2}} \div 8^{-\frac{2}{3}}$.   **28.** $(2\,x^3)^0 - (-2\,x^0)^3$.

29. $(\frac{1}{4})^{\frac{1}{2}} + (4)^{-\frac{1}{2}}$.   **30.** $(\frac{2}{3})^{-2} + (\frac{1}{64})^{\frac{1}{3}}$.

31. $(2^{-1} + 2^{-2})^{-1}$.   **32.** $(1^1 + 2^2 + 3^3)^{\frac{1}{5}}$.

33. $(4^{-\frac{1}{2}} + 8^{-\frac{1}{3}})^6$.   **34.** $(1^0 + 2^0 + 3^0 + 4^0)^{-\frac{1}{2}}$.

35. $[3^0 - 5(3)^{-2}]^{-\frac{1}{2}}$.   **36.** $(3^{-1} + 3^{-2})^{\frac{1}{2}}$.

Perform the indicated operations, using the laws of exponents:

37. $a^{\frac{1}{3}} \cdot a^{\frac{1}{3}}$.   **38.** $m^{-1} \cdot m^{-3}$.   **39.** $b \cdot b^{-\frac{1}{2}}$.   **40.** $x^{\frac{3}{2}} \cdot x^{-\frac{2}{3}}$.

41. $c^{\frac{5}{6}} \div c^{\frac{1}{3}}$.   **42.** $2^{\frac{3}{4}} \div 2^{-\frac{1}{4}}$.   **43.** $x^0 \div x^{-3}$.   **44.** $y^{-\frac{1}{2}} \div y^{-\frac{3}{2}}$.

45. $(a^{\frac{2}{3}})^6$.   **46.** $(x^{-2})^{-3}$.   **47.** $(z^{10})^{\frac{3}{5}}$.   **48.** $(b^{-4})^{\frac{1}{2}}$.

49. $(x^{-2})^{-2} \cdot (x^2)^{-1}$.   **50.** $(-2\,a^{-\frac{1}{2}}b^{\frac{1}{4}})^{-4}$.   **51.** $5\,ax^{\frac{1}{2}} \cdot 7\,a^{\frac{1}{3}}x^{-\frac{1}{3}}$.

52. $\left(\dfrac{m^{-2}}{n}\right)^{-1} \cdot \left(\dfrac{m}{n^{-2}}\right)^2$.   **53.** $\dfrac{(ab^2)^{\frac{1}{2}}}{(a^2b^3)^{-1}}$.   **54.** $\dfrac{(2\,x^{\frac{1}{2}}y^{\frac{1}{3}})^6}{8\,x^{-1}y}$.

55. $(xy^{\frac{1}{2}})^3 \cdot (x^{\frac{1}{2}}y)^4$.   **56.** $(2\,x^{\frac{1}{2}})^3 \cdot (4\,x^3)^{-\frac{1}{2}}$.   **57.** $(8\,x^{-2})^{\frac{1}{3}} \cdot (2\,x^0)^{-3}$.

58. $\left(\dfrac{a^{\frac{1}{2}}}{b}\right)^{-2} \cdot \left(\dfrac{a^4}{b^6}\right)^{\frac{1}{2}}$.   **59.** $\dfrac{(2\,x^{-1})^2(4\,x^4)^{\frac{1}{2}}}{(8\,x^{-3})^{\frac{1}{3}}}$.   **60.** $\dfrac{3\,ax^{-\frac{1}{2}} \cdot 6^{-1}a^{\frac{1}{2}}x}{4^{-1}a^{-\frac{1}{2}}x^2}$.

Express the following in simplest form with positive exponents:

61. $ab^{-1} + a^{-1}b$.   **62.** $(a-b)^{-1}$.   **63.** $2\,a^{-1} - (2\,b)^{-1}$.

64. $\dfrac{x^{-1} + y^{-1}}{x^{-2} - y^{-2}}$.   **65.** $\dfrac{x}{y} + \dfrac{y^{-1}}{x^{-1}}$.   **66.** $\dfrac{x^{-2} + y^{-2}}{x^{-2}y^{-2}}$.

67. $\sqrt{(x+y)^{-2}}$.   **68.** $\dfrac{x^2 - y^2}{x^{-1} + y^{-1}}$.   **69.** $(1 - x^{-1})^{-1}$.

70. $\dfrac{(\frac{1}{2}\,xy^2)^{-1}}{x^{-1} + y^{-2}}$.   **71.** $\sqrt[3]{a^{-1}\sqrt{a^3}}$.   **72.** $(a^{-1} - b^{-1})^{-1}$.

73. $\dfrac{x - y^{-1}z^2}{xyz^{-1} - z}$.   **74.** $\dfrac{a - a^{-1}b^2}{1 - a^{-1}b}$.   **75.** $\dfrac{1 - a^{-3}}{a^0 + a^1 + a^2}$.

Perform the indicated operations, using the laws of exponents:

76. $x^{-n} \cdot x^{\frac{1}{2}(n+3)}$.   **77.** $x^{\frac{1}{2}-k} \cdot x^{\frac{1}{2}+k}$.

78. $(a^{-2}b^n)^{-\frac{1}{n}}$.   **79.** $(x^{-a}y^{1-a})^{-2}$.

80. $\dfrac{(p^r q^{-1})^r}{(p^{-1}q^r)^r}$.

81. $\left(\dfrac{x^{n^2-1}}{x^{n-1}}\right)^{\frac{1}{n}}$.

82. $\dfrac{m^{x+2}n^{2x-1}}{(m^x n^{x+1})^2}$.

83. $\left(\dfrac{a^{(k+1)^2}}{a^{(k-1)^2}}\right)^{\frac{1}{4}}$.

84. $(x^{\frac{1}{2}} + y^{\frac{1}{2}})(x^{\frac{1}{2}} - y^{\frac{1}{2}})$.

85. $(x^{\frac{1}{3}} - y^{\frac{1}{3}})(x^{\frac{2}{3}} + x^{\frac{1}{3}}y^{\frac{1}{3}} + y^{\frac{2}{3}})$.

86. $(x^{\frac{1}{3}} - 2\,x^{-\frac{1}{3}})^3$.

87. $(2\,a^{-1} - b^{\frac{1}{2}})(a^{\frac{3}{2}} + 3\,b^{-\frac{1}{2}})$.

88. Divide $(2\,x^2 + 3\,x^{\frac{3}{2}}y^{\frac{1}{2}} - 4\,xy + 8\,y^2)$ by $(x^{\frac{1}{2}} + 2\,y^{\frac{1}{2}})$.

89. Divide $(2\,a^2 - 5\,a + 1 + 2\,a^{-1})$ by $(2 + a^{-1})$.

Simplify:

90. $\left[\dfrac{125^{\frac{2}{3}} - 2(-8)^{-\frac{2}{3}}}{2\,a^0 + (\frac{1}{4})^{-2}}\right]^{\frac{1}{2}}$.

91. $\left[\dfrac{9^{n+\frac{1}{4}} \cdot 3^{\frac{1}{2}(n+1)}}{3^{1-\frac{1}{2}n}}\right]^{\frac{1}{n}}$.

92. $\left[\left(\dfrac{m^{-\frac{1}{2}}n^{\frac{2}{3}}}{m^{-\frac{3}{2}}n^{\frac{1}{3}}}\right)^{-2} \div \dfrac{2\,m^{-\frac{3}{2}}}{n}\right]^{-2}$.

93. $\dfrac{2 + 4\,x(x+1)^{-\frac{1}{3}}}{2\,x + (x+1)^{\frac{1}{3}}}$.

94. $\dfrac{(x-1)^{-\frac{1}{2}} - (x-1)^{\frac{1}{2}}}{x(x-1)^{-\frac{1}{2}} - (x-1)^{\frac{1}{2}}}$.

95. $\dfrac{(1 + x^{-1})(x - x^{-1})^{-1}}{(1 - x^{-1})^{-2}}$.

46. Radicals. The symbol $\sqrt[n]{a}$, denoting the principal nth root of a, is called a **radical.** The operation of extracting roots is indicated by the symbol $\sqrt{}$, called the **radical sign;** the number n is called the **index** or **order** of the root, and a is called the **radicand.** Thus, in the expression $\sqrt[3]{8} = 2$, the radicand is 8, the index is 3, the root is 2, and the radical is said to be of the third order. If $n = 2$, the radical is called a quadratic radical and the index is not usually written.

An irrational number which is an indicated root of a rational number is called a **surd.** Thus, $\sqrt{2}$ and $\sqrt[3]{5}$ are surds. $\sqrt[3]{8}$ is not a surd because $\sqrt[3]{8} = 2$ is a rational number. $\sqrt{1 + \sqrt{2}}$ is not a surd because $(1 + \sqrt{2})$ is not a rational number.

A surd of the second order is called a **quadratic surd.** A binomial in which at least one term is a quadratic surd is called a **binomial quadratic surd.** Thus, $(2 - \sqrt{5})$ and $(2\sqrt{3} + \sqrt{7})$ are binomial quadratic surds.

47. Laws of Radicals. By definition the radical $\sqrt[n]{a}$ can be written in the form $a^{\frac{1}{n}}$, and hence any operations performed with the radical must be made in conformity with the laws of exponents. The most important of these laws written in radical form are called the **laws of radicals.** *

Law I. $\sqrt[n]{a} \cdot \sqrt[n]{b} = \sqrt[n]{ab}.$

Law II. $\dfrac{\sqrt[n]{a}}{\sqrt[n]{b}} = \sqrt[n]{\dfrac{a}{b}}.$

Law III. $\sqrt[m]{\sqrt[n]{a}} = \sqrt[mn]{a}.$

The above laws may be used to *simplify* radicals. A radical $\sqrt[n]{a}$ is said to be in simplest form when

1. The radicand contains no factor to the power n,

Example 1. Simplify $\sqrt{18}$, $\sqrt[3]{-16}$, and $\sqrt{8\,a^2 b^5}$.
Solution: By Law I, we have

$$\sqrt{18} = \sqrt{9 \cdot 2} = \sqrt{9} \cdot \sqrt{2} = 3\sqrt{2},$$
$$\sqrt[3]{-16} = \sqrt[3]{-8 \cdot 2} = \sqrt[3]{-8} \cdot \sqrt[3]{2} = -2\sqrt[3]{2},$$
$$\sqrt{8\,a^2 b^5} = \sqrt{4\,a^2 b^4 \cdot 2\,b} = \sqrt{4\,a^2 b^4} \cdot \sqrt{2\,b} = 2\,ab^2\sqrt{2\,b}.$$

2. The radicand contains no fractions,

Example 2. Simplify $\sqrt[3]{2\tfrac{4}{9}}$, $\sqrt{\dfrac{3\,a^3}{8\,b}}$, and $\dfrac{1}{\sqrt[5]{8}}.$

Solution: To eliminate fractions in the radicand, we multiply the numerator and denominator by the smallest number which will make the denominator a perfect nth power; then we apply Law II.

$$\sqrt[3]{2\tfrac{4}{9}} = \sqrt[3]{\tfrac{2\,2}{9}} = \sqrt[3]{\dfrac{22 \cdot 3}{27}} = \dfrac{\sqrt[3]{66}}{3} = \tfrac{1}{3}\sqrt[3]{66},$$

$$\sqrt{\dfrac{3\,a^3}{8\,b}} = \sqrt{\dfrac{3\,a^3 \cdot 2\,b}{16\,b^2}} = \sqrt{\dfrac{a^2 \cdot 6\,ab}{16\,b^2}} = \dfrac{a\sqrt{6\,ab}}{4\,b} = \dfrac{a}{4\,b}\sqrt{6\,ab},$$

$$\dfrac{1}{\sqrt[5]{8}} = \dfrac{1}{\sqrt[5]{8}} \cdot \dfrac{\sqrt[5]{4}}{\sqrt[5]{4}} = \dfrac{\sqrt[5]{4}}{\sqrt[5]{32}} = \dfrac{\sqrt[5]{4}}{2} = \tfrac{1}{2}\sqrt[5]{4}.$$

NOTE. The above simplification is also known as **rationalizing the denominator.**

3. The index is the smallest possible positive integer.

Example 3. Simplify $\sqrt[8]{9}$ and $\sqrt[6]{8\,m^3}$.
Solution: By Law III, we have

$$\sqrt[8]{9} = \sqrt[4]{\sqrt{9}} = \sqrt[4]{3},$$
$$\sqrt[6]{8\,m^3} = \sqrt{\sqrt[3]{8\,m^3}} = \sqrt{2\,m}.$$

* Subject to the restriction of Article 42, NOTE.

Express each of the following in radical form:

1. $x^{\frac{3}{4}}$.
2. $3\,a^{\frac{1}{2}}$.
3. $(3\,a)^{\frac{1}{2}}$.
4. $b^{0.4}$.
5. $x^{\frac{1}{2}} + y^{\frac{1}{2}}$.

6. $2\,x^{\frac{4}{5}}$.
7. $a^{\frac{1}{2}}b^{\frac{1}{3}}$.
8. $(8\,x)^{\frac{2}{3}}$.
9. $2^{\frac{1}{3}}a^{\frac{1}{6}}$.
10. $(x+y)^{\frac{1}{2}}$.

Express each of the following in exponent form:

11. $\sqrt[3]{x^5}$.
12. $\sqrt[5]{x^3}$.
13. $2\sqrt{a}$.
14. $\sqrt{2\,a}$.
15. $\sqrt[6]{a^5}\sqrt{b}$.

16. $\sqrt{2}\sqrt[3]{b}$.
17. $\sqrt[4]{16\,x^3}$.
18. $a\sqrt[3]{ab^2}$.
19. $\sqrt[3]{\sqrt{a}}$.
20. $\sqrt[4]{x\sqrt{x}}$.

Simplify each of the following radicals:

21. $\sqrt{75}$.
22. $\sqrt{800}$.
23. $\sqrt[3]{54}$.
24. $\sqrt[4]{32}$.
25. $\sqrt[3]{-40}$.

26. $\sqrt{\frac{3}{5}}$.
27. $\sqrt[4]{\frac{7}{8}}$.
28. $\sqrt{5\frac{2}{5}}$.
29. $\sqrt[3]{-\frac{3}{4}}$.
30. $\sqrt[3]{7\frac{1}{9}}$.

31. $\sqrt{0.49}$.
32. $\sqrt{63\,a^2}$.
33. $\sqrt[3]{-2\,a^7}$.
34. $\sqrt[4]{a^5b^3}$.
35. $\sqrt[3]{81\,b^7}$.

36. $\sqrt[3]{\dfrac{x}{y}}$.
37. $\sqrt{\dfrac{3\,a}{2\,b^2}}$.
38. $\sqrt[5]{\dfrac{32}{x^2}}$.
39. $\sqrt[6]{\dfrac{a^{10}}{8\,b^4}}$.
40. $\sqrt{\dfrac{28}{45\,n}}$.

Reduce each radical to lowest order:

41. $\sqrt[4]{4}$.
42. $\sqrt[6]{27}$.
43. $\sqrt[9]{64}$.
44. $\sqrt[8]{81}$.
45. $\sqrt[10]{32}$.

46. $\sqrt[6]{8\,a^3}$.
47. $\sqrt[8]{16\,x^2}$.
48. $\sqrt[12]{a^6b^9}$.
49. $\sqrt[8]{4\,a^4}$.
50. $\sqrt[4]{9\,x^{2n}}$.

Express as radicals of the same order:

51. $\sqrt{3},\ \sqrt[3]{5}$.
52. $\sqrt{\frac{3}{2}},\ \sqrt[4]{\frac{7}{3}}$.
53. $\sqrt[4]{x^3},\ \sqrt[6]{3\,x^5}$.

54. $\sqrt{2},\ \sqrt[4]{4},\ \sqrt[8]{8}$.
55. $\sqrt{3},\ \sqrt[3]{4},\ \sqrt[4]{5}$.
56. $\sqrt{a},\ \sqrt[3]{b^2},\ \sqrt[6]{c^5}$.

48. Addition and Subtraction of Radicals.

Radicals of the same order which have the same radicand are called **similar** or **like radicals.** Thus, $5\sqrt{2}$, $\frac{1}{2}\sqrt{2}$, and $x\sqrt{2}$ are similar radicals, whereas $\sqrt{2}$, $\sqrt{3}$, and $\sqrt[3]{2}$ are dissimilar radicals.

Similar radicals, regarded as similar terms, may be added or subtracted accordingly. Thus, $7\sqrt[3]{3} - 5\sqrt[3]{3} = 2\sqrt[3]{3}$. If radicals are not similar their algebraic sum can only be indicated.

Example. Combine $\sqrt{12} - \dfrac{1}{\sqrt{2}} - \sqrt[4]{9} + \sqrt{4\frac{1}{2}}$.

Solution:

$$\sqrt{12} - \frac{1}{\sqrt{2}} - \sqrt[4]{9} + \sqrt{4\tfrac{1}{2}} = \sqrt{4 \cdot 3} - \frac{\sqrt{2}}{\sqrt{2}\sqrt{2}} - \sqrt[4]{\sqrt{9}} + \sqrt{\tfrac{9}{4} \cdot 2}$$

$$= 2\sqrt{3} - \tfrac{1}{2}\sqrt{2} - \sqrt{3} + \tfrac{3}{2}\sqrt{2} = \sqrt{3} + \sqrt{2}.$$

EXERCISE 33

Simplify and collect similar radicals:

1. $3\sqrt{50} - 2\sqrt{18}$.   **2.** $x\sqrt{8} + 4\sqrt{2\,x^2}$.   **3.** $\sqrt{150} - 6\sqrt{2\tfrac{2}{3}}$.

4. $2\sqrt[3]{16} + \sqrt[3]{-54}$.   **5.** $\sqrt[3]{\tfrac{1}{2}} - \sqrt[3]{\tfrac{4}{27}}$.   **6.** $\sqrt[4]{2\,a^4} - \sqrt[4]{2\,b^4}$.

7. $4\sqrt{63} - 5\sqrt{28} + 3\sqrt{20}$.   **8.** $3\sqrt{98} + \tfrac{1}{2}\sqrt{48} + \sqrt{72}$.

9. $\sqrt{\tfrac{4}{3}} - \sqrt{\tfrac{3}{4}} - \sqrt{\tfrac{1}{12}}$.   **10.** $\tfrac{5}{2}\sqrt[3]{\tfrac{3}{4}} + \tfrac{3}{4}\sqrt[3]{-\tfrac{2}{9}} - 3\sqrt[3]{\tfrac{2}{3}}$.

11. $\sqrt{32} + \sqrt[3]{-40} - 5\sqrt[4]{324}$.   **12.** $3\sqrt{8\tfrac{1}{3}} - 2\sqrt{5\tfrac{1}{3}} - 2\sqrt{1\tfrac{1}{3}}$.

13. $8\sqrt{\tfrac{1}{12}} - \dfrac{5}{\sqrt{75}} + 10\sqrt{\tfrac{3}{5}}$.   **14.** $\dfrac{\sqrt{3}}{\sqrt{2}} - \dfrac{1}{\sqrt{6}} + \dfrac{\sqrt{24}}{3}$.

15. $\dfrac{3}{\sqrt[3]{2}} + \dfrac{6}{\sqrt{3}} - \sqrt[4]{144}$.   **16.** $\dfrac{8}{\sqrt[3]{3}} - \tfrac{1}{3}\sqrt[3]{72} - \sqrt[3]{13\tfrac{1}{2}}$.

If letters represent positive numbers, simplify the following:

17. $\sqrt{a^2 b} - \sqrt{b^3} + \sqrt{bc^2}$.   **18.** $\sqrt[3]{ax^3} + \sqrt[3]{-ay^3} - \sqrt[3]{8\,a}$.

19. $\sqrt{a^3 - a^2 b} - \sqrt{ab^2 - b^3}$.   **20.** $\sqrt[3]{x^3 + x^4} + \sqrt[3]{8\,x + 8}$.

21. $\sqrt{\dfrac{x}{y}} + \sqrt{\dfrac{y}{x}} - \dfrac{2}{\sqrt{xy}}$.   **22.** $\sqrt{\dfrac{x+y}{x-y}} - \sqrt{\dfrac{x-y}{x+y}}$.

23. $\sqrt[3]{\dfrac{x+3\,y}{y^2}} + \dfrac{3\,x+y}{x^2} - \sqrt[3]{\dfrac{x}{y^2}}$.   **24.** $\sqrt{\dfrac{a^2+b^2}{ab} + 2} - \sqrt{\dfrac{b}{a}}$.

49. Multiplication of Radicals. The product of two radicals of the same order is determined by Law I. Thus, $\sqrt[3]{3} \cdot \sqrt[3]{5} = \sqrt[3]{15}$. When two radicands of a product contain common factors, the simplification can often be made easier by factoring.

Illustration. To multiply and simplify the product $\sqrt{65} \cdot \sqrt{91}$, we proceed as follows:

$$\sqrt{65} \cdot \sqrt{91} = \sqrt{13 \cdot 5} \cdot \sqrt{13 \cdot 7} = \sqrt{13}\sqrt{5}\sqrt{13}\sqrt{7} = 13\sqrt{35}.$$

Example 1. Multiply $(\sqrt{45} - \sqrt{32})$ by $(\sqrt{20} + \sqrt{18})$.
Solution: Simplifying before multiplying, we have

$$(\sqrt{45} - \sqrt{32})(\sqrt{20} + \sqrt{18}) = (3\sqrt{5} - 4\sqrt{2})(2\sqrt{5} + 3\sqrt{2})$$
$$= 6\sqrt{25} + 9\sqrt{10} - 8\sqrt{10} - 12\sqrt{4} = 6 + \sqrt{10}.$$

To multiply radicals of different orders, it is first necessary to express the given radicals as equivalent radicals of some common order.

Example 2. Multiply $\sqrt{2}$ by $\sqrt[3]{4}$.

Solution: Reducing each of the given radicals to the same lowest order, we have

$$\sqrt{2} = 2^{\frac{1}{2}} = 2^{\frac{3}{6}} = \sqrt[6]{2^3} \quad \text{and} \quad \sqrt[3]{4} = 4^{\frac{1}{3}} = 4^{\frac{2}{6}} = \sqrt[6]{4^2}.$$

Since $4 = 2^2$, on multiplying and simplifying we have

$$\sqrt{2} \cdot \sqrt[3]{4} = \sqrt[6]{2^3} \cdot \sqrt[6]{4^2} = \sqrt[6]{2^3 \cdot 4^2} = \sqrt[6]{2^7} = 2\sqrt[6]{2}.$$

EXERCISE 34

Perform the indicated operations and simplify:

1. $3\sqrt{48} \cdot 2\sqrt{75}$.   **2.** $4\sqrt{\frac{3}{2}} \cdot 3\sqrt{\frac{3}{8}}$.   **3.** $4\sqrt[3]{12} \cdot 5\sqrt[3]{18}$.

4. $\frac{2}{5}\sqrt[3]{\frac{9}{16}} \cdot \frac{2}{9}\sqrt[3]{\frac{3}{4}}$.   **5.** $\sqrt{42} \cdot \sqrt{77}$.   **6.** $\sqrt[3]{33} \cdot \sqrt[3]{90}$.

7. $\frac{2}{5}\sqrt{8\frac{1}{6}}\sqrt{8\frac{1}{3}}$.   **8.** $(-2\sqrt{18})^2$.   **9.** $(\frac{1}{2}\sqrt[3]{\frac{3}{4}})^2$.

10. $(3\sqrt{2\,a})^3$.   **11.** $\sqrt[3]{4} \cdot \sqrt[6]{32}$.   **12.** $\sqrt[5]{a^4b^3} \cdot \sqrt[6]{a^3b^5}$.

13. $\sqrt{10}(2\sqrt{5} - 5\sqrt{2} + 3\sqrt{15})$.   **14.** $\sqrt{12}(3\sqrt{27} - 5\sqrt{8} - 2\sqrt{15})$.

15. $\sqrt{\frac{2}{3}}(\sqrt{\frac{1}{2}} + 2\sqrt{\frac{3}{4}} - \frac{1}{2}\sqrt{\frac{8}{3}})$.   **16.** $2\sqrt[3]{4}(\sqrt[3]{6} - 2\sqrt[3]{10} - \sqrt[3]{18})$.

17. $\sqrt{ab}(\sqrt{a} + \sqrt{b})$.   **18.** $\sqrt{x}(\sqrt{ax} - \sqrt{bx} + \sqrt{cx})$.

19. $(3\sqrt{7} + 2\sqrt{3})(2\sqrt{7} - 5\sqrt{3})$.   **20.** $(5\sqrt{5} + \sqrt{3})(2\sqrt{5} - 9\sqrt{3})$.

21. $(\sqrt{\frac{1}{2}} + 2\sqrt{\frac{1}{3}})(2\sqrt{\frac{3}{10}} - \sqrt{\frac{5}{9}})$.   **22.** $(3\sqrt{5} - 2\sqrt{10})^2$.

23. $(\sqrt[3]{2} + \sqrt[3]{4})(\sqrt[3]{2} - \sqrt[3]{4})$.   **24.** $(\sqrt{3} - 1)^2 + 2(\sqrt{3} - 1)$.

25. $(\sqrt[3]{5} + \sqrt[3]{2})^3$.   **26.** $(3\sqrt{72} - 2\sqrt{27})^3$.

27. $(\sqrt{a} - 3\sqrt{b})^2$.   **28.** $(\sqrt{x} - \sqrt{y})(\sqrt{x} + \sqrt{y})$.

29. $(2\sqrt{x} + 3\sqrt{y})(2\sqrt{x} - \sqrt{y})$.   **30.** $(2\sqrt[3]{x} - 1)(3\sqrt[3]{x^2} + 2)$.

31. $(\sqrt[3]{ax} + \sqrt[3]{x^2})(\sqrt[3]{ax} - \sqrt[3]{a^2})$.   **32.** $(1 - \sqrt{2 - a})(2 + \sqrt{2 - a})$.

33. $\sqrt{\sqrt{5} + 1} \cdot \sqrt{\sqrt{5} - 1}$.   **34.** $\sqrt[3]{2\sqrt{3} + 2} \cdot \sqrt[3]{2\sqrt{3} - 2}$.

35. $(\sqrt{a + x} - \sqrt{a - x})^2$.   **36.** $(\sqrt{2} + \sqrt{6} + \sqrt{10})^2$.

37. $(\sqrt[3]{x} - \sqrt[3]{y})(\sqrt[3]{x^2} + \sqrt[3]{xy} + \sqrt[3]{y^2})$.

38. $(\sqrt{x} + \sqrt[4]{4\,x} + 1)(\sqrt{x} - \sqrt[4]{4\,x} + 1)$.

Find the value of each of the following:

39. $x^2 - 2\,x - 17$, when $x = 1 - 3\sqrt{2}$.

40. $2\,x^2 - 6\,x - 3$, when $x = \frac{1}{2}(3 - \sqrt{15})$.

41. $ax^2 + bx + c$, when $x = (-b + \sqrt{b^2 - 4\,ac})/2\,a$.

42. $x^3 - 3\,x^2 + 3\,x - 3$, when $x = 1 + \sqrt[3]{2}$.

50. Division of Radicals. The quotient of two radicals of the same order is determined by Law II. Thus, $\sqrt[3]{12} \div \sqrt[3]{4} = \sqrt[3]{3}$.

To divide by a single radical, we may divide term by term and simplify. In general, however, it is usually more convenient to multiply the dividend and the divisor by a radical which will eliminate the radical in the divisor. This process is known as **rationalizing** the divisor.

Illustration. $\dfrac{4-\sqrt{6}}{2\sqrt{3}} = \dfrac{(4-\sqrt{6})\cdot\sqrt{3}}{2\sqrt{3}\cdot\sqrt{3}} = \dfrac{4\sqrt{3}-3\sqrt{2}}{6}.$

If we multiply the sum and the difference of two quadratic surds, we obtain a **rational product.** Thus,

$$(\sqrt{a}+\sqrt{b})(\sqrt{a}-\sqrt{b}) = (\sqrt{a})^2 - (\sqrt{b})^2 = a - b.$$

Hence, if the divisor is a binomial quadratic surd of the form $(a\sqrt{b} + c\sqrt{d})$, we may *rationalize the divisor* by multiplying both the dividend and the divisor by $(a\sqrt{b} - c\sqrt{d})$.

Example 1. Divide $\sqrt{14}$ by $(2\sqrt{2}-\sqrt{7})$.
Solution: Multiplying the numerator and denominator by $(2\sqrt{2}+\sqrt{7})$, we have

$$\frac{\sqrt{14}}{2\sqrt{2}-\sqrt{7}} = \frac{\sqrt{14}(2\sqrt{2}+\sqrt{7})}{(2\sqrt{2}-\sqrt{7})(2\sqrt{2}+\sqrt{7})} = \frac{4\sqrt{7}+7\sqrt{2}}{8-7} = 4\sqrt{7}+7\sqrt{2}.$$

Example 2. Divide $\sqrt[6]{16\,a^5}$ by $\sqrt{2\,a}$.
Solution: $\dfrac{\sqrt[6]{16\,a^5}}{\sqrt{2\,a}} = \dfrac{\sqrt[6]{16\,a^5}}{\sqrt[6]{8\,a^3}} = \sqrt[6]{2\,a^2}.$

EXERCISE 35

Perform the indicated operations and simplify:

1. $\dfrac{5\sqrt{3}}{2\sqrt{20}}.$

2. $\dfrac{4\sqrt{34}}{\sqrt{51}}.$

3. $\dfrac{5\sqrt[3]{15}}{3\sqrt[3]{5}}.$

4. $\dfrac{2\sqrt[3]{13}}{3\sqrt[3]{26}}.$

5. $\dfrac{\sqrt{7\frac{1}{2}}}{\frac{1}{2}\sqrt{\frac{5}{9}}}.$

6. $\dfrac{\sqrt{0.315}}{\sqrt{0.045}}.$

7. $\dfrac{2\sqrt[4]{18}}{5\sqrt{6}}.$

8. $\dfrac{2\sqrt[3]{4}}{3\sqrt{2}}.$

9. $\dfrac{x\sqrt{y}}{y\sqrt{x}}.$

10. $\dfrac{a\sqrt[3]{5\,a}}{3\sqrt[3]{4\,a^2}}.$

11. $\dfrac{\sqrt[6]{x^5y^3}}{\sqrt[6]{x^2y}}.$

12. $\dfrac{6\,y\sqrt{2\,x^3y}}{5\,x\sqrt[4]{4\,xy^3}}.$

13. $\dfrac{3\sqrt{6} - 9\sqrt{15} + 12\sqrt{21}}{3\sqrt{3}}.$

14. $\dfrac{\sqrt{10} - 5\sqrt{7} - 3\sqrt{15}}{4\sqrt{5}}.$

15. $\dfrac{\sqrt{\frac{1}{2}} + \sqrt{\frac{1}{3}} + \sqrt{\frac{1}{4}}}{\sqrt{\frac{1}{5}}}.$

16. $\dfrac{2\sqrt[3]{2} - 6\sqrt[3]{9} + \sqrt[3]{-24}}{2\sqrt[3]{3}}.$

17. $\dfrac{a\sqrt{b} + b\sqrt{a} + \sqrt{ab}}{\sqrt{ab}}.$

18. $\dfrac{a\sqrt[3]{b} + b\sqrt[3]{a} + \sqrt[3]{ab}}{\sqrt[3]{ab}}.$

19. $\dfrac{1 - \sqrt{10}}{\sqrt{5} + \sqrt{2}}.$

20. $\dfrac{3\sqrt{7} + 12}{2\sqrt{7} - 1}.$

21. $\dfrac{2\sqrt{3}}{3\sqrt{2} - 2\sqrt{3}}.$

22. $\dfrac{\sqrt{27} - \sqrt{18}}{\sqrt{75} - \sqrt{72}}.$

23. $\dfrac{\sqrt{7} - \sqrt{5}}{\sqrt{7} + \sqrt{5}}.$

24. $\dfrac{16 - \sqrt{35}}{2\sqrt{5} + \sqrt{7}}.$

25. $\dfrac{x - 18}{\sqrt{x} + 3\sqrt{2}}.$

26. $\dfrac{a + \sqrt{ab}}{b + \sqrt{ab}}.$

27. $\dfrac{\sqrt{a} - \sqrt{a - 1}}{\sqrt{a} + \sqrt{a - 1}}.$

28. $\dfrac{2x + 3y + 5\sqrt{xy}}{\sqrt{x} + \sqrt{y}}.$

29. $\dfrac{2y}{\sqrt{x + y} + \sqrt{x - y}}.$

30. $\left[\dfrac{\sqrt{a^2 + 4} - 2}{\sqrt{a^2 + 4} + 2} \right]^{\frac{1}{2}}.$

31. $\dfrac{2 - 3\sqrt{2} + \sqrt{6}}{1 + \sqrt{2} + \sqrt{3}}.$

32. $\dfrac{5 + 2\sqrt{21}}{\sqrt{3} - \sqrt{5} + \sqrt{7}}.$

33. $\dfrac{3\sqrt{3} - \sqrt{7}}{\sqrt{5}} \div \dfrac{\sqrt{2}}{3\sqrt{3} + \sqrt{7}}.$

34. $\dfrac{\sqrt{2}}{\sqrt{2} + 2} \cdot \dfrac{5 + 4\sqrt{2}}{\sqrt{2} + 3}.$

35. $\dfrac{\sqrt{2}}{\sqrt{2} - 1} + \dfrac{7\sqrt{2}}{2\sqrt{2} - 1}.$

36. $\dfrac{3\sqrt{2} - \sqrt{3}}{\sqrt{3} - \sqrt{2}} - \dfrac{\sqrt{2} - 2\sqrt{3}}{\sqrt{3} + \sqrt{2}}.$

37. $\dfrac{1}{\sqrt{3} - \sqrt{2}} \cdot \dfrac{4 - \sqrt{6}}{1 + \sqrt{6}}.$

38. $\dfrac{8 - 2\sqrt{15}}{\sqrt{5} - \sqrt{3}} \div \dfrac{\sqrt{6}}{6 + 2\sqrt{15}}.$

39. Simplify $\sqrt{4 + \sqrt{15}} + \sqrt{4 - \sqrt{15}}$. Hint: Square the expression, simplify, and then extract the square root.

51. Imaginary Numbers. When P is positive, we have defined the symbol $\sqrt{P}$ to represent a positive real number whose square is P. Similarly we might expect the expression $\sqrt{-P}$ to represent a number whose square is $(-P)$. However, by the rule of signs, we know that no real number exists whose square is negative. For this reason, we **define** the expression $\sqrt{-P}$, $P > 0$ to represent a new type of number called an **imaginary number,** and we **define** the multiplication of two imaginary numbers to be such that $\sqrt{-P} \cdot \sqrt{-Q} = -\sqrt{P \cdot Q}$ where $P > 0$ and $Q > 0$.

NOTE. Observe that the laws of radicals do not hold for the multiplication of imaginary numbers.

The imaginary number $\sqrt{-1}$ is called the **imaginary unit** and is usually denoted by the letter i; hence $i^2 = -1$. We shall assume* that i, considered as a literal number, can be combined with the real numbers in accordance with the usual laws of algebra.

Illustration 1. $2i + 3i = 5i,$ $(2i)(3i) = 6i^2 = -6.$

If P is a positive number, then $(\pm i\sqrt{P})^2 = i^2P = -P$. Thus, $(-P)$ has the two square roots $\pm i\sqrt{P}$. We agree, however, that the symbol $\sqrt{-P}$ represents the single value $i\sqrt{P}$, that is, i multiplied by a positive real number. Thus, for example, $\sqrt{-4} = \sqrt{4}\sqrt{-1} = 2i,$ and $\sqrt{-9a^2} = \sqrt{9a^2}\sqrt{-1} = 3ai,$ if $a > 0$.

By the above definition of i, it follows that $i^3 = i^2 \cdot i = -i,$ $i^4 = (i^2)^2 = (-1)^2 = 1$. In this manner we see that higher powers of i can always be reduced to one of the four values $i,$ $-1, -i, 1$ in accordance with the following table:

$$i = i^5 = i^9 = \cdots = i, \qquad i^3 = i^7 = i^{11} = \cdots = -i,$$
$$i^2 = i^6 = i^{10} = \cdots = -1, \qquad i^4 = i^8 = i^{12} = \cdots = 1.$$

A number of the form $(a + bi)$, where a and b are real numbers, is called a **complex number.** The number a is called the **real part,** and bi is called the **imaginary part** of the complex number, b being the coefficient of the imaginary part. If $b \neq 0$, the complex number is also called an **imaginary number,** and if $a = 0$ when $b \neq 0$, it is called a **pure imaginary number.** When $b = 0$, the complex number reduces to the real number a.

Illustration 2. $(3 + 2i)$ and $(5 - \sqrt{-2})$ are imaginary numbers; $-3i$ and $\sqrt{-5}$ are pure imaginary numbers; $\frac{1}{2}$ and $-\sqrt{2}$ are real numbers; and all of these are complex numbers.

If two complex numbers differ only in the sign of their imaginary parts, they are called **conjugate complex numbers,** and either is called the conjugate of the other.

Illustration 3. $(a + bi)$ is the conjugate of $(a - bi)$, bi is the conjugate of $-bi$, and a real number is its own conjugate.

* A more detailed study would justify this assumption.

In algebraic operations involving imaginary numbers,

1. Express all imaginary numbers in terms of the unit i; then

2. Complete the indicated operations, considering i as an ordinary literal number, and make the substitution $i^2 = -1$ whenever possible.

Illustration 4. $\sqrt{-9}(3-\sqrt{-4})=3\,i(3-2\,i)=9\,i-6\,i^2=6+9\,i.$

To express the quotient of two complex numbers in the form $(a + bi)$, we rationalize the divisor by multiplying the dividend and divisor by the conjugate of the divisor.

Example. Divide $(8 + i)$ by $(3 + 2\,i)$.

Solution:

$$\frac{8+i}{3+2\,i}=\frac{(8+i)(3-2\,i)}{(3+2\,i)(3-2\,i)}=\frac{24-13\,i-2\,i^2}{9-4\,i^2}=\frac{26-13\,i}{13}=2-i.$$

EXERCISE 36

If letters represent positive numbers, express each of the following in terms of i and simplify:

1. $\sqrt{-25}.$ **2.** $\sqrt{-64}$ **3.** $\sqrt{-8}.$ **4.** $2\sqrt{-45}.$

5. $\sqrt{-\frac{1}{9}}.$ **6.** $\sqrt{-\frac{1}{32}}.$ **7.** $\sqrt{-0.04}.$ **8.** $\sqrt{-4\,a^4}.$

9. $\sqrt{-20\,x^4}.$ **10.** $\sqrt{-a^6b^4}.$ **11.** $\sqrt{-\frac{2}{3}\,x^3}.$ **12.** $\sqrt{-\frac{1}{2}\,ab^2}.$

Using $i^2 = -1$, evaluate each of the following:

13. $i^7.$ **14.** $i^{19}.$ **15.** $i^{57}.$ **16.** $i^{82}.$ **17.** $i^{100}.$

18. $(-i)^3.$ **19.** $(-i^3)^4.$ **20.** $(-i)^6.$ **21.** $(-i^7)^7.$ **22.** $(-i^4)^3.$

Perform the indicated operations and reduce to the form $(a + bi)$:

23. $(3 + 2\,i) + (5 - 4\,i).$ **24.** $(7 - i) - (5 + i).$

25. $(2 -\sqrt{-4}) - (3 +\sqrt{-9}).$ **26.** $(4+\sqrt{-8})+(-1+\sqrt{-18}).$

27. $\sqrt{-8}\sqrt{-24}\sqrt{-27}.$ **28.** $(3 +\sqrt{-4})(2 +\sqrt{-9}).$

29. $(2 + 3\,i)(4 - 5\,i).$ **30.** $(4 - 6\,i)(-2 + 7\,i).$

31. $(3 -\sqrt{-12}) \div \sqrt{-4}.$ **32.** $2 \div (1 + i).$

33. $(19 - 8\,i) \div (3 + 4\,i).$ **34.** $(17 - i) \div (5 - 2\,i).$

35. $(3\,i^4 - i)(4\,i^3 - 1).$ **36.** $(2\,i^4 - 3\,i^2 + 2\,i - 1)^2.$

37. $(3 - 2\,i)^3.$ **38.** $(3 + 2\,i)^2 \div i.$

39. $(i + i^{-1})^2.$ **40.** $(3 - i)^{-1}.$

41. $(1 + i)^2 + (1 + i)^{-2}.$ **42.** $(1 - i)^{10}.$

43. Find the value of $(2\,x^2 - 3\,x + 1)$ when $x = 4 + 3\,i.$

44. Find the value of $(4 - x - x^2)$ when $x = -3 - 2\,i.$

45. Find the value of $(x^3 + x - 5)$ when $x =\sqrt{2} - i.$

46. Find the value of $(2\,x^3 - x^2 - 1)$ when $x = 1 + i\sqrt{3}.$

Solve each of the following equations for x:

47. $i(x + 1) + x(i + 1) = 0.$ 48. $(x + i)/(x - i) = i.$

49. $\dfrac{x + 2}{x} = \dfrac{i}{3}.$ 50. $\dfrac{x + 2i}{x - i} = \dfrac{x + i}{x - 3i}.$

52. Equations Involving Radicals. An equation containing the unknown quantity in the radicand of a radical is called a **radical equation.**

Illustration: $2\sqrt[3]{x} = 5$ and $\sqrt{x^2 - 5} = x + 1$ are radical equations, whereas $x\sqrt{2} = 3 + \sqrt{5}$ is not.

Radicals may be eliminated in certain radical equations by raising both members to some appropriate power. Thus, in $\sqrt{x} = 7$, by squaring we have $x = 49$.

NOTE 1. Not all radical equations have solutions. For example, consider $\sqrt{x} = -7$. By squaring both sides, it appears that $x = 49$ is a solution. But this value does not satisfy the given radical equation since $\sqrt{49}$ equals 7 and not -7.

Such apparent solutions are called **extraneous solutions** and should be rejected when solving radical equations. Hence, it is **necessary** to check all solutions of radical equations.

NOTE 2. The operation of raising both sides of an equation to a positive integral power may or may not introduce extraneous roots. Thus, on squaring both sides of the equation $A = B$, we obtain $A^2 = B^2$, and this new equation contains all the solutions of $A = -B$ as well as those of $A = B$.

Example. Solve $\sqrt{4x - 11} = 2\sqrt{x} - 1.$

Solution: Squaring both sides of the given equation, we obtain

$$4x - 11 = 4x - 4\sqrt{x} + 1.$$

Solving, we obtain $\sqrt{x} = 3$; hence $x = 9$. Substituting this value for x in the original equation, we obtain the numerical identity $\sqrt{25} = 2\sqrt{9} - 1$. Therefore, $x = 9$ is a valid solution.

EXERCISE 37

Solve, and eliminate extraneous solutions:

1. $\sqrt{x - 5} = 3.$ 2. $\sqrt[3]{x + 2} = -3.$ 3. $(5x + 6)^{\frac{1}{2}} = -2.$

4. $(3x + 1)^{\frac{1}{4}} = 2.$ 5. $\sqrt{2 + \sqrt{x}} = 2.$ 6. $\sqrt{5x - 2} = \sqrt{x}.$

7. $\sqrt{5x - 1} = 2\sqrt{x + 1}.$ 8. $\sqrt[3]{9x - 4} = 2\sqrt[3]{x - 1}.$

9. $\sqrt{x} + \sqrt{x + 5} = 5.$ 10. $\sqrt{x - 4} + 3 = \sqrt{x + 11}.$

11. $\sqrt{2x-1} + 2 = \sqrt{2x+11}.$ **12.** $\sqrt{x-5} + \sqrt{x+10} = 3.$

13. $\sqrt{x+4} + \sqrt{x+16} = 2.$ **14.** $\sqrt{5x} + \sqrt{5x-9} = 1.$

15. $\sqrt{x+31} - \sqrt{x+14} = 1.$ **16.** $\sqrt{x+12} - \sqrt{x-12} = 2.$

17. $\sqrt{9x+40} = 3\sqrt{x} + 2.$ **18.** $2 + \sqrt{x+3} = 3 + \sqrt{x+2}.$

19. $\sqrt{x+5} - 1 = \dfrac{x}{\sqrt{x+5}}.$ **20.** $\dfrac{\sqrt{x+2}+1}{\sqrt{x+2}-1} = 2.$

21. $\sqrt[3]{x^3 + 3x^2} = x + 1.$ **22.** $\sqrt[3]{\sqrt{x+3} - \sqrt{x}} = 1.$

23. $\dfrac{1}{\sqrt{x-6}} - \dfrac{1}{\sqrt{x+6}} = \dfrac{2}{\sqrt{x^2-36}}.$ **24.** $\dfrac{\sqrt{x}+1}{3\sqrt{x}-5} = \dfrac{2\sqrt{x}+5}{6\sqrt{x}-7}.$

CHAPTER 8

Quadratic Equations

53. Quadratic Equations in One Unknown. An equation of the form

$$ax^2 + bx + c = 0, \quad a \neq 0, \tag{1}$$

where **a, b,** and **c** are constants, is called a **general quadratic equation in x,** and an equation written in the form of (1) is said to be in **standard form.**

If $b = 0$, the equation is called an **incomplete** or **pure quadratic equation;** and if $b \neq 0$, it is called a **complete quadratic equation.** Thus, $4x^2 - 9 = 0$ is a pure quadratic equation, and $2x^2 + x = 6$ is a complete quadratic equation. A pure quadratic equation can be considered as a linear equation in which we first find the square of the unknown.

Example. Solve $\dfrac{11}{x^2 + 6} = \dfrac{6}{x^2 - 4}$.

Solution: Clearing of fractions, we obtain

$$11x^2 - 44 = 6x^2 + 36, \quad \text{or} \quad 5x^2 = 80, \quad \text{or} \quad x^2 = 16.$$

Hence, taking square roots, we have $x = \pm 4$.

54. Solution by Factoring. The solution of any algebraic equation by factoring depends on the following important principle:

Rule. *If the product of two or more factors is equal to zero, then at least one of the factors must be equal to zero.*

Thus, if $A \cdot B = 0$, then $A = 0$ or $B = 0$, or both $A = 0$ and $B = 0$.

In solving quadratic equations by factoring, the work is simplified by (1) *making the coefficient of the squared term positive* and (2) *reducing the coefficients to their lowest integral form.*

Example 1. Solve $98\,x - 6\,x^2 = 400$.
Solution: Transposing and rearranging terms, we have

$$- 6\,x^2 + 98\,x - 400 = 0,$$

or $\qquad 3\,x^2 - 49\,x + 200 = 0.$

Factoring, $\qquad (x - 8)(3\,x - 25) = 0.$

Hence, from $x - 8 = 0$ and $3\,x - 25 = 0$, we obtain

$$x = 8 \quad \text{or} \quad x = 8\tfrac{1}{3}.$$

Example 2. Solve for x: $ax^2 + x - abx - b = 0$.
Solution: We factor by grouping terms:

$$(ax^2 + x) - (abx + b) = 0,$$
$$x(ax + 1) - b(ax + 1) = 0,$$
$$(ax + 1)(x - b) = 0,$$
$$x = -1/a \quad \text{or} \quad b.$$

EXERCISE 38

Solve the following equations for x:

1. $9\,x^2 = 49.$

2. $5\,x^2 - 12 = x^2 + 24.$

3. $(2\,x - 1)^2 = 17 - 4\,x.$

4. $(x + 3)(x - 3) = 2\,x^2 - 25.$

5. $\dfrac{2}{x^2 + 1} = \dfrac{3}{2\,x^2 - 3}.$

6. $\dfrac{x^2 - 1}{3} - \dfrac{2\,x^2 - 3}{5} = \dfrac{x^2 - 4}{2}.$

7. $\dfrac{5\,a^2}{2} - x^2 = \dfrac{3\,x^2}{2}.$

8. $\dfrac{x^2 - 9\,a^2}{16\,a^2} = \dfrac{x^2 - 16\,a^2}{9\,a^2}.$

Solve and leave answers in terms of simplified radicals:

9. $\dfrac{x + 1}{2\,x + 1} = \dfrac{2\,x + 3}{x + 7}.$

10. $\dfrac{1}{x} + \dfrac{1}{x + 3} = \dfrac{5}{x + 6}.$

11. $\dfrac{x^2 + 3}{x^2} = \dfrac{x^2 + 9}{x^2 + 4}.$

12. $\dfrac{x + 5}{x} - \dfrac{5}{4} = \dfrac{x - 1}{4}.$

Solve each of the following formulas for the letter indicated:

13. $V = \tfrac{1}{3}\,\pi r^2 h$, for r.

14. $E = \tfrac{1}{2}\,mv^2 + k$, for v.

15. $F = \dfrac{mM}{d^2}$, for d.

16. $\dfrac{1}{a^2} + \dfrac{1}{b^2} = \dfrac{1}{c^2}$, for a.

Solve the following equations by factoring:

17. $x^2 + 2x - 8 = 0$.   **18.** $2x^2 + 7x - 4 = 0$.
19. $2x^2 - 11x + 5 = 0$.   **20.** $3x^2 - 2x - 5 = 0$.
21. $6x^2 + 15x - 9 = 0$.   **22.** $8 - 4x - 12x^2 = 0$.
23. $30x^2 - 85x + 25 = 0$.   **24.** $12x^2 - 42x - 24 = 0$.
25. $10x^2 + 48x - 10 = 0$.   **26.** $21x^2 - 77x + 42 = 0$.
27. $x^2 + 0.2x - 0.03 = 0$.   **28.** $x^2 - 1.3x + 0.22 = 0$.
29. $(x - 2)^2 = 36$.   **30.** $(3x + 4)^2 = 9$.

Solve the following equations for x:

31. $x^2 - 8nx + 12n^2 = 0$.   **32.** $a^2x^2 - 11abx + 18b^2 = 0$.
33. $x^2 - bx + ab - a^2 = 0$.   **34.** $(a + b)x = x^2 + ab$.
35. $px^2 - p^2x - x + p = 0$.   **36.** $x^2 - 2ax + a^2 - b^2 = 0$.

55. Solution by Completing the Square. Any quadratic equation, whether factorable or not, can be solved by a method known as **completing the square.**

This process depends essentially on the fact that *the binomial* $(x^2 + kx)$ *becomes a perfect square if we add the square of one-half the coefficient of* x. That is,

$$(x^2 + kx) + \tfrac{1}{4}k^2 = (x + \tfrac{1}{2}k)^2.$$

Example. Solve by completing the square: $2x^2 - 6x + 1 = 0$.

Solution:

Transpose the constant term: $2x^2 - 6x = -1$.

Divide by the coefficient of x^2: $x^2 - 3x = -\tfrac{1}{2}$.

Add $(\tfrac{1}{2}k)^2$ to both sides: $x^2 - 3x + (\tfrac{3}{2})^2 = -\tfrac{1}{2} + \tfrac{9}{4} = \tfrac{7}{4}$.

Take the square root of both sides: $x - \tfrac{3}{2} = \pm \tfrac{1}{2}\sqrt{7}$.

Hence: $x = \tfrac{1}{2}(3 + \sqrt{7})$ or $\tfrac{1}{2}(3 - \sqrt{7})$.

Since $\sqrt{7} = 2.646$: $x = \tfrac{1}{2}(3 + 2.646) = 2.82$, or $x = \tfrac{1}{2}(3 - 2.646) = 0.18$.

NOTE. The above decimal answers are only approximate and do not satisfy the given equation exactly. Unless numerical values of the roots are required, the roots should be expressed in terms of simplified radicals.

56. Solution by the Quadratic Formula. The general quadratic equation

$$ax^2 + bx + c = 0$$

can be solved using the method of completing the square. Thus, transposing c and dividing by a, we have

$$x^2 + \frac{b}{a}x = -\frac{c}{a}.$$

Completing the square on the left side by adding $(b/2\,a)^2$, we obtain

$$x^2 + \frac{b}{a}\,x + \left(\frac{b}{2\,a}\right)^2 = -\frac{c}{a} + \frac{b^2}{4\,a^2},$$

or

$$\left(x + \frac{b}{2\,a}\right)^2 = \frac{b^2 - 4\,ac}{4\,a^2}.$$

Taking the square root of each side, we have

$$x + \frac{b}{2\,a} = \pm\,\frac{\sqrt{b^2 - 4\,ac}}{2\,a};$$

hence,

$$x = \frac{-b \pm \sqrt{b^2 - 4\,ac}}{2\,a}.$$

This important result is called the **quadratic formula,** and should be carefully *memorized*.

Example 1. Solve $9\,x^2 - 18\,x + 14 = 0$.
Solution: Since $a = 9$, $b = -18$, and $c = 14$, we have

$$x = \frac{-(-18) \pm \sqrt{(-18)^2 - 4(9)(14)}}{2(9)} = \frac{18 \pm \sqrt{36(9 - 14)}}{18}$$

$$= \frac{18 \pm 6\,i\sqrt{5}}{18} = \frac{3 \pm i\sqrt{5}}{3}.$$

NOTE. To facilitate the simplification of the radical expression, we may factor out of $(b^2 - 4\,ac)$ such square numbers as are evidently common to both terms.

Example 2. Solve for x: $\quad px^2 - (2\,p + q)x + (p + q) = 0$.
Solution: Since $a = p$, $b = -(2\,p + q)$, and $c = (p + q)$, we have

$$x = \frac{(2\,p + q) \pm \sqrt{(2\,p + q)^2 - 4\,p(p + q)}}{2\,p}$$

$$= \frac{2\,p + q \pm \sqrt{q^2}}{2\,p} = \frac{p + q}{p} \quad \text{or} \quad 1.$$

EXERCISE 39

What should be added to each of the following in order to have a perfect square of a binomial?

1. $x^2 + 4\,x$.　**2.** $x^2 - 10\,x$.　**3.** $x^2 - 3\,x$.　**4.** $x^2 - \frac{1}{3}\,x$.
5. $x^2 + \frac{2}{5}\,x$.　**6.** $x^2 - 6\,ax$.　**7.** $x^2 - \frac{4}{7}\,mx$.　**8.** $x^2 + \frac{3}{4}\,bx$.

Verify by substitution that

9. $x = \frac{1}{2}(3 + \sqrt{2})$ is a root of $4\,x^2 - 12\,x + 7 = 0$.
10. $x = \frac{1}{3}(-1 + i)$ is a root of $9\,x^2 + 6\,x + 2 = 0$.

Solve by completing the square. Express radicals in the simplest form:

11. $x^2 + 2\,x = 8$.   **12.** $x^2 - 4\,x = 12$.
13. $2\,x^2 - 5\,x - 3 = 0$.   **14.** $3\,x^2 - 4\,x - 4 = 0$.
15. $x^2 - x - 1 = 0$.   **16.** $2\,x^2 - 4\,x + 1 = 0$.
17. $8\,x^2 - 10\,x - 3 = 0$.   **18.** $9\,x^2 - 12\,x - 8 = 0$.
19. $5\,x^2 - 8\,x + 4 = 0$.   **20.** $3\,x^2 - 16\,x + 4 = 0$.
21. $4\,x^2 - 8\,ax + 3\,a^2 = 0$.   **22.** $6\,x^2 + 11\,ax + 4\,a^2 = 0$.
23. $3\,x^2 - 2\,ax - 3\,a^2 = 0$.   **24.** $4\,x^2 - 6\,ax - 3\,a^2 = 0$.

Solve, using the quadratic formula. Express radicals in the simplest form:

25. $2\,x^2 + 5\,x + 2 = 0$.   **26.** $3\,x^2 - 2\,x - 5 = 0$.
27. $3\,x^2 - 2\,x - 7 = 0$.   **28.** $x^2 + 10\,x + 5 = 0$.
29. $4\,x^2 + 0.4\,x - 0.05 = 0$.   **30.** $3\,x^2 - 4\,x + 4 = 0$.
31. $12\,x^2 - 14\,x + 3 = 0$.   **32.** $8\,x^2 - 16\,x + 5 = 0$.

Solve and express answers correct to two decimal places:

33. $x^2 - 4\,x - 7 = 0$.   **34.** $2\,x^2 + 3\,x - 6 = 0$.
35. $5\,x^2 - 7\,x - 2 = 0$.   **36.** $4\,x^2 + 6\,x - 27 = 0$.
37. $6\,x^2 - 18\,x + 9 = 0$.   **38.** $2\,x^2 + 2.3\,x + 0.4 = 0$.

Solve for x, using the quadratic formula:

39. $x^2 - 9\,abx + 20\,a^2b^2 = 0$.   **40.** $6\,m^2x^2 + 5\,mnx + n^2 = 0$.
41. $6\,x^2 - 2\,x - 4 = ax - a$.   **42.** $x^2 + a^2 - 2\,b^2 = 2\,ax$.
43. $x^2 - 2\,ax = a$.   **44.** $x^2 + a^2 = 2\,ax + b^2x^2$.

Solve for y in terms of x, and for x in terms of y:

45. $x^2 - y^2 - 3\,x + 3\,y = 0$.   **46.** $x^2 + xy - 2\,y^2 - y = 1$.
47. $4\,x^2 - y^2 - 2\,x + y = 2$.   **48.** $x^2 - 4\,xy + 4\,y^2 = x + 1$.
49. $x^2 + 2\,xy + y^2 - 9\,x = 0$.   **50.** $y^2 + 2\,xy = x - 2$.

57. Problems Reducing to Quadratic Equations. A complete quadratic equation should be solved by *factoring*, if the factors are easily recognized; otherwise the *quadratic formula* should be used.

Example 1. Solve $\sqrt{2\,x + 3} - \sqrt{4\,x - 1} = 1$.

Solution:

Transpose: $\sqrt{2x+3} = 1 + \sqrt{4x-1}.$

Square both sides: $2x+3 = 1 + 2\sqrt{4x-1} + 4x - 1.$

Combine terms: $3 - 2x = 2\sqrt{4x-1}.$

Square both sides: $9 - 12x + 4x^2 = 4(4x-1).$

Combine terms: $4x^2 - 28x + 13 = 0.$

Factor: $(2x-1)(2x-13) = 0.$

$$x = \tfrac{1}{2} \quad \text{or} \quad \tfrac{13}{2}.$$

Checking for extraneous roots:

when $x = \frac{1}{2}$,

$\sqrt{1+3} - \sqrt{2-1} = 1,$

$2 - 1 = 1.$

when $x = \frac{13}{2}$,

$\sqrt{13+3} - \sqrt{26-1} = 1,$

$4 - 5 \neq 1.$

Hence, the only valid solution of the given radical equation is $x = \frac{1}{2}$.

Example 2. Solve $x^3 - 8 = 0$.

Solution: Factoring, we have $(x-2)(x^2 + 2x + 4) = 0$. Hence

$$x - 2 = 0 \quad \text{or} \quad x = 2,$$

$$x^2 + 2x + 4 = 0 \quad \text{or} \quad x = \frac{-2 \pm \sqrt{4-16}}{2} = -1 \pm i\sqrt{3}.$$

If the equation obtained in solving a stated problem is a quadratic equation, we have two solutions. Both solutions may have a reasonable meaning as an answer to the problem, but more often only one of the solutions has any real significance. In giving an answer to such problems, reject any solutions which have absurd meanings.

Example 3. *A* alone can do a piece of work in 5 days less than the time required by *B* alone to do the job. Working together, they complete the work in 6 days. How long does it take each alone to do the job?

Analysis: Let x = the time in days required by A; then

$x + 5$ = the time in days required by B, and

$6/x$ = fraction of work done by A in 6 days, and

$6/(x+5)$ = fraction of work done by B in 6 days; hence

Solution:
$$\frac{6}{x} + \frac{6}{x+5} = 1,$$
$$6x + 30 + 6x = x^2 + 5x,$$
$$x^2 - 7x - 30 = 0,$$
$$(x-10)(x+3) = 0,$$
$$x = 10, -3.$$

Answer: *A* requires 10 days and *B* requires 15 days.

EXERCISE 40

Solve the following equations for x:

1. $(x+1)(x+5) = 45$.
2. $(x-2)(x+3) = 6$.
3. $x(3x+2) = (x+2)^2$.
4. $x^2 + (x+2)^2 = 650$.
5. $x^3 - (x-1)^3 = 19$.
6. $(c+x)(2c-3x) = 3x^2$.
7. $x(x^2-1) = 64 - x$.
8. $(x+1)^3 = 3x(x+1)$.

9. $(4x+1)(3x+1) - (2x+1)(x+1) = 14$.
10. $(3x-1)^2 + 5(3x-1) + 6 = 0$.
11. $(x+3c)^2 - (x+2c)^2 = (x+c)^2$.
12. $(x-1)(2x-1)(3x-1) = 6x^3 - 33$.

13. $\dfrac{x+6}{2x+1} = \dfrac{2x-3}{x+2}$.
14. $\dfrac{9}{x-1} + \dfrac{4}{x+3} = 1$.

15. $\dfrac{15}{x+5} + \dfrac{12}{x+10} = 1$.
16. $\dfrac{2x}{3x+1} = \dfrac{x-2}{2x-1}$.

17. $\dfrac{1}{3x-4} - \dfrac{3}{3x+4} = \dfrac{2}{5x}$.
18. $\dfrac{x+5}{x+2} + \dfrac{x-3}{x-2} = \dfrac{3(x-5)}{x^2-4}$.

19. $\dfrac{3}{x+1} + \dfrac{2}{2x-1} = \dfrac{13}{18}$.
20. $\dfrac{1}{x} + \dfrac{1}{x-3} = \dfrac{7}{3x-5}$.

21. $\dfrac{1}{x} + \dfrac{1}{x+3d} = \dfrac{1}{x-d}$.
22. $x(x-2a) = \dfrac{2a^2+1}{a^2}$.

23. $\sqrt{6x-11} = 2x - 7$.
24. $\sqrt{10-x} = 2(x+4)$.

25. $\sqrt{2x-5} - \sqrt{x-3} = 1$.
26. $\sqrt{3x+5} + \sqrt{6x+3} = 3$.

27. $\sqrt{2-x} + \sqrt{5-x} = \sqrt{x+8}$.
28. $\sqrt{5x-1} = 4 - \sqrt{x-1}$.

29. $\sqrt{b(ax-2b)} = ax - 2b$.
30. $\sqrt{n(3x+n)} = 3n - \sqrt{nx}$.

31. Find three consecutive integers the sum of whose squares equals 434.

32. A rectangular lawn 40 feet long and 26 feet wide has a path of uniform width around it. Find the width of the path if its area is 432 square feet.

33. A man bought some pigs for $120. If each pig had cost a dollar more, he would have obtained 6 less pigs for the same money. How many pigs did he buy?

34. The sum of the reciprocals of two consecutive even integers is $\frac{7}{24}$. Find the integers.

35. A skilled worker can do a certain job in 9 days less time than an unskilled worker, and together they can do the job in 20 days. How long would it take each alone to do the job?

36. The sum of two numbers is 10, and the sum of their cubes is 280. What are the numbers?

37. A boy bought some candy bars for $1.50. He ate two bars and sold the rest at 2 cents profit on each bar. If he made 90 cents on the deal, how many bars did he buy?

38. The tens' digit of a two-figure number is 2 more than the units' digit, and the number itself is 1 more than the sum of the squares of its digits. Find the number.

39. The sum of a number and its square root is 56. Find the number.

40. A floor can be paved with 720 square tiles of a certain size. If each tile were 1 inch longer each way, it would take 500 tiles. Find the size of each tile.

41. One pipe takes 36 minutes longer to drain a tank than it takes another pipe to fill it. When both pipes are open, it takes 55 minutes to fill the tank. How long would it take to fill the tank if the drain were shut off?

42. A motorboat takes 1 hour longer to make a trip of 48 miles up a stream than it takes on the return trip downstream. If the average rate of the current is 4 miles per hour, what is the rate of the boat in still water?

43. The longer leg of a right triangle is 2 feet more than twice the shorter leg. If the hypotenuse is 13 feet long, find the legs of the triangle.

44. A train travels 150 miles at a uniform rate. If the rate had been 5 miles per hour more, the journey would have taken 1 hour less time. Find the rate of the train.

45. A man has a certain investment which annually yields $200 interest. If he had $1000 less invested at a rate 1 per cent higher, he would receive the same yearly interest. How much has he invested, and at what rate?

46. The circumference of a rear wheel of a wagon is 40 inches longer than that of a front wheel, and the rear wheel performs 50 less revolutions than the front wheel in traveling a distance of 1000 feet. How large are the wheels?

47. The denominator of a fraction exceeds twice the numerator by 1. If the numerator is increased by 4 and the denominator is decreased by 4, the resulting fraction will be the reciprocal of the given fraction. Find the given fraction.

48. A 2-inch square is cut from each corner of a rectangular piece of cardboard whose length exceeds the width by 4 inches. The sides are then turned up and an open box is formed. Find the three dimensions of this box, if the volume is 64 cubic inches.

49. A can do a piece of work in 7 days less than B, and together they can do the work in 9 days less than A alone. Find the time they take when they work together.

50. If an object is thrown vertically into the air with a velocity v in feet per second, the height s of the object in feet after t seconds is given by the formula $s = vt - \frac{1}{2} gt^2$, where $g = 32$. (a) Solve the formula for t, (b) find t when $v = 200$ feet per second and $s = 500$ feet, and (c) using the data in (b), find when the object will hit the ground.

58. Equations in Quadratic Form. An equation is said to be in **quadratic form** if it is quadratic with respect to some function of the unknown.

Illustration: $x^4 - 8 x^2 - 9 = 0$ is a quadratic in x^2;

$$x^{-3} - 9 x^{-\frac{3}{2}} + 8 = 0 \text{ is a quadratic in } x^{-\frac{3}{2}};$$

and $2(x - 3) - \sqrt{x - 3} - 3 = 0$ is a quadratic in $\sqrt{x - 3}$.

Example 1. Solve $4 x^4 + 7 x^2 - 36 = 0$.
Solution: Factoring, we have

$$(4 x^2 - 9)(x^2 + 4) = 0.$$

Setting each factor equal to zero, we obtain

$$x^2 = \tfrac{9}{4}, \quad \text{hence } x = \pm \tfrac{3}{2}; \text{ and}$$
$$x^2 = -4, \text{ hence } x = \pm 2 i.$$

Note 1. The details in the solution are often simpler if a new variable is introduced.

Example 2. Solve $\dfrac{x^2 - 3}{x} - \dfrac{8 x}{x^2 - 3} = 2$.

Solution: Let $y = \dfrac{x^2 - 3}{x}$, then $y - \dfrac{8}{y} = 2$; hence

$$y^2 - 2 y - 8 = 0, (y + 2)(y - 4) = 0, \text{ and } y = -2 \text{ or } 4.$$

From $\dfrac{x^2 - 3}{x} = -2$, we have $x^2 + 2 x - 3 = 0$; hence $x = 1 \text{ or } -3$.

From $\dfrac{x^2 - 3}{x} = 4$, we have $x^2 - 4 x - 3 = 0$; hence $x = 2 \pm \sqrt{7}$.

Note 2. The above examples illustrate the fact that *an integral rational equation of the nth degree has exactly n roots.*

EXERCISE 41

Solve the following equations:

1. $4 x^4 - 9 x^2 + 2 = 0.$

2. $x^4 - 6 x^2 - 27 = 0.$

3. $x^{-4} - 10 x^{-2} + 9 = 0.$

4. $x - x^{\frac{1}{2}} - 2 = 0.$

5. $8 x^6 + 7 x^3 - 1 = 0.$

6. $2 x^{\frac{1}{2}} + 2 x^{-\frac{1}{2}} = 5.$

7. $x^{\frac{4}{3}} - 7 x^{\frac{2}{3}} + 12 = 0.$

8. $x^{-3} - 7 x^{-\frac{3}{2}} - 8 = 0.$

9. $(x - 1)^2 - 2(x - 1) = 1.$

10. $(2 x - 3)^4 - (2 x - 3)^2 = 12.$

11. $(x^2 + x)^2 + 3(x^2 + x) = 10.$

12. $(2 x^2 + 1)^2 - 2(2 x^2 + 1) = 15.$

13. $\left(x - \dfrac{6}{x} \right)^2 + \left(x - \dfrac{6}{x} \right) = 20.$

14. $\left(2 - \dfrac{1}{x} \right)^2 - 3\left(2 - \dfrac{1}{x} \right) = 4.$

15. $\left(\dfrac{x^2}{x + 1} \right) + 2\left(\dfrac{x + 1}{x^2} \right) = 3.$

16. $(x^2 + 2 x) - \dfrac{6}{(x^2 + 2 x)} = 5.$

17. $x^2 + 3x - 8 = \dfrac{20}{x^2 + 3x}$.

18. $\dfrac{x^2 - 6}{x} + \dfrac{5x}{x^2 - 6} = 6$.

19. $x^8 - 17x^4 + 16 = 0$.

20. $(x^2 - 6x + 4)^2 = 16$.

21. $(2x - 1) - 3\sqrt{2x - 1} = 40$.

22. $2\sqrt{x - 3} + 5\sqrt[4]{x - 3} = 3$.

23. $x^2 + 3x = \sqrt{x^2 + 3x + 12}$.

24. $x^2 + 4x - 8 = \sqrt{x^2 + 4x - 2}$.

25. $\left(3 - \dfrac{1}{x}\right) = \sqrt{3 - \dfrac{1}{x}}$.

26. $\sqrt{\dfrac{x}{x - 5}} + \sqrt{\dfrac{x - 5}{x}} = \dfrac{13}{6}$.

27. $(x^2 - 2)(x^2 + 1) = 10$.

28. $(x + 1)^4 - 28 = 4x(x^2 + 1)$.

29. $\dfrac{5}{x^{-2}} + \dfrac{5}{x^{-2} + 1} = 24$.

30. $\dfrac{9}{x^2 - 1} + \dfrac{7}{x^2 + 3} = 4$.

59. Character of the Roots. If r_1 and r_2 represent the roots of the quadratic equation $ax^2 + bx + c = 0$, then, by the formula,

$$r_1 = \frac{-b + \sqrt{b^2 - 4ac}}{2a} \quad \text{and} \quad r_2 = \frac{-b - \sqrt{b^2 - 4ac}}{2a}.$$

The expression $(b^2 - 4ac)$, which appears under the radical sign, is called the **discriminant** of the quadratic equation, and its value determines the character of the roots, as is shown below.

If a, b, and c are real numbers, then r_1 and r_2 are

> *real and unequal when $b^2 - 4ac$ is positive;*
> *real and equal when $b^2 - 4ac$ is zero;*
> *imaginary when $b^2 - 4ac$ is negative.*

NOTE 1. If a, b, and c are rational numbers, then r_1 and r_2 are rational when the discriminant is a perfect square or zero; otherwise the roots are irrational or imaginary.

NOTE 2. If the discriminant is negative, the roots have the form $(m + ni)$ and $(m - ni)$; that is, they are conjugate imaginary numbers.

Illustration. For $8x^2 - 14x - 15 = 0$, we have

$$b^2 - 4ac = (-14)^2 - 4(8)(-15) = 676 = (26)^2.$$

Hence, the roots are real, unequal, and rational.

Example. Determine the values of k for which the equation $kx^2 + 3kx + (2k + 1) = 0$ has equal roots.

Solution: If the roots are to be equal, the discriminant must be zero. Hence, since $a = k$, $b = 3k$, and $c = 2k + 1$, we have

$$(3k)^2 - 4(k)(2k + 1) = k^2 - 4k = 0; \text{ hence } k = 0, 4.$$

When $k = 0$, the equation is not quadratic; therefore the roots are equal only when $k = 4$.

60. Sum and Product of the Roots. Adding the two roots of the quadratic equation $ax^2 + bx + c = 0$, we have

$$r_1 + r_2 = \left(\frac{-b + \sqrt{b^2 - 4ac}}{2a}\right) + \left(\frac{-b - \sqrt{b^2 - 4ac}}{2a}\right) = -\frac{b}{a}.$$

Multiplying these roots, we obtain

$$r_1 r_2 = \left(\frac{-b + \sqrt{b^2 - 4ac}}{2a}\right)\left(\frac{-b - \sqrt{b^2 - 4ac}}{2a}\right)$$

$$= \frac{b^2 - (b^2 - 4ac)}{4a^2} = \frac{4ac}{4a^2} = \frac{c}{a}.$$

Rule. *In the quadratic equation $ax^2 + bx + c = 0$, the sum of the roots is $-b/a$ and the product of the roots is c/a.*

If r_1 and r_2 are the roots of a quadratic equation, the equation can be written as $(x - r_1)(x - r_2) = 0$, or

$$x^2 - (r_1 + r_2)x + r_1 r_2 = 0.$$

This result is consistent with the above rule, and in general a quadratic equation can be given in the form

$$x^2 - Sx + P = 0,$$

where S is the sum of the roots and P is the product of the roots.

Example 1. Form a quadratic equation whose roots are $(2 \pm 2i)$.
Solution: Since $r_1 = 2 + 2i$ and $r_2 = 2 - 2i$, we have

$S = (2 + 2i) + (2 - 2i) = 4$ and $P = (2 + 2i)(2 - 2i) = 4 - 4i^2 = 8.$

Hence, the required equation is $x^2 - 4x + 8 = 0$.

Example 2. Determine the values of k for which one root of the equation $x^2 - (k + 2)x + 2 = 0$ is twice the other.
Solution: From the equation, we have $S = k + 2$ and $P = 2$. Hence, if r and $2r$ denote the roots, then $r(2r) = 2$ or $r = \pm 1$. Thus, the roots are 1 and 2, or -1 and -2. Finding the sums, we obtain $k = 1$ or $k = -5$.

EXERCISE 42

Without solving the following equations, (*a*) determine the character of the roots and (*b*) give the sum and the product of the roots:

1. $x^2 - 7x + 10 = 0.$
2. $2x^2 + 4x - 1 = 0.$
3. $3x^2 - 4x - 9 = 0.$
4. $4x^2 - 20x + 25 = 0.$
5. $32x^2 - 8x + 5 = 0.$
6. $\frac{1}{2}x^2 + \frac{3}{4}x - \frac{2}{3} = 0.$
7. $0.7x^2 - 3.2x - 0.25 = 0.$
8. $1234x^2 - 923x = 0.$
9. $\frac{2}{5}x^2 - \frac{4}{3}x - \frac{1}{2} = 0.$
10. $4x^2 - 2.4x + 0.36 = 0.$
11. $2x^2 + 2\sqrt{2}x - 3 = 0.$
12. $2x^2 + 4x + \sqrt{3} = 0.$

Form a quadratic equation, with integral coefficients, having the roots:

13. $4, -5$.
14. $2, \frac{1}{2}$.
15. $-3, 3$.
16. $\frac{1}{2}, -\frac{3}{4}$.
17. $-\frac{2}{7}, -\frac{2}{7}$.
18. $\frac{4}{5}, \frac{3}{5}$.
19. $0.2, -0.7$.
20. $2.3, 1.7$.
21. $-1.3, -0.2$.
22. $\pm 3i$.
23. $\pm \frac{1}{4}\sqrt{5}$.
24. $\pm 2i\sqrt{3}$.
25. $4 \pm 2i\sqrt{3}$.
26. $-2 \pm 5\sqrt{3}$.
27. $3 \pm \frac{1}{2}i$.
28. $\frac{1}{2}(3 \pm 2\sqrt{2})$.
29. $\frac{1}{3}(-1 \pm i)$.
30. $\frac{2}{3}(2 \pm \sqrt{3})$.

Determine the values of k for which the following equations have equal roots:

31. $kx^2 - 12x + 9 = 0$.
32. $9x^2 + 2kx + 16 = 0$.
33. $x^2 + kx = 1 - k$.
34. $kx^2 + 4x = 2k - 9$.
35. $5x^2 - x + 6 = kx$.
36. $(k-3)x^2 = (x-3)k^2$.
37. $(x+k)^2 + 4x = 0$.
38. $x^2 + x = kx + k$.
39. $k(x^2 + x) = 4 + 2x - x^2$.
40. $(x+1)^2 = (2x+k)^2$.

Determine the values of k for which the roots of the following equations satisfy the indicated condition:

41. $x^2 + 5x - (k+3) = 0$; one root is zero.
42. $2x^2 - 3kx + 7 = x$; one root is the negative of the other.
43. $2x^2 - (k-2)x - 7 = 0$; one root is -2.
44. $3x^2 - (2k+1)x = 4$; sum of roots is $\frac{1}{2}$.
45. $kx^2 - 5x + 3 = 0$; product of roots is -4.
46. $4x^2 - kx - 3 = 0$; sum of roots equals product of roots.
47. $2x^2 - 6x + k = 0$; difference of roots is 2.
48. $x^2 + x + 5 = kx + k$; one root is $(1 + i)$.
49. $2x^2 + kx + k = 0$; one root is twice the other.
50. $kx^2 - 2kx + 5 = 4x$; one root exceeds the other by 2.
51. $kx^2 + 7x + 2k = 0$; the quotient of the roots is $\frac{3}{4}$.
52. $ax^2 + x = k - k^2x$; one root is the reciprocal of the other.
53. $akx^2 + 2x = k^2 + 4a^2$; one root is 2.
54. $x^2 - akx + a^2(k-1) = 0$; one root is a times the other.

61. Graphs of Quadratic Functions.

A polynomial in x of the form $f(x) = ax^2 + bx + c$, where $a \neq 0$, is called a **quadratic function in** x.

Example 1. Graph $f(x) = x^2 - 4x + 3$.

Solution: Selecting arbitrary values for x, we compute the corresponding values of $f(x)$,

x	-1	0	1	2	3	4	5
$f(x)$	8	3	0	-1	0	3	8

and obtain the graph given in Figure 10. This curve is called a **parabola** and it is symmetric with respect to a vertical line called the **axis of the parabola.** The point V where the axis cuts the parabola is called the **vertex of the parabola,** and the ordinate of the vertex represents the smallest or **minimum value** attained by $(x^2 - 4x + 3)$ for any real value of x.

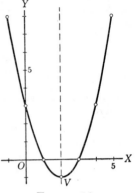

The following facts are proved in more advanced works.

1. The graph of $f(x) = ax^2 + bx + c$ *is a parabola whose axis is vertical; it opens upward if* **a** *is positive and opens downward if* **a** *is negative.*

2. The equation of the axis is **x = − b/2 a.**

FIGURE 10.

3. The function f(x) *has a minimum or maximum value according as* **a** *is positive or negative, and its value is given by*

$$f\left(-\frac{b}{2\,a}\right) = c - \frac{b^2}{4\,a}.$$

Graphically the real roots of the equation $f(x) = ax^2 + bx + c = 0$ are those values of x where the graph of $f(x)$ either crosses or touches the x-axis. Thus, if the graph of $f(x)$ crosses the x-axis at two distinct points, touches the x-axis at one point, or does not touch the x-axis, the real roots of the equation $f(x) = 0$ are respectively real and unequal, real and equal, or imaginary.

Example 2. Find two numbers whose sum is 100 and whose product is a maximum.

Solution: Let x and $(100 - x)$ represent the numbers; then the product $x(100 - x)$ will be a maximum at the vertex of the parabola $f(x) = -x^2 + 100x$. Hence, $x = -b/2a = -100/(-2) = 50$.

Answer: The numbers are 50 and 50.

EXERCISE 43

Find graphically the real roots of the following equations to the nearest tenth in decimals:

1. $x^2 + x - 4 = 0$.
3. $2x^2 - 6x + 3 = 0$.
5. $0.4 + 1.4x - x^2 = 0$.

2. $7 + 4x - x^2 = 0$.
4. $9x^2 - 12x - 8 = 0$.
6. $5x^2 - 8x + 3.2 = 0$.

Graph the following functions and find (a) the coordinates of the vertex, and (b) the equation of the axis:

7. $x^2 - 2x + 4$.
8. $2x^2 - 3x - 7$.
9. $5 + 4x - x^2$.
10. $5x^2 - 3x + 2$.
11. $3x^2 - 4x$.
12. $x^2 + 8$.
13. $3 - x - 5x^2$.
14. $4x^2 + 5x + 6$.
15. $2x^2 - 9x - 5$.

State whether the following functions have a maximum or a minimum value, and find this value without graphing:

16. $2x^2 - 3x + 4$.
17. $7 - x - x^2$.
18. $3 - 2x + x^2$.
19. $8x^2 - 7x - 1$.
20. $\frac{1}{2}x^2 - 5x - 1$.
21. $0.4 - 3x - 2.1x^2$.
22. $-x^2 - x - 1$.
23. $7x^2 - x + 15$.
24. $6 - 4x^2 - 3x$.

25. Divide 40 into two parts whose product is a maximum.

26. Divide 50 into two parts such that the sum of their squares is a minimum.

27. What number exceeds its square by the greatest amount?

28. A man has 600 yards of fencing and wants to fence three sides of a rectangular field which borders on a straight river. What dimensions give a maximum area?

29. If a projectile is shot vertically upward, its height in feet at time t in seconds is given by the formula $s = v_0 t - \frac{1}{2} gt^2$ where v_0 is the initial velocity in feet per second and $g = 32$. When v_0 is 650 feet per second, find the maximum height reached.

30. The average profit on a manufactured article is $15 per article when 100 per day are produced. When more are produced, the average profit is decreased 1 cent for each additional article made. Find the production number per day which yields the greatest profit.

CHAPTER 9

Systems of Quadratic Equations

62. Quadratic Equations in Two Unknowns. An equation of the form

$$ax^2 + bxy + cy^2 + dx + ey + f = 0, \qquad (1)$$

where a, b, c, d, e, and f are constants and a, b, and c are not all zero, is called a **general quadratic equation in x and y.** We shall limit the discussion in this chapter to those equations in which the coefficients are real numbers.

It is shown in more advanced courses that the graph of an equation of the form of (1) is generally a **circle,** an **ellipse,** a **parabola,** or a **hyperbola,** although exceptional cases exist in which the equation has no graph at all, or a graph consisting of a single point, one line, two intersecting lines, or two parallel lines. The above curves as a group are often called the **conic sections** inasmuch as they are the curves obtained in taking plane sections of a right circular cone.

NOTE. When the left member of Equation (1) can be expressed as the product of two real rational factors, its graph consists of two lines, one corresponding to each factor.

63. Standard Forms of Quadratic Equations.

I. Circle. *An equation of the form $ax^2 + ay^2 = c$, where the constants are positive, represents a circle whose center is at the origin and whose radius is $\sqrt{c/a}$.*

94

Illustration. The graph of the equation $4\,x^2 + 4\,y^2 = 25$ is a circle of radius $\frac{5}{2}$, as shown in Figure 11.

II. Ellipse. *An equation of the form* $ax^2 + by^2 = c$, *where the constants are positive and* $a \neq b$, *represents an ellipse whose center is at the origin and whose axes lie on the coordinate axes.*

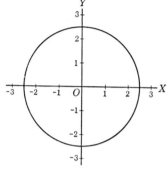

FIGURE 11.

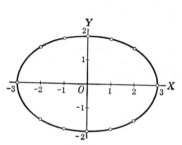

FIGURE 12.

Example 1. Graph $4\,x^2 + 9\,y^2 = 36$.

Solution: Setting $x = 0$, we obtain the y-intercepts, ± 2; and setting $y = 0$, we obtain the x-intercepts, ± 3.

Solving the given equation for y, we may use the equivalent equation

$$y = \pm\, \tfrac{2}{3}\sqrt{9 - x^2}$$

to obtain other points of the curve. In tabular form, we have

x	0	± 3	± 1	± 2
y	± 2	0	± 1.9	± 1.5

NOTE 1. Observe that the radical equation $y = \frac{2}{3}\sqrt{9 - x^2}$ represents only the half of the curve that lies above the x-axis.

III. Hyperbola. *An equation of the form* $ax^2 - by^2 = c$ *or* $by^2 - ax^2 = c$, *where the constants are positive, represents a hyperbola which is symmetric to the coordinate axes.*

Example 2. Graph $4\,x^2 - 9\,y^2 = 36$.

Solution: Setting $y = 0$, we obtain the x-intercepts, ± 3.

Solving the given equation for y, we may use the equivalent equation

$$y = \pm\, \tfrac{2}{3}\sqrt{x^2 - 9}$$

to obtain other points of the curve. In the radical form of the equation it is evident that any values of x numerically less than 3 will give

imaginary values for y and hence no points on the curve. Setting
$x = \pm\, 4, \pm\, 5, \pm\, 6$, we obtain the points

x	± 3	± 4	± 5	± 6
y	0	± 1.8	± 2.7	± 3.5

NOTE 2. As indicated in Figure 13, every hyperbola is bounded by
two straight lines which are called its **asymptotes.** The extremities
of the curve approach these lines
but never reach them. The equations of the asymptotes may be determined from the equation of the
hyperbola by changing the constant
term to zero. Thus, in Example 2,
the equation of the asymptotes
is $4\,x^2 - 9\,y^2 = 0$. Hence, from
$(2\,x + 3\,y)(2\,x - 3\,y) = 0$, we
have the equations $2\,x + 3\,y = 0$
and $2\,x - 3\,y = 0$.

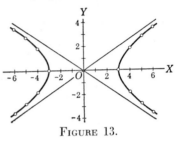

FIGURE 13.

NOTE 3. *An equation of the form $xy = k$, where k is not zero, represents
a hyperbola which has the coordinate axes as asymptotes.*

IV. Parabola. *An equation of the form $x = ay^2 + by + c$,
where $a \neq 0$, represents a parabola whose axis is horizontal.*

NOTE 4. *An equation of the form $y = ax^2 + bx + c$ represents a
parabola whose axis is verti-
cal.* This equation was discussed in Article 61.

Example 3. Graph
$x = y^2 - 2$.

Solution: Setting $x = 0$,
we obtain the y-intercepts,
$\pm\sqrt{2}$; and setting $y = 0$, we
obtain the x-intercept, -2.
Expressing the given equation in the explicit form

$$y = \pm\sqrt{x + 2},$$

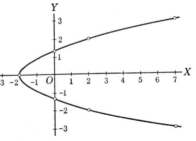

FIGURE 14.

we see that the values of y are imaginary when x is less than -2. For
values of x greater than 2, we have

x	-2	0	2	7
y	0	± 1.4	± 2	± 3

EXERCISE 44

Name each of the following conics, obtain a table of points including the intercepts, and plot the graph:

1. $x^2 + y^2 = 16$.
2. $xy = 6$.
3. $x^2 - 4y^2 = 16$.
4. $9x^2 + 4y^2 = 36$.
5. $4x = y^2$.
6. $9x^2 + 16y^2 = 144$.
7. $2y = x^2 - 5x$.
8. $4y^2 - 9x^2 = 36$.
9. $x = y^2 - y - 2$.
10. $5x^2 - y^2 = 20$.
11. $2x^2 + 3y^2 = 30$.
12. $xy = -12$.

Factor the following equations, and graph:

13. $x^2 + xy = 3x$.
14. $x^2 - y^2 + 2x + 1 = 0$.
15. $x^2 + x = y^2 + y$.
16. $x^2 + 3x + 2 = y^2 - y$.

Graph each of the following equations:

17. $xy = x^2 + 1$.
18. $xy + x = y$.
19. $x^2 + 2xy + y^2 = x$.
20. $x^2 - x = xy - y$.
21. $x^2 + 4y^2 = 0$.
22. $x^2 + xy + y^2 = 3$.
23. $(x - 2)^2 + 4(y + 1)^2 = 4$.
24. $4(x - 1)^2 - (y - 2)^2 = 16$.

64. Graphic Solution of Systems Involving Quadratics.

Plotting the graphs of the two equations

$$\begin{cases} x^2 + y^2 = 25, \\ x - y + 1 = 0, \end{cases}$$

on the same coordinate system, we see that their graphs intersect at the points $(3, 4)$ and $(-4, -3)$. It is evident that each of these pairs of values satisfies both of the given equations; and hence corresponding to each point of intersection we have a *real solution* of those equations.

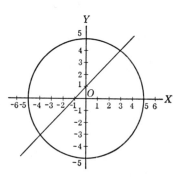

FIGURE 15.

From a study of the various combinations of conic sections it is apparent that any two of these curves cannot intersect in

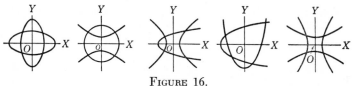

FIGURE 16.

more than four points. Hence, the respective systems of equations cannot have more than four real solutions.

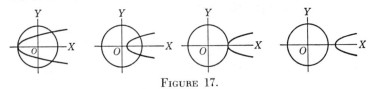

FIGURE 17.

Figure 17 illustrates that there may be less than four real solutions.

Example. Solve graphically:

$$\begin{cases} 4\,x^2 + y^2 = 16, \\ y^2 = x + 4. \end{cases}$$

Solution: Plotting the graph of each equation on the same coordinate system, we see that they intersect at four points. Each of these points represents a solution of the given system of equations, and approximating them to the nearest tenth in decimals, we have

$$\begin{cases} x = 1.6, \quad 1.6, \, -1.9, \, -1.9, \\ y = 2.4, \, -2.4, \quad 1.5, \, -1.5. \end{cases}$$

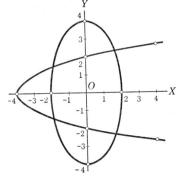

FIGURE 18.

EXERCISE 45

Solve the following systems of equations graphically:

1. $\begin{cases} x^2 + y^2 = 100, \\ y = x + 2. \end{cases}$
2. $\begin{cases} y^2 = 4\,x + 4, \\ y = 2\,x - 2. \end{cases}$
3. $\begin{cases} x^2 + 4\,y^2 = 25, \\ x + 1 = 2\,y. \end{cases}$

4. $\begin{cases} x^2 + y^2 = 17, \\ x^2 + 9\,y^2 = 25. \end{cases}$
5. $\begin{cases} y^2 - x^2 = 4, \\ y = x + 2. \end{cases}$
6. $\begin{cases} x^2 + y^2 = 9, \\ x^2 - 3\,y^2 = 12. \end{cases}$

7. $\begin{cases} 2\,x + y^2 = 6, \\ x^2 + y^2 = 5. \end{cases}$
8. $\begin{cases} x^2 - 3\,y^2 = 1, \\ x^2 + 4\,y^2 = 8. \end{cases}$
9. $\begin{cases} x^2 + 4\,y^2 = 9, \\ y^2 = 12(x + 3). \end{cases}$

10. $\begin{cases} y^2 = 4\,x - 4, \\ x^2 = 4\,y - 4. \end{cases}$
11. $\begin{cases} x^2 - y^2 = 9, \\ 5\,x - 4\,y = 9. \end{cases}$
12. $\begin{cases} 4\,x^2 - y^2 = 12, \\ 4\,y^2 - x^2 = 12. \end{cases}$

Solve the following systems of equations graphically and express the solutions correct to the nearest tenth in decimals:

13. $\begin{cases} xy = 5, \\ y = x^2. \end{cases}$
14. $\begin{cases} x^2 + y^2 = 16, \\ 2\,x + 3\,y = 6. \end{cases}$
15. $\begin{cases} x^2 + y^2 = 25, \\ y^2 = 1 - x. \end{cases}$

16. $\begin{cases} 2\,x^2 + y^2 = 6, \\ 5\,x + y = 9. \end{cases}$
17. $\begin{cases} xy + 6 = 0, \\ 2\,x + y = 2. \end{cases}$
18. $\begin{cases} x^2 + 4\,y^2 = 4, \\ xy - 1 = 0. \end{cases}$

65. Algebraic Solution of Systems Involving Quadratics. In Article 64 it was illustrated geometrically that a system of two quadratic equations in two unknowns could not have more than four real solutions. This fact is a special instance of the following general theorem, whose proof is beyond the scope of this book:

Theorem. *A system of two independent integral rational equations in two unknowns, of degrees* **m** *and* **n** *respectively, have at most* **mn** *real and imaginary solutions.*

Thus, a system of two quadratic equations can have at most 2×2 or 4 real and imaginary solutions. Occasionally such systems have less than four solutions.

Illustration. The system of equations $xy = 1$, $xy = x - 1$ has one solution, namely, $x = 2$ and $y = \frac{1}{2}$; and the system of equations $xy = 1$, $xy = 2$ has no solutions.

Solving a system of two quadratic equations in two unknowns usually involves solving a fourth-degree equation in one unknown. Thus, in eliminating y from the system of equations $y = x^2$, $y^2 + 5x - 6 = 0$, we obtain $x^4 + 5x - 6 = 0$. The general method of solving a fourth-degree equation is given in Article 121. In this chapter we shall consider only the systems of equations that can be solved by more elementary means.

66. Systems Involving One Linear Equation. A system of equations involving one linear equation is solved as follows:

1. Solve the linear equation for one of the unknowns.

2. Substitute the value (1) in the second equation.

3. Solve the equation obtained in (2).

4. Substitute the values (3) in (1) to find the corresponding values of the second unknown.

Example. Solve: $\begin{cases} 2x^2 + 2y^2 = 5xy, \\ x + 2y = 4. \end{cases}$

Solution: Following the procedure outlined above, we have

(1) $x = 4 - 2y.$
(2) $2(4 - 2y)^2 + 2y^2 = 5y(4 - 2y).$

(3)
$$32 - 32\,y + 8\,y^2 + 2\,y^2 = 20\,y - 10\,y^2,$$
$$20\,y^2 - 52\,y + 32 = 0,$$
$$5\,y^2 - 13\,y + 8 = 0,$$
$$(y - 1)(5\,y - 8) = 0,$$
$$y = 1,\ \tfrac{8}{5}.$$

(4) Since
$$x = 4 - 2\,y,$$
$$\text{when } y = 1,\ x = 2,$$
$$\text{when } y = \tfrac{8}{5},\ x = \tfrac{4}{5}.$$

EXERCISE 46

Solve algebraically for x and y:

1. $\begin{cases} x - y = 1, \\ x^2 + y^2 = 13. \end{cases}$
   2. $\begin{cases} x + 6\,y = 3, \\ xy + y = -2. \end{cases}$
   3. $\begin{cases} y = 2\,x - 3, \\ 2\,x^2 - xy = 15. \end{cases}$

4. $\begin{cases} x + y = 2, \\ x^2 - 2\,y^2 = 8. \end{cases}$
   5. $\begin{cases} x - 2\,y = 1, \\ xy - 10 = 0. \end{cases}$
   6. $\begin{cases} x - y = 1, \\ x^2 + xy + y^2 = 7. \end{cases}$

7. $\begin{cases} x + 4\,y = 9, \\ x^2 + 4\,y = 9. \end{cases}$
   8. $\begin{cases} 2\,x + y = 5, \\ x^2 - y^2 = 7. \end{cases}$
   9. $\begin{cases} y = \tfrac{3}{4}\,x, \\ 3\,xy - 2\,x^2 = 4. \end{cases}$

10. $\begin{cases} 5\,x - 3\,y = 6, \\ 2\,x^2 - 3\,x = y^2. \end{cases}$
    11. $\begin{cases} 4\,x - 3\,y = 25, \\ x^2 + y^2 = 25. \end{cases}$
    12. $\begin{cases} 3\,x + 4\,y = 7, \\ x^2 + x = 2\,y^2. \end{cases}$

13. $\begin{cases} x + y = 1, \\ \dfrac{1}{x} + \dfrac{1}{y} = 4. \end{cases}$
    14. $\begin{cases} x - 2\,y = 2, \\ \dfrac{x + y}{x - y} = y. \end{cases}$
    15. $\begin{cases} x^2 - 5\,y^2 = 4, \\ \dfrac{x + 3}{y + 2} = 2. \end{cases}$

16. $\begin{cases} x - y = b, \\ xy = a^2 + ab. \end{cases}$
    17. $\begin{cases} x - y = 2, \\ xy + 1 = c^2. \end{cases}$
    18. $\begin{cases} x + y = 2\,m, \\ x^2 - y^2 = 4\,mn. \end{cases}$

67. Systems Involving Two Quadratic Equations.

The algebraic solution of a system of two quadratic equations can often be found by applying methods of elimination similar to those previously studied. In all cases it is important to indicate clearly the pairs of values which together are solutions of the given system.

Example 1. Solve: $\begin{cases} 4\,x^2 + y^2 = 13, & (1) \\ xy = 3. & (2) \end{cases}$

Solution: Solving Equation (2) for y, we have $y = 3/x$. Substituting this value for y in Equation (1) gives

$$4\,x^2 + \frac{9}{x^2} = 13,$$
$$4\,x^4 + 9 = 13\,x^2,$$
$$4\,x^4 - 13\,x^2 + 9 = 0.$$

Factoring, $(x^2 - 1)(4\,x^2 - 9) = 0.$

Hence, $x = \pm\,1,\ \pm\,\tfrac{3}{2}.$

Substituting each of these four values of x in (2), we obtain the four distinct solutions:

$$\begin{cases} x = + 1, \ - 1, \ + \tfrac{3}{2}, \ - \tfrac{3}{2}, \\ y = + 3, \ - 3, \ + 2, \ - 2. \end{cases}$$

Example 2. Solve for x and y: $\begin{cases} 3\,x^2 - 2\,y^2 = 10\,a^2, & (3) \\ 2\,x^2 + 3\,y^2 = 11\,a^2. & (4) \end{cases}$

Solution: Multiplying both members of Equation (3) by 3, and both members of Equation (4) by 2, we obtain

$$\begin{cases} 9\,x^2 - 6\,y^2 = 30\,a^2, \\ 4\,x^2 + 6\,y^2 = 22\,a^2. \end{cases}$$

Adding these equations, we have $13\,x^2 = 52\,a^2$ or $x^2 = 4\,a^2$. Hence, $x = \pm\,2\,a$; and substituting either $+\,2\,a$ or $-\,2\,a$ for x in Equation (4) we find that $y = \pm\,3\,a$. Thus, we have the four distinct solutions:

$$\begin{cases} x = 2\,a, \quad 2\,a, \ - 2\,a, \ - 2\,a, \\ y = 3\,a, \ - 3\,a, \quad 3\,a, \ - 3\,a. \end{cases}$$

EXERCISE 47

Solve the following systems of equations algebraically:

1. $\begin{cases} x^2 + y^2 = 13, \\ 4\,x^2 - y^2 = 7. \end{cases}$ 2. $\begin{cases} x^2 + 4\,y^2 = 20, \\ 4\,x^2 + y^2 = 20. \end{cases}$ 3. $\begin{cases} x^2 + y^2 = 25, \\ xy = 12. \end{cases}$

4. $\begin{cases} 4\,x^2 + y^2 = 16, \\ xy + 4 = 0. \end{cases}$ 5. $\begin{cases} x^2 - 6\,y^2 = 3, \\ 3\,x^2 + 2\,y^2 = 29. \end{cases}$ 6. $\begin{cases} 3\,x^2 - y^2 = 3, \\ y + 2\,x^2 = 5. \end{cases}$

7. $\begin{cases} 4\,x^2 + 3\,y^2 = 19, \\ 7\,x^2 - 2\,y^2 = 26. \end{cases}$ 8. $\begin{cases} x^2 + 3 = xy, \\ 2\,x^2 - 6 = xy. \end{cases}$ 9. $\begin{cases} 3\,x^2 + 2 = 2\,y^2, \\ y^2 - x^2 = 9. \end{cases}$

10. $\begin{cases} 5\,x^2 + 19 = 4\,y^2, \\ 8\,x^2 - 20 = 5\,y^2. \end{cases}$ 11. $\begin{cases} 3\,x^2 - 2\,y^2 = 0, \\ 5\,x^2 - 3\,y^2 = 1. \end{cases}$ 12. $\begin{cases} 4\,x^2 - y = 15, \\ 2\,x^2 + 3\,y = 11. \end{cases}$

Solve and express results correct to two decimal places:

13. $\begin{cases} 3\,x^2 + 2\,y^2 = 10, \\ xy + 2 = 0. \end{cases}$ 14. $\begin{cases} x^2 + 7\,y^2 = 21, \\ 2\,x^2 - 3\,y^2 = 6. \end{cases}$ 15. $\begin{cases} 5\,x^2 + 2\,y^2 = 14, \\ y^2 = 2\,x + 1. \end{cases}$

Solve for x and y:

16. $\begin{cases} 2\,x^2 + 3\,y^2 = 7\,a^2, \\ 5\,y^2 - x^2 = 3\,a^2. \end{cases}$ 17. $\begin{cases} x^2 + 4\,y^2 = 20\,a^2, \\ xy = 4\,a^2. \end{cases}$ 18. $\begin{cases} x^2 + xy = 1 + a, \\ x - xy = 1 - a. \end{cases}$

68. Reduction to Simpler Systems by Factoring. In order for a product of two or more quantities to be equal to zero, we know that one or more of the factors of that product must be equal to zero. We may use this property to reduce a particular system of equations to two or more simpler systems of equations.

Example. Solve: $\begin{cases} x^2 + y^2 = 8, & (1) \\ x^2 - 3\,xy + 2\,y^2 = 0. & (2) \end{cases}$

Solution: Factoring (2), we have $(x - y)(x - 2y) = 0$. Hence (2) is satisfied if either $(x - y) = 0$ or $(x - 2y) = 0$.

Thus any solution of (1) and (2) is a solution of one of the following systems, and conversely any solution of either of the following systems is a solution of the given system:

I. $\begin{cases} x^2 + y^2 = 8, \\ x - y = 0. \end{cases}$ II. $\begin{cases} x^2 + y^2 = 8, \\ x - 2y = 0. \end{cases}$

Solving each of the above systems separately, we have the solutions

I'. $\begin{cases} x = 2, -2, \\ y = 2, -2. \end{cases}$ II'. $\begin{cases} x = \frac{4}{5}\sqrt{10}, -\frac{4}{5}\sqrt{10}, \\ y = \frac{2}{5}\sqrt{10}, -\frac{2}{5}\sqrt{10}. \end{cases}$

Thus the complete solution of the given system of equations consists of the four solutions in I' and II'.

69. Equations of the Form $ax^2 + bxy + cy^2 = d$.

The solution of a system of equations, in which all terms containing variables are of the second degree, can be obtained by a method known as **eliminating the constant.**

1. Eliminate the constant term between the two given equations to obtain an equation of the form $Ax^2 + Bxy + Cy^2 = 0$.

2. Factor the equation obtained in (1), and solve each factor with either of the given equations.

Example. Solve: $\begin{cases} x^2 + xy = 12, & \text{(1)} \\ y^2 + 4xy = 48. & \text{(2)} \end{cases}$

Solution: Multiplying (1) by 4 and subtracting (2) gives

$$4x^2 - y^2 = 0 \quad \text{or} \quad (2x - y)(2x + y) = 0.$$

Hence, we solve the two systems of equations

I. $\begin{cases} 2x - y = 0, \\ x^2 + xy = 12. \end{cases}$ II. $\begin{cases} 2x + y = 0, \\ x^2 + xy = 12. \end{cases}$

The solutions of these systems are

I'. $\begin{cases} x = 2, -2, \\ y = 4, -4. \end{cases}$ II'. $\begin{cases} x = 2i\sqrt{3}, -2i\sqrt{3}, \\ y = -4i\sqrt{3}, 4i\sqrt{3}. \end{cases}$

Thus the complete solution of the given system of equations consists of the real and imaginary solutions in I' and II'.

NOTE. Systems of equations of the above form may also be solved by making the substitution $y = vx$. Thus, Equations (1) and (2) become

$$\begin{cases} x^2 + vx^2 = 12, \\ v^2 x^2 + 4vx^2 = 48. \end{cases}$$

Eliminating x, we have

$$\frac{12}{1 + v} = \frac{48}{v^2 + 4 v}; \text{ hence } v^2 = 4.$$

When $v = 2$, we obtain $x^2 = 12/(1 + v) = 4$, or $x = 2, -2$; and from $y = vx$, we have respectively $y = 4, -4$.

When $v = -2$, we obtain $x^2 = 12/(1 + v) = -12$, or $x = 2\,i\sqrt{3}$, $-2\,i\sqrt{3}$; and from $y = vx$, we have respectively $y = -4\,i\sqrt{3}, 4\,i\sqrt{3}$.

EXERCISE 48

Reduce to simpler systems and solve:

1. $\begin{cases} x^2 + y^2 = 25, \\ (3\,x - 4\,y)(x + y + 5) = 0. \end{cases}$ 2. $\begin{cases} x^2 - y^2 = 16, \\ (3\,x + 5\,y)(x + y - 4) = 0. \end{cases}$

3. $\begin{cases} 8\,x^2 - 3\,xy = 14, \\ (2\,x + 3\,y)(3\,x - 2\,y) = 0. \end{cases}$ 4. $\begin{cases} 2\,xy - y^2 = 3, \\ (x + y)(2\,x - y - 3) = 0. \end{cases}$

Reduce to simpler systems by factoring and solve:

5. $\begin{cases} 2\,xy - y^2 = 9, \\ x^2 - y^2 = 0. \end{cases}$ 6. $\begin{cases} x^2 + xy + y^2 = 49, \\ x^2 - xy - 2\,y^2 = 0. \end{cases}$

7. $\begin{cases} 3\,xy + y^2 = 4, \\ (x + y)^2 - 4 = 0. \end{cases}$ 8. $\begin{cases} x^2 + 4\,y^2 = 9, \\ x^2 + 2\,xy = 0. \end{cases}$

Reduce to four systems of linear equations and solve:

9. $\begin{cases} (x + y)(x - y - 2) = 0, \\ (x - 3\,y)(2\,x - y - 3) = 0. \end{cases}$ 10. $\begin{cases} x^2 + 2\,xy + y^2 = 25, \\ 12\,x^2 - 16\,xy - 3\,y^2 = 0. \end{cases}$

Solve by the method of eliminating constants:

11. $\begin{cases} x^2 + 2\,xy = 8, \\ 3\,x^2 - 4\,y^2 = 8. \end{cases}$ 12. $\begin{cases} x^2 + xy = 6, \\ 2\,x^2 + y^2 = 27. \end{cases}$

13. $\begin{cases} x^2 - xy + y^2 = 21, \\ 2\,xy - y^2 = 15. \end{cases}$ 14. $\begin{cases} x^2 - xy + y^2 = 3, \\ 2\,x^2 + y^2 = 6. \end{cases}$

15. $\begin{cases} x^2 + xy = 6, \\ xy + y^2 = 3. \end{cases}$ 16. $\begin{cases} x^2 - 2\,xy + 2\,y^2 = 5, \\ 7\,x^2 + 2\,y^2 = 15. \end{cases}$

17. $\begin{cases} x^2 - 2\,xy + y^2 = 9, \\ 2\,x^2 - 3\,xy + y^2 = 15. \end{cases}$ 18. $\begin{cases} 2\,x^2 - xy + 3\,y^2 = 18, \\ x^2 + 2\,xy - 3\,y^2 = 12. \end{cases}$

19. $\begin{cases} x(2\,y - x) = 16, \\ y(2\,y + x) = 60. \end{cases}$ 20. $\begin{cases} (x + y)^2 + x^2 = 5, \\ (x + y)^2 + y^2 = 10. \end{cases}$

Solve for x and y by any method:

21. $\begin{cases} y^2 = x^2 + 2\,x + 1, \\ x^2 + xy = 6. \end{cases}$ 22. $\begin{cases} x^2 - 5\,xy = 4, \\ x^2 - x = y^2 - y. \end{cases}$

23. $\begin{cases} x^2 + xy = a + 1, \\ y^2 + xy = a^2 + a. \end{cases}$ 24. $\begin{cases} x^2 - a^2 y^2 = 0, \\ y^2 = y - x. \end{cases}$

70. Miscellaneous Methods of Reduction. An equation is said to be **symmetric in x and y** if the equation remains the same when x and y are interchanged. A system of two symmetric quadratic equations in two unknowns can be solved by changing variables, as indicated in the following example.

Example 1. Solve:
$$\begin{cases} 2\,x^2 + 2\,y^2 + x + y = 6, \\ 4\,xy + x + y = -2. \end{cases}$$

Solution: Let $x = u + v$, and $y = u - v$; then the given system becomes
$$\begin{cases} 4\,u^2 + 4\,v^2 + 2\,u = 6, \\ 4\,u^2 - 4\,v^2 + 2\,u = -2. \end{cases}$$

The solutions of this new system are readily found to be
$$\begin{cases} u = \tfrac{1}{2},\ -1, \quad \tfrac{1}{2},\ -1, \\ v = 1, \quad\ 1,\ -1,\ -1. \end{cases}$$

Hence, from $x = u + v$ and $y = u - v$, we have the following solutions for the given system:
$$\begin{cases} x = \quad \tfrac{3}{2}, \quad\ 0,\ -\tfrac{1}{2},\ -2, \\ y = -\tfrac{1}{2},\ -2, \quad \tfrac{3}{2}, \quad 0. \end{cases}$$

Example 2. Solve:
$$\begin{cases} (x - 2\,y)(x - y) = 3, & (1) \\ (x - 2\,y)(x + y) = 7. & (2) \end{cases}$$

Solution: Dividing the corresponding members of (1) and (2), we have
$$\frac{x - y}{x + y} = \frac{3}{7}; \text{ hence } y = \tfrac{2}{5}\,x. \tag{3}$$

Solving (3) with either of the given equations, we obtain the two solutions
$$\begin{cases} x = 5,\ -5, \\ y = 2,\ -2. \end{cases}$$

Example 3. Solve:
$$\begin{cases} x^2 + y^2 + x - y = 6, & (4) \\ xy = 2. & (5) \end{cases}$$

Solution: Multiplying (5) by 2 and subtracting from (4), we obtain
$$x^2 - 2\,xy + y^2 + x - y = 2,$$
or
$$(x - y)^2 + (x - y) - 2 = 0;$$
hence
$$[(x - y) - 1][(x - y) + 2] = 0.$$

Solving the systems of equations

I. $\begin{cases} x - y - 1 = 0, \\ xy = 2, \end{cases}$ II. $\begin{cases} x - y + 2 = 0, \\ xy = 2, \end{cases}$

we obtain the solutions

I'. $\begin{cases} x = 2,\ -1, \\ y = 1,\ -2. \end{cases}$ II'. $\begin{cases} x = -1 + \sqrt{3},\ -1 - \sqrt{3}, \\ y = \quad 1 + \sqrt{3}, \quad 1 - \sqrt{3}. \end{cases}$

EXERCISE 49

Solve, using the method of Example 1:

1. $\begin{cases} xy + x - y = 1, \\ \quad x^2 + y^2 = 17. \end{cases}$ **2.** $\begin{cases} (x + y)^2 + (x - y) = 4, \\ \quad\quad x^2 + y^2 = 5. \end{cases}$

3. $\begin{cases} x^2 + xy + y^2 = 7, \\ \quad xy + x + y = 5. \end{cases}$ **4.** $\begin{cases} x^2 + y^2 + 2x + 2y = 6\frac{1}{2}, \\ \quad\quad 3xy - x - y = \frac{1}{4}. \end{cases}$

Solve, using the method of Example 2:

5. $\begin{cases} (x + y)(x - y) = 16, \\ (x + y)(2x - y) = 56. \end{cases}$ **6.** $\begin{cases} \quad\quad x^2 - y^2 = 2, \\ x^2 - 2xy - 3y^2 = 3. \end{cases}$

7. $\begin{cases} \quad\quad x^3 - y^3 = 7\frac{5}{8}, \\ x^2 + xy + y^2 = 15\frac{1}{4}. \end{cases}$ **8.** $\begin{cases} x^2 - y^2 - x - y = 9, \\ \quad x^2 - xy - x = 6. \end{cases}$

Solve, using the method of Example 3:

9. $\begin{cases} x^2 + y^2 = x + y, \\ \quad\quad xy = 1. \end{cases}$ **10.** $\begin{cases} 4x^2 + y^2 = 2x + y + 8, \\ \quad\quad xy = 3. \end{cases}$

11. $\begin{cases} x^2 + 9y^2 = 40, \\ \quad xy = x - 3y. \end{cases}$ **12.** $\begin{cases} x^2 + xy + y = 137, \\ y^2 + xy + x = 205. \end{cases}$

Solve the following systems by any method:

13. $\begin{cases} x^3 + y^3 = 9, \\ x^3 - 2y^3 = 6. \end{cases}$ **14.** $\begin{cases} x - 2y = 2, \\ \sqrt{x} + \sqrt{y} = 3. \end{cases}$ **15.** $\begin{cases} x^{\frac{1}{3}}y^{\frac{1}{3}} - y^{\frac{2}{3}} = 2, \\ x^{\frac{2}{3}} - x^{\frac{1}{3}}y^{\frac{1}{3}} = 6. \end{cases}$

16. $\begin{cases} xy^2 = 3, \\ xy - y = 2. \end{cases}$ **17.** $\begin{cases} x^3 + y^3 = 37, \\ x + y = 1. \end{cases}$ **18.** $\begin{cases} x^2 - xy = a + 1, \\ xy - y^2 = a. \end{cases}$

19. $\begin{cases} x^2 - 2xy + y^2 = 4, \\ xy + 2x - 5 = 0. \end{cases}$ **20.** $\begin{cases} x^2 - xy + x = 10, \\ xy - y^2 + y = 8. \end{cases}$

21. $\begin{cases} x^2 + y^2 + z^2 = 14, \\ 2x - y + z = 3, \\ x + 2y - 2z = -1. \end{cases}$ **22.** $\begin{cases} x^2 + y^2 - z = 9, \\ x + y - z = 1, \\ xy - z = 2. \end{cases}$

EXERCISE 50

Solve each problem, using two or more unknowns:

1. Find the sides of a rectangle whose perimeter is 60 feet and whose area is 221 square feet.

2. The sum of the reciprocals of two numbers is 5 and the product of the numbers is $\frac{9}{56}$. Find the numbers.

3. Find the legs of a right triangle whose hypotenuse is 13 feet and whose area is 30 square feet.

4. The product of two integers divided by their sum gives a quotient of 2 and a remainder of 2; and their sum divided by their difference gives a quotient of 2 and a remainder of 1. Find the integers.

5. A milkman covers his route, which is 15 miles long, by 11 A.M. each day. If his average rate of travel were half a mile faster each hour, he would be through by 10 A.M. What time does he start in the morning?

6. How much should be added to the width and how much should be taken from the length of a rectangle 10 inches by 24 inches, in order to increase its area by 12 square inches and decrease its perimeter by 2 inches?

7. In a two-figure number the sum of the squares of the digits is 45, and the product of the number and the number with digits reversed is 2268. Find the number.

8. A rectangular door has two equal rectangular panels one above the other. The border surrounding them is everywhere 5 inches wide except between the panels, where it is 6 inches wide. Find the length and width of the door if the area of the borders is 1280 square inches and the area of the door is 3200 square inches.

9. Towns A and B are 216 miles apart. P leaves B to travel to A, and Q leaves A at the same time, traveling to B. They pass after 4 hours, and P reaches A 1 hour and 48 minutes before Q reaches B. At what rates do they travel?

10. The product of two integers exceeds their sum by 54, and the quotient of the two integers is 4 less than their difference. Find the integers.

11. The fore wheel of a wagon makes 4 revolutions more than a hind wheel in traveling a distance of 144 feet. If the circumference of each were increased 1 foot, the fore wheel would make 3 revolutions more than the hind wheel in traveling a distance of 130 feet. Find the circumference of each wheel.

12. The product of two integers is 15 more than the square of the smaller and 16 less than the square of the larger. What are the integers?

13. The difference between a fraction and its reciprocal is $\frac{5}{6}$. Find the fraction if it equals $\frac{3}{10}$ the sum of its numerator and denominator.

14. The hypotenuse of a right triangle is 17, and it becomes 20 if the sides of the triangle are increased by 1 and 4 respectively. Find the sides of the triangle.

15. A group of students rented a motorboat and shared the cost equally. If the number of students had been 5 less, they could have used a smaller boat costing half as much, and the expense to each would have been 50 cents less. If there had been 10 more students, they would have required a larger boat costing 20 per cent more, but the expense to each would have been 30 cents less. How many students were in the group?

16. A certain fraction is 5 per cent of the sum of its numerator and denominator, and the reciprocal of the fraction is 80 per cent of the sum of the numerator and denominator. Find the fraction.

17. A, B, and C start together to solve a certain number of problems. A solved 6 per day and finished them 2 days after B. C solved 4 more per day than B and finished 2 days before he did. Find the total number of problems.

18. A closed rectangular box with a square base has a total surface area of 144 square inches and a diagonal of 9 inches. What are its dimensions?

19. A and B plan to make 80 boxes in two days, making 40 each day. On the first day A works for 3 hours and B works for 2 hours and 45 minutes. On the second day A makes 12 boxes before B arrives, and then together they finish the other 28 boxes 4 hours after A began working. How many boxes does each make per hour?

20. A man has three adjacent square lots of different dimensions. If these lots fronted on a street with the largest lot between the other two, the perimeter of his property would be 340 yards; but if the smallest lot were in the center the perimeter would be 364 yards. Find the size of his lots, if their total area is 4897 square yards.

CHAPTER 10

Ratio, Proportion, and Variation

71. Ratio. *When two like quantities are compared by division, the quotient obtained is called the* **ratio** *of the two quantities.*

Thus, the ratio of a to b is the quotient a/b, and is sometimes written as $a : b$.

Illustration. The ratio of 5 inches to 2 feet is $\frac{5}{24}$, or $5 : 24$.

72. Proportion. *An equality of two ratios is called a* **proportion.**

Thus, $a : b = c : d$ is a proportion in which a and d are the **extremes,** b and c the **means,** and d is the **fourth proportional** to a, b, and c.

In a proportion of the form $a : b = b : c$, c is called the **third proportional** to a and b, and b is the **mean proportional** between a and c.

If we wish to compare three or more quantities in the above sense, we may write a relation such as the following:

$$a : b : c = 2 : 3 : 5.$$

Each side of this equality is called a **continued ratio** and the above is read "a is to b is to c as 2 is to 3 is to 5." This single relation is an abbreviated notation for expressing the following ordinary proportions:

$$a : b = 2 : 3 \quad \text{and} \quad a : c = 2 : 5.$$

Example 1. Divide 70 into three numbers whose ratio is $2:3:5$.

Solution: If $2x$ represents the smallest number, then $3x$ and $5x$ represent the others. Hence, $2x + 3x + 5x = 70$, and $x = 7$. Thus, the numbers are 14, 21, and 35.

If $a:b = c:d$, the following properties of proportions can be verified by the student:

1. $ad = bc$; the product of the means equals the product of the extremes.

2. $a:c = b:d$; proportion by **alternation.**

3. $b:a = d:c$; proportion by **inversion.**

4. $(a+b):b = (c+d):d$; proportion by **composition.**

5. $(a-b):b = (c-d):d$; proportion by **division.**

6. $(a+b):(a-b) = (c+d):(c-d)$; proportion by **composition** and **division.**

Example 2. If $\dfrac{a}{b} = \dfrac{c}{d}$, prove that $\dfrac{a+b}{b} = \dfrac{c+d}{d}$.

Solution: Adding 1 to both sides of the given proportion, we have

$$\frac{a}{b} + 1 = \frac{c}{d} + 1; \text{ hence } \frac{a+b}{b} = \frac{c+d}{d}.$$

EXERCISE 51

Express each of the following ratios in its simplest form:

1. $35:56$. **2.** $\frac{3}{4}:\frac{1}{5}$. **3.** $0.08:0.4$. **4.** $6x^4:3x^5$. **5.** $a^2b^3:a^3b^2$.

Find the ratio of the given quantities:

6. 2 feet to $7\frac{1}{2}$ yards.   **7.** 6 pints to 5 quarts.
8. 12 ounces to 3 pounds.   **9.** 220 yards to 1 mile.

Find the fourth proportional to the following:

10. 21, 14, 27.   **11.** 10, $16\frac{2}{3}$, $23\frac{1}{3}$.   **12.** a, ab, b.   **13.** a, b, c.

Find the third proportional to the following:

14. 5, 8.   **15.** $2\frac{1}{2}$, $1\frac{2}{3}$.   **16.** a^2, ab.   **17.** a, b.

Find the mean proportional between the following:

18. 8 and 18.   **19.** $2\frac{1}{2}$ and $22\frac{1}{2}$.   **20.** a and a^3.   **21.** a and b.

Solve the equations:

22. $3:(6-x) = 4:5$.   **23.** $(x-1):3 = (x+2):4$.
24. $2:x = (x-2):4$.   **25.** $x:(x+1) = (x+3):(x+5)$.

26. $(x - 1) : (x + y) = (x + 1) : 5\,y = 2 : 5.$

27. $(2\,x - y) : (x + 1) = (2\,x + 3) : (3\,x + y) = 7 : 3.$

28. Divide 78 in two parts whose ratio is 6 : 7.

29. What is the ratio of the area of a circle to the area of a circumscribing square? Use $\pi = \frac{22}{7}$.

30. What number must be subtracted from each member of the ratio 53 : 79 in order to have the ratio 3 : 5?

31. Find three numbers in the ratio 2 : 5 : 7, whose sum is 238.

32. The ratio of the dimensions of a rectangle is 5 : 7. If 2 feet are added to each dimension, the area is increased 100 square feet. Find the dimensions.

33. Two positive integers are in the ratio 4 : 7. If 18 is added to the smaller and 6 is taken from the larger, the resulting numbers have the ratio 2 : 3. Find the integers. Are two answers possible? Why or why not?

34. At a boxing match the contestants agree to split the proceeds in the ratio 5 : 3, the winner getting the larger share. If the net gate receipts are \$95,624.56, how much does each receive?

35. According to the terms of a will, a man leaves \$5000 to charity; then one-half and one-third of the remainder are willed to his wife and son respectively. What was left is given to his niece. If the man's property amounted to \$65,000, in what ratio was the money divided?

36. If $x{:}y = 2{:}3$, find the numerical value of the ratio $(x+y) : (x+2\,y)$. Hint: Note that $x = \frac{2}{3}\,y$.

37. A merchant maintains a " selling price to cost " ratio of 7 : 5 on all his merchandise. If, at a sale, he sells his goods at " $\frac{1}{4}$ off," what is the ratio of the new selling price to cost?

If $a : b = c : d$, prove that:

38. $(a - b) : b = (c - d) : d.$　　　**39.** $(ad + bc) : ac = 2\,b : a.$

40. If $\dfrac{a}{b} = \dfrac{c}{d} = \dfrac{e}{f}$, prove that $\dfrac{a + c + e}{b + d + f} = \dfrac{a}{b} = \dfrac{c}{d} = \dfrac{e}{f}.$

　　　Hint: Let $\dfrac{a}{b} = \dfrac{c}{d} = \dfrac{e}{f} = k$, then $a = kb$, $c = kd$, $e = kf$.

73. Direct Variation. *One variable y is said to* **vary directly** *as another variable x when they change in such a way that their ratio is constant.* Thus, " y varies directly as x " means that $y/x = k$, or $y = kx$; the constant k is called the **constant of variation.** The symbol $\propto$ is sometimes used to denote variation. Thus, $y \propto x$ is read " y varies directly as x."

Note. The word *directly* is often omitted, and y is said to vary as x.

Illustration. The circumference C of a circle varies as the diameter d, and from $C = \pi d$ we see that the constant of proportionality is π.

Example. The weight of a solid spherical ball varies as the cube of its diameter. If a ball 2 inches in diameter weighs 1.6 pounds, how much will a ball 3 inches in diameter weigh?

Solution: Since the weight (w) varies as the cube of the diameter (d), we have $w = kd^3$. When $w = 1.6$, $d = 2$; hence

$$1.6 = k \cdot 2^3 \quad \text{or} \quad k = 0.2.$$

Thus, $w = 0.2\, d^3$; and when $d = 3$, we have

$$w = 0.2 \cdot 3^3 = 5.4 \text{ pounds.}$$

74. Inverse Variation. *One variable y is said to* **vary inversely** *as another variable x when y varies directly as the reciprocal of x.* Thus, "y varies inversely as x" means that $y = k \cdot \dfrac{1}{x}$, or $xy = k$, k being the constant of variation.

Illustration. The time T required to travel a given distance D is inversely proportional to rate, and from $T = D/R$ we see that the constant of proportionality is the given distance D.

Example. If p varies inversely as q, and $p = 6$ when $q = 4$, find p when $q = 3$.

Solution: Since p varies inversely as q, we have $pq = k$. Substituting $p = 6$ and $q = 4$, we find that $k = 24$. Hence the exact relation satisfied by p and q is $pq = 24$. Now substituting 3 for q, we find that $p = 8$.

75. Combined Variation. The relationship among three or more variables can often be described by means of direct and inverse variations, as is illustrated.

Illustration 1. If $z = kxy$, where k is a constant, then z is said to *vary jointly* as x and y.

Illustration 2. If $u = kxy^3/\sqrt{z}$, where k is a constant, then u is said to vary directly as x, directly as the cube of y, and inversely as the square root of z.

Applications of variations consist in determining one or more of the following in the order given:

1. Finding the equation involving the constant of variation k.

2. Finding a value of k, using the equation determined in 1.

3. Finding an unknown part, using k as determined in 2.

EXERCISE 52

Express the relations in 1–4 by an equation:

1. P varies directly as x^2 and inversely as $\sqrt{y}$.
2. The altitude of a triangle varies directly as the area and inversely as the base. What is the constant of proportionality?
3. R varies jointly as p and q, and $R = 56$ when $p = 2$ and $q = 4$.
4. W varies inversely as $(m + \sqrt{n})$, and $W = 4$ when $m = \frac{1}{2}$ and $n = \frac{1}{8}$.
5. If a varies directly as b, and b varies directly as c, show that a varies directly as c.
6. If a varies inversely as b, and b varies inversely as c, show that a varies directly as c.
7. If p varies directly as q, and $p = 54$ when $q = 3$, find p when $q = 5$.
8. If m varies directly as n, and $m = 0.02$ when $n = 0.7$, find m when $n = 0.035$.
9. If z varies directly as $(2x - 3y)$, and $z = 12$ when $x = 5$ and $y = 2$, find z when $x = 7$ and $y = 3$.
10. If x varies directly as y, with $x = x_1$ when $y = y_1$ and $x = x_2$ when $y = y_2$, show that $x_1 : x_2 = y_1 : y_2$.
11. If a varies inversely as b, and $a = 3\frac{1}{2}$ when $b = 5\frac{1}{3}$, find a when $b = 2\frac{2}{3}$.
12. If s varies inversely as t^2, and $s = 32$ when $t = 6$, find s when $t = 8$.
13. If m varies inversely as $d^{\frac{3}{2}}$, and $m = 6\frac{3}{4}$ when $d = 2\frac{1}{4}$, find m when $d = 6\frac{1}{4}$.
14. If x varies inversely as y, with $x = x_1$ when $y = y_1$ and $x = x_2$ when $y = y_2$, show that $x_1 : x_2 = y_2 : y_1$.
15. If z varies jointly as x and y, and $z = 30$ when $x = 2$ and $y = 5$, find z when $x = 3$ and $y = 7$.
16. If p varies directly as a and inversely as b, and $p = 2\frac{1}{2}$ when $a = 1\frac{2}{3}$ and $b = 2\frac{2}{3}$, find p when $a = 3\frac{1}{2}$ and $b = 2\frac{1}{3}$.
17. If R varies directly as x^2 and inversely as $\sqrt{y}$, and $R = 10$ when $x = 2$ and $y = 8$, find R when $x = 3$ and $y = 18$.
18. If L varies jointly as x and y and inversely as z^2, and $L = 1.8$ when $x = 0.1$, $y = 0.7$, and $z = 1.4$, find L when $x = 0.2$, $y = 2.8$, and $z = 2.1$.
19. If the weight of a hollow statue varies directly as the square of its height, what would a statue 6 feet high weigh, when a similar one 10 inches high weighs $8\frac{1}{3}$ pounds?
20. The distance through which a body falls in a given time varies directly as the square of the time. If it is observed that a body falls 64 feet in 2 seconds, how far will it fall in 5 seconds?

21. The weight of a body above the surface of the earth varies inversely as the square of its distance from the center of the earth. How much would a body weigh at a distance 500 miles above the earth's surface, if the body weighs 100 pounds on the earth's surface? Assume the radius of the earth to be 4000 miles.

22. The amount of paint needed to paint a spherical ball varies as the square of the diameter of the ball. If 1 pint of paint is needed for 100 balls of diameter 2 inches, how much paint is needed for 150 balls of diameter 3 inches?

23. The strength of a beam varies inversely as the cube of its length. If a beam 9 feet long can support 1280 pounds, how much can a similar 12-foot beam support?

24. The length of a piece of wire varies directly as its weight and inversely as the square of its diameter. If a wire 100 feet long and $\frac{1}{8}$ of an inch in diameter weighs 6 pounds, how long a wire of the same material and $\frac{1}{12}$ of an inch in diameter must be taken to weigh 10 pounds?

25. In a motorboat, the required power of the motor varies directly as the cube of the desired speed of the boat. If a 32-horsepower motor can run a boat at a speed of 8 miles per hour, how many horsepower are needed to run the boat at 12 miles per hour?

26. The number of vibrations of a string per second varies directly as the square root of the tension and inversely as the product of its length and diameter. If a string 2 feet long and $\frac{1}{4}$ inch in diameter vibrates 250 times per second when the tension is 150 pounds, how many vibrations per second are made by a 3-foot string $\frac{1}{6}$ inch in diameter under a tension of 96 pounds?

27. The cost of a certain article varies inversely as the square root of the demand for the article. If it costs 45 cents when the company is producing 200,000, what should the cost be if production jumps to 450,000?

28. The electrical resistance of a wire varies directly as the length and inversely as the square of the diameter. If a wire 1000 feet long and 0.09 of an inch in diameter has a resistance of 1 ohm, what is the resistance of a wire of the same material which is 3000 feet long and 0.16 of an inch in diameter?

29. Two persons are given pensions varying as the square root of the number of years of service. One has served 9 years longer than the other and receives a pension $250 greater. If the length of service of the first had exceeded that of the second by $4\frac{1}{4}$ years, their pensions would have been in the ratio 9 : 8. How long had they served?

30. The cost of publishing a pamphlet is $1000 plus an amount varying with the number of copies published. An author figures that an additional 50 copies would cost $100 more, while an additional 100 copies would increase the cost 10%. Find the number of copies published.

CHAPTER 11

Progressions

76. **Progressions.** A succession of numbers formed according to some fixed law is called a **progression.** The individual numbers are called **terms** of the progression and are named from left to right as the first term, the second term, and so on.

An **arithmetic progression,** *or A. P., is a progression in which the successive terms increase or decrease by a constant amount, which is called the* **common difference.**

Any term of an A. P. decreased by the preceding term gives the common difference.

Illustration 1. The numbers 2, 5, 8, 11, ⋯ form an A. P. whose common difference is 3; and 4, $1\frac{1}{2}$, -1, $-3\frac{1}{2}$, ⋯ is an A. P. with the common difference $-2\frac{1}{2}$.

A **geometric progression,** *or G. P., is a progression in which the successive terms increase or decrease by a constant factor, which is called the* **common ratio.**

Any term of a G. P. divided by the preceding term gives the common ratio.

Illustration 2. The numbers 3, -6, 12, -24, ⋯ form a G. P. whose common ratio is -2; and 4, 2, 1, $\frac{1}{2}$, ⋯ is a G. P. with the common ratio $\frac{1}{2}$.

In order that three quantities will form either an A. P. or a G. P. it follows from the definitions that one of the following conditions must be satisfied:

1. Necessary condition that A, B, and C form an A. P. *is*

$$B - A = C - B \quad \text{or} \quad A + C = 2\,B.$$

2. Necessary condition that A, B, and C form a G. P. *is*

$$\frac{B}{A} = \frac{C}{B} \qquad \text{or} \qquad B^2 = AC.$$

NOTE. Three quantities A, B, and C cannot form an A. P. and a G. P. at the same time except for the trivial case in which $A = B = C$.

Example 1. Find the value of x for which the three quantities $(2\,x - 3)$, $(x + 4)$, and $(3\,x - 1)$ form an A. P.

Solution: We have $A = 2\,x - 3$, $B = x + 4$, and $C = 3\,x - 1$. Hence, applying the condition $A - B = B - C$, we have

$$(2\,x - 3) - (x + 4) = (x + 4) - (3\,x - 1).$$

Solving, we obtain $x = 4$.

Check: Substituting 4 for x in the given expressions, we obtain 5, 8, and 11, which is an A. P. with the common difference 3.

Example 2. Find the values of x for which the three quantities $(x^2 + 2)$, $(2\,x - 1)$, and 3 form a G. P.

Solution: We have $A = x^2 + 2$, $B = 2\,x - 1$, and $C = 3$. Hence, applying the condition $B^2 = AC$, we have

$$(2\,x - 1)^2 = 3(x^2 + 2).$$

Solving, we obtain $x = 5$ or -1.

Check: Substituting 5 for x, we obtain 27, 9, and 3, which is a G. P. with $\frac{1}{3}$ as the common ratio. Setting $x = -1$, we obtain 3, -3, and 3, which is a G. P. with -1 as the common ratio.

EXERCISE 53

Determine which of the following progressions are arithmetic progressions and which are geometric progressions:

1. 4, 7, 10, 13, 16.   2. 6, 4, 2, -2, -4.

3. $\frac{1}{2}$, -1, 2, -4, 8.   4. 81, 54, 36, 24, 16.

5. 0, 1, 3, 9, 27.   6. -7, -3, 1, 3, 7.

7. 3, $\frac{9}{2}$, 6, $\frac{15}{2}$, 9.   8. 2.8, 1.4, 0, -1.4, -2.8.

9. 1, $\sqrt{2}$, 2, $2\sqrt{2}$, 4.   10. $-2\sqrt{2}$, $-\sqrt{2}$, 0, $\sqrt{2}$, $2\sqrt{2}$.

Determine the values of x for which the following form an A. P.:

11. $-3, 5, x$.   12. $3, x - 2, -13$.

13. $2, 2\,x - 1, 3\,x$.   14. $2\,x - 3, 5, 3\,x + 2$.

15. $3\,x - 2, x + 5, 2\,x - 3$.   16. $x + 1, \frac{1}{2}\,x, 2\,x - 7$.

17. $x - \frac{1}{2}, x - \frac{1}{3}, 2\,x + \frac{1}{6}$.   18. $x + 3, 2\,x + 1, 3\,x - 1$.

19. $x^2, 3\,x + 1, 4\,x - 1$.   20. $2\,x + 1, x^2 - 1, 3\,x$.

Determine the values of x for which the following form a G. P.:

21. $8, -12, x$.

22. $4, x, 9$.

23. $x - 2, x, x + 6$.

24. $x + 1, 3x, 5x + 2$.

25. $x + 1, x + 3, x + 7$.

26. $x^2 + 1, x + 3, 2$.

27. $2 - x, 4 - x, 8 - 3x$.

28. $x - 4, x - 1, x + 4$.

29. $x + 1, x + 2, 2(x + 1)$.

30. $2, 2x, x^2 + 2$.

77. The nth Term of an A. P. If the first term of an A. P. is denoted by a and the common difference by d, the terms of the progression will be represented by

$$a, a + d, a + 2d, a + 3d, a + 4d, \text{ and so on.}$$

It is evident that in any term the coefficient of d is always 1 less than the number of the term. Hence if l represents the last, or nth, term, we have the formula

$$l = a + (n - 1)d.$$

Example 1. Find the 37th term of the A. P. $-7, -4, -1, 2, \cdots$.
Solution: Since $a = -7$, $d = 3$, and $n = 37$, we have

$$l = -7 + (37 - 1)3 = 101.$$

Example 2. If the 3rd and 14th terms of an A. P. are respectively 3 and -19, what are the first five terms of the progression?
Solution: Let a be the first term and d the common difference; then $(a + 2d)$ and $(a + 13d)$ represent respectively the 3rd and the 14th terms. Thus, we have

$$\begin{cases} a + 13d = -19, \\ a + 2d = 3. \end{cases}$$

Solving this system of equations, we obtain $a = 7$ and $d = -2$. Hence, the first five terms of the progression are $7, 5, 3, 1, -1$.

78. Arithmetic Means. In any A. P. the terms between two given terms are called the **arithmetic means** between those two terms.

Thus, in the progression $1, 4, 7, 10, 13$, the numbers 4, 7, and 10 are the *three* arithmetic means between 1 and 13; whereas in the progression $1, 5, 9, 13$, the numbers 5 and 9 are the *two* arithmetic means between 1 and 13.

Example. Insert four arithmetic means between 1 and 13.

Solution: The two given terms, together with the four means, make an A. P. of six terms; that is $n = 6$. Also it is given that $a = 1$ and $l = 13$. Hence, substituting in $l = a + (n - 1)d$, we have

$$13 = 1 + (6 - 1)d.$$

Solving, we obtain $d = 2\frac{2}{5}$. Thus the four means are $3\frac{2}{5}$, $5\frac{4}{5}$, $8\frac{1}{5}$, and $10\frac{3}{5}$.

The most important instance of arithmetic means is that of *one* arithmetic mean between two given numbers. This mean is also called the *arithmetic average* of the two numbers. If M is the arithmetic mean between a and b, then by the definition of an A. P.,

$$M - a = b - M.$$

Solving for M, $$M = \frac{a + b}{2}.$$

Thus, the arithmetic mean of the numbers 1 and 13 is

$$\tfrac{1}{2}(1 + 13) = 7.$$

79. The Sum of n Terms of an A. P. Let S represent the sum of n terms of an arithmetic progression; that is,

$$S = a + (a + d) + (a + 2\,d) + \cdots + (l - d) + l.$$

Writing the terms in reverse order, we have

$$S = l + (l - d) + (l - 2\,d) + \cdots + (a + d) + a.$$

Adding the corresponding terms of these two equations, we obtain

$$2\,S = (a + l) + (a + l) + (a + l) + \cdots + (a + l) + (a + l)$$
$$= n(a + l).$$

Therefore,

$$S = \frac{n}{2}\,(a + l). \tag{1}$$

Since, $$l = a + (n - 1)d, \tag{2}$$

$$S = \frac{n}{2}\,[2\,a + (n - 1)d]. \tag{3}$$

If any three of the numbers l, a, n, d, S are known, the remaining two may be determined by means of the above formulas.

Example 1. Find the sum of the first 17 terms of the progression $3\frac{1}{2}$, $4\frac{1}{4}$, 5, $\cdots$.

Solution: In the given progression $a = 3\frac{1}{2}$, $d = \frac{3}{4}$, and $n = 17$. Substituting in (3), we obtain

$$S = \tfrac{17}{2}[2(\tfrac{7}{2}) + 16(\tfrac{3}{4})] = \tfrac{17}{2}[7 + 12] = \tfrac{17}{2} \cdot 19 = 161\tfrac{1}{2}.$$

Example 2. If $a = 4$, $l = 36$, and $S = 500$, find n and d.

Solution: Substituting in (1), we obtain

$$500 = \frac{n}{2}(4 + 36).$$

Solving, $\qquad\qquad n = 25.$

Now substituting in (2), we obtain

$$36 = 4 + 24\,d.$$

Hence, $\qquad\qquad d = 1\tfrac{1}{3}.$

Example 3. How many terms of the progression -1, 1, 3, 5, $\cdots$ must be added to give a sum of 360?

Solution: In the given progression $a = -1$, $d = 2$, and $S = 360$. Substituting in (3), we have

$$360 = \frac{n}{2}[2(-1) + (n-1)2].$$

Simplifying, $\quad n^2 - 2\,n - 360 = 0.$

Solving, $\qquad\qquad n = 20 \quad\text{or}\quad -18.$

Since $n = -18$ has no meaning, we reject it as a solution. Thus 20 terms of the progression must be taken.

EXERCISE 54

Find l and S for each of the following progressions:

1. 4, 7, 10, $\cdots$ to 17 terms.   **2.** -3, 1, 5, $\cdots$ to 22 terms.

3. 29, 17, 5, $\cdots$ to 9 terms.   **4.** 11, 25, 39, $\cdots$ to 13 terms.

5. $3\frac{1}{3}$, $3\frac{2}{3}$, 4, $\cdots$ to 25 terms.   **6.** $7\frac{1}{4}$, $6\frac{3}{4}$, $6\frac{1}{4}$, $\cdots$ to 35 terms.

7. $-1\frac{1}{3}$, $\frac{1}{2}$, $2\frac{1}{3}$, $\cdots$ to 19 terms.   **8.** $-0.7, 1.2, 3.1, \cdots$ to 21 terms.

9. $1.24, 2.11, 2.98, \cdots$ to 8 terms.   **10.** 6.4, 4.6, 2.8, $\cdots$ to 30 terms.

Insert the number of arithmetic means as indicated:

11. Five, between 9 and 33.   **12.** Four, between 5 and -10.

13. Four, between $2\frac{2}{3}$ and 6.   **14.** Five, between $5\frac{1}{2}$ and $\frac{1}{2}$.

15. Six, between 6.2 and 8.3.   **16.** Eight, between -0.7 and 11.9.

17. Find the arithmetic mean of (a) 5 and 23, (b) $3\frac{5}{6}$ and $7\frac{1}{2}$.

18. Find the arithmetic mean of (a) -12 and 47, (b) 2.2 and 1.45.

19. In an A. P. whose common difference is 3, the 13th term is 50. Find the sum of the first two terms.

20. The 6th term of an A. P. is 40 and the 34th term is -16. Find a and d.

21. The 12th term of an A. P. is 28 and the 25th term is 67. Find the 8th term.

22. The 19th term of an A. P. is 17.8 and the 49th term is 38.8. Find the 30th term.

23. Find the sum of the first 10 terms of an A. P. whose 8th term is $13\frac{1}{2}$ and whose 37th term is -1.

24. Find the sum of the first 50 terms of an A. P. whose 20th term is 37 and whose 60th term is 157.

25. The 16th term of an A. P. is 23 and the 37th term is 47. Find the sum of the 17th term and the 36th term.

26. The 7th term of an A. P. is 2.7 and the 24th term is 24.8. Find the sum of the first 10 odd terms of the A. P.

In each of the following, three of the elements l, a, n, d, S are given. Find the missing elements.

27. $a = 6, d = 3, l = 54$.   **28.** $a = 5, n = 8, l = 40$.

29. $d = 2, n = 7, l = 50$.   **30.** $a = -5, n = 12, d = 2\frac{1}{2}$.

31. $a = 4, l = 22, S = 169$.   **32.** $a = 2, n = 16, S = 9\frac{1}{3}$.

33. $d = 2, n = 9, S = 27$.   **34.** $n = 7, l = 5\frac{1}{2}, S = 28$.

35. $d = -2, l = -1, S = 99$.   **36.** $a = 13, d = -3, S = 35$.

37. The 5th, 27th, and last terms of an A. P. are respectively 11, 55, and 81. Find the 1st term and the number of terms.

38. Find the sum of the first 20 terms of an A. P. whose nth term is $(3n - 2)$.

39. The 3rd term of an A. P. is 4 times the 1st term, and the 6th term is $25\frac{1}{2}$. Find the progression.

40. Find the first 5 terms of an A. P. in which the 5th term is twice the 3rd term, and 6 more than the 2nd term.

41. If p and q are the first two terms of an A. P., find the 5th term.

42. Insert two arithmetic means between p and q.

43. Show that the quantities $\dfrac{1}{1-\sqrt{x}}, \dfrac{1}{1-x}, \dfrac{1}{1+\sqrt{x}}$ form an A. P. and find the 4th term.

44. If the 3rd term of an A. P. is zero, show that the sum of the first 5 terms is zero.

45. Find a formula for the sum of the first n positive integers.

46. Find a formula for the sum of the first n positive odd integers.

47. Find formulas for n and S when a, d, and l are given.

48. Find formulas for a and d when n, l, and S are given.

49. Prove that the sum of an odd number of terms in A. P. is equal to the middle term multiplied by the number of terms.

50. If the pth term of an A. P. is q, and the qth term is p, show that the $(p + q)$th term is zero when $p \neq q$.

80. The nth Term of a G. P. If the first term of a G. P. is denoted by a and the common ratio by r, the terms of the progression will be represented by

$$a, \ ar, \ ar^2, \ ar^3, \ ar^4, \text{ and so on.}$$

It is evident that in any term the exponent of r is always 1 less than the number of the term. Hence if l represents the last, or nth, term, we have the formula

$$l = ar^{n-1}.$$

Example. Find the 9th term of the G. P. 64, 32, 16, $\cdots$.
Solution: Since $a = 64$, $r = \frac{1}{2}$, and $n = 9$, we have

$$l = 64(\tfrac{1}{2})^{9-1} = \tfrac{1}{4}.$$

Note. In arithmetical computations involving exponents, cancel as much as possible before actually computing the result. Thus in the above example, we would proceed as follows:

$$l = 64(\tfrac{1}{2})^8 = \frac{64}{2^8} = \frac{2^6}{2^8} = \frac{1}{2^2} = \frac{1}{4}.$$

81. Geometric Means. In any G. P. the terms between two given terms are called the **geometric means** between those two terms.

Thus, in the progression $\frac{1}{16}$, $\frac{1}{2}$, 4, 32, 256, the numbers $\frac{1}{2}$, 4, and 32 are the *three* geometric means between $\frac{1}{16}$ and 256; whereas in the progression $\frac{1}{16}$, 1, 16, 256, the numbers 1 and 16 are the *two* geometric means between $\frac{1}{16}$ and 256.

Example. Insert two geometric means between 2 and 54.
Solution: The two given terms, together with the two means, make a G. P. of four terms; that is $n = 4$. Also it is given that $a = 2$ and $l = 54$. Hence, substituting in $l = ar^{n-1}$, we have $54 = 2 \cdot r^3$.
Solving, we obtain $r = 3$. Thus the two means are 6 and 18.

Note 1. In finding geometric means, we are interested only in the *real* means. Thus, in the above example, we disregard the imaginary cube roots of 27.

The most important instance of geometric means is that of *one* geometric mean between two given numbers. This mean is also called the *mean proportional* between two numbers. If M

is the geometric mean between a and b, then by the definition of a G. P., we have

$$\frac{M}{a} = \frac{b}{M}; \text{ hence } M = \pm \sqrt{ab}.$$

Thus, the geometric mean of 3 and 12 is $\sqrt{3 \cdot 12} = 6$.

NOTE 2. Although $3, -6, 12$ also forms a G. P., the value -6 does not fall between 3 and 12. It is called an *improper mean*. On the other hand, -6 would be the *proper geometric mean* between -3 and -12.

82. The Sum of n Terms of a G. P. Let S represent the sum of n terms of a geometric progression; that is,

$$S = a + ar + ar^2 + \cdots + ar^{n-2} + ar^{n-1}.$$

Multiplying both sides by r, we have

$$rS = ar + ar^2 + ar^3 + \cdots + ar^{n-1} + ar^n.$$

Hence, by subtraction,

$$S - rS = a - ar^n,$$
$$(1 - r)S = a(1 - r^n).$$

Therefore, if $r \neq 1$, we have

$$S = a\frac{1 - r^n}{1 - r}. \tag{1}$$

Since

$$l = ar^{n-1}, \tag{2}$$

$$S = \frac{a - rl}{1 - r}. \tag{3}$$

If any three of the numbers l, a, n, r, S are known, the remaining two may be determined by means of the above formulas.

Example 1. Find the sum of $9, -3, 1, \cdots$ to 6 terms.
Solution: In the given progression $a = 9$, $r = -\frac{1}{3}$, and $n = 6$. Hence, substituting in (1), we have

$$S = 9 \cdot \frac{1 - (-\frac{1}{3})^6}{1 - (-\frac{1}{3})} = 9 \cdot \frac{1 - \frac{1}{729}}{1 + \frac{1}{3}} = 9 \cdot \frac{\frac{728}{729}}{\frac{4}{3}} = 9 \cdot \frac{728}{729} \cdot \frac{3}{4} = \frac{182}{27}.$$

Example 2. If $a = 3$, $l = 96$, and $S = 189$, find r and n.
Solution: Substituting in (3), we have

$$189 = \frac{3 - 96\,r}{1 - r}.$$

Solving, $\qquad\qquad r = 2.$

Now, substituting in (2),
$$96 = 3 \cdot 2^{n-1}.$$
Hence,
$$32 = 2^{n-1}.$$
Since $32 = 2^5$, we obtain $\quad n = 6.$

EXERCISE 55

Find l and S for each of the following progressions:

1. 3, 6, 12, $\cdots$ to 6 terms.   **2.** 16, 8, 4, $\cdots$ to 8 terms.
3. $\frac{1}{3}$, -1, 3, $\cdots$ to 6 terms.   **4.** 16, 24, 36, $\cdots$ to 7 terms.
5. 27, -18, 12, $\cdots$ to 7 terms.   **6.** $\frac{1}{8}$, $\frac{1}{4}$, $\frac{1}{2}$, $\cdots$ to 6 terms.
7. .04, .2, 1, $\cdots$ to 8 terms.   **8.** 100, -10, 1, $\cdots$ to 7 terms.
9. $\sqrt{2}$, 2, $2\sqrt{2}$, $\cdots$ to 7 terms.   **10.** $\frac{8}{9}$, $\frac{4}{3}$, 2, $\cdots$ to 6 terms.

Insert the number of geometric means as indicated:

11. Two, between 7 and 56.   **12.** Two, between -54 and 2.
13. Three, between $2\frac{1}{4}$ and 36.   **14.** Three, between $\frac{2}{3}$ and 54.
15. Five, between 1 and 8.   **16.** Four, between 3^4 and 3^9.

17. Find the geometric mean between (a) 20 and 125, and (b) $3\frac{1}{3}$ and $7\frac{1}{2}$.

18. Find the geometric mean between (a) 7.5 and 14.7, (b) $1\frac{2}{3}$ and $3\frac{3}{4}$.

19. The 4th and 5th terms of a G. P. are respectively 5 and 10. Write the first 3 terms of the progression.

20. In a G. P. the 1st term is $\frac{1}{2}$, the 2nd term is -2, and the last term is -8192. Find the next to the last term.

21. Find the 3rd term of a G. P. whose 5th term is 18 and whose 9th term is $3\frac{5}{9}$.

22. The 4th term of a G. P. is 5 and the common ratio is -3. Which term is equal to -135?

23. The 1st term of a G. P. is 0.0003 and the common ratio is 10. Which term is equal to 3,000,000?

24. The 3rd term of a G. P. is 6 and the 5th term is 12. Find the sum of the first 8 terms.

In each of the following, three of the elements l, a, n, r, S are given. Find the missing elements.

25. $a = 8$, $n = 6$, $l = 60\frac{3}{4}$.   **26.** $r = 2$, $n = 5$, $S = 77\frac{1}{2}$.
27. $a = 6\frac{3}{4}$, $r = \frac{2}{3}$, $l = \frac{4}{3}$.   **28.** $a = 6$, $r = -2$, $S = -126$.
29. $a = 7$, $n = 3$, $S = 91$.   **30.** $a = \frac{3}{4}$, $l = 48$, $S = 32\frac{1}{4}$.

Find the sum of each of the following:

31. -32, 16, -8, $\cdots$, $-\frac{1}{8}$.   **32.** 4, 6, 9, $\cdots$, $20\frac{1}{4}$.
33. 0.512, 2.56, 12.8, $\cdots$, 1600.   **34.** $5\frac{1}{3}$, 8, 12, $\cdots$, $40\frac{1}{2}$.
35. 2^0, $2^{\frac{1}{2}}$, 2^1, $\cdots$, 2^5.   **36.** $\sqrt{3}$, $\sqrt{6}$, $2\sqrt{3}$, $\cdots$, $4\sqrt{6}$.

37. Find a formula for a in terms of (a) r, n, and S; (b) r, n, and l.

38. Find a formula for r in terms of (a) a, l, and S; (b) a, l, and n.

39. Find a formula for l in terms of (a) a, r, and S; (b) r, n, and S.

40. Find a formula for S in terms of (a) r, n, and l; (b) a, n, and l.

41. The 1st, 4th, and last terms of a G. P. are respectively 48, 162, and $546\frac{3}{4}$. Find the number of terms.

42. Find the sum of 10 terms of a G. P. whose nth term is $1/2^n$.

43. If $(1.06)^9 = 1.6895$, find the value of
$$1 + (1.06) + (1.06)^2 + \cdots + (1.06)^8.$$

44. If $(1.04)^{10} = 1.4802$, find the value of
$$1 + (1.04)^{-1} + (1.04)^{-2} + \cdots + (1.04)^{-9}.$$

45. If p and q are the first 2 terms of a G. P., find the 5th term.

46. Insert two geometric means between p and q.

47. Show that the quantities $(x + x\sqrt{x})$, $(x + \sqrt{x})$, and $(1 + \sqrt{x})$ form a G. P. and find the 4th term.

Show that the following also form a G. P.:

48. The reciprocals of the terms of a G. P.

49. Like powers of the terms of a G. P.

50. Like principal roots of the terms of a G. P.

83. Infinite Geometric Progressions. The sum of any geometric progression of n terms may be written in the form

$$S = a + ar + ar^2 + \cdots + ar^{n-1} = \frac{a - ar^n}{1 - r}.$$

If r is numerically less than 1, the successive terms of the sum continually decrease in numerical value. Thus, if $r = \frac{1}{2}$, we have $r^2 = \frac{1}{4}$, $r^3 = \frac{1}{8}$, $r^4 = \frac{1}{16}$, $\cdots$, $r^{10} = \frac{1}{1024}$, and so on.

By increasing n, the value of r^n may be made as small as we please. Hence as n increases indefinitely, the limiting value of ar^n is zero, and the formula for the sum of the infinite geometric progression becomes

$$S = \frac{a}{1 - r}.$$

NOTE 1. Observe that the sum of an infinite G. P. is not a sum in the usual sense, but is the limit approached by the G. P. as more and more terms are taken. For more details on limits, see Chapter 23.

Example 1. Find the sum of the infinite G. P. 6, $- 4$, $2\frac{2}{3}$, $\cdots$.
Solution: Since $a = 6$ and $r = - \frac{2}{3}$, we have

$$S = \frac{6}{1 - (- \frac{2}{3})} = 6 \cdot \frac{3}{5} = 3\frac{3}{5}.$$

Example 2. Express the infinite repeating decimal $0.2181818 \cdots$ as an equivalent numerical fraction.
Solution: The given decimal may be written in the form

$$0.2 + 0.018 + 0.00018 + 0.0000018 + \cdots$$

where the first term contains the non-repeating part of the decimal. It is evident that the terms following the first term form an infinite geometric progression with $a = 0.018$ and $r = 0.01$. Therefore the value of the given decimal may be reduced to

$$0.2 + \frac{0.018}{1 - 0.01} = \frac{2}{10} + \frac{18}{990} = \frac{1}{5} + \frac{1}{55} = \frac{12}{55}.$$

NOTE 2. The above example can also be solved as follows: let $x = 0.21818 \cdots$; then $100 \, x = 21.81818 \cdots$; and subtracting, we have $99 \, x = 21.6$. Hence, $x = 12/55$.

EXERCISE 56

Find the sum of the following infinite G. P.:

1. 18, 6, 2, $\cdots$.   **2.** 6, $- 3$, $1\frac{1}{2}$, $\cdots$.
3. 2, $\frac{4}{3}$, $\frac{8}{9}$, $\cdots$.   **4.** $- \frac{4}{3}$, $- 1$, $- \frac{3}{4}$, $\cdots$.
5. 3, $- 1.2$, 0.48, $\cdots$.   **6.** 1.728, 1.44, 1.2, $\cdots$.
7. 5, $\sqrt{5}$, 1, $\cdots$.   **8.** $\sqrt{2}$, 1, $\frac{1}{2}\sqrt{2}$, $\cdots$.
9. $\sqrt{2} - 1$, $2\sqrt{2} - 3$, $5\sqrt{2} - 7$, $\cdots$.   **10.** $\frac{1}{4} \, x$, $\frac{1}{16} \, x$, $\frac{1}{64} \, x$, $\cdots$.

Find the fractions equivalent to the following repeating decimals:

11. $0.555555 \cdots$.   **12.** $0.636363 \cdots$.   **13.** $0.153153 \cdots$.
14. $2.242222 \cdots$.   **15.** $0.324545 \cdots$.   **16.** $1.242424 \cdots$.
17. $3.269444 \cdots$.   **18.** $2.234234 \cdots$.   **19.** $0.468787 \cdots$.

20. Find the 2nd and 3rd terms of an infinite G. P. whose 1st term is 4 and whose sum is $5\frac{1}{7}$.

21. The sum of an infinite G. P. is $25\frac{3}{5}$ and the 2nd term is $1\frac{3}{5}$ less than the 1st term. Find the 1st term.

22. In an infinite G. P., the sum of the odd terms is 2 and the sum of the even terms is 1. Find the first 4 terms of the G. P.

84. Harmonic Progressions. *A progression of numbers whose reciprocals form an arithmetic progression is called a* **harmonic progression** *or* H. P. Thus, the numbers 1, $\frac{1}{2}$, $\frac{1}{3}$, $\frac{1}{4}$, $\cdots$

form a harmonic progression, since their reciprocals, 1, 2, 3, 4, $\cdots$, form an A. P.

Example 1. Find the 8th term of the H. P. 6, 4, 3, $\cdots$.

Solution: The 8th term of the corresponding A. P. $\frac{1}{6}, \frac{1}{4}, \frac{1}{3}, \cdots$ is

$$l = \frac{1}{6} + (8 - 1)\frac{1}{12} = \frac{3}{4}.$$

Hence, the 8th term of the H. P. is $\frac{4}{3}$.

In any H. P. the terms between two given terms are called the **harmonic means** between those two terms.

Example 2. Insert 3 harmonic means between $-\frac{3}{2}$ and $\frac{3}{14}$.

Solution: We first insert 3 arithmetic means in the corresponding A. P. whose 1st term is $-\frac{2}{3}$ and whose 5th term is $\frac{14}{3}$. Thus,

$$\tfrac{14}{3} = -\tfrac{2}{3} + (5 - 1)d, \quad \text{or} \quad d = \tfrac{4}{3}.$$

Hence the arithmetic means are $\frac{2}{3}$, 2, and $\frac{10}{3}$; and the corresponding harmonic means are $\frac{3}{2}, \frac{1}{2}$, and $\frac{3}{10}$.

EXERCISE 57

Find the last term of the following H. P.:

1. $\frac{1}{4}, \frac{1}{7}, \frac{1}{10}, \cdots$ to 7 terms. $\qquad$ 2. $-\frac{2}{3}, -2, 2, \cdots$ to 8 terms.
3. $3, 1\frac{1}{5}, \frac{3}{4}, \cdots$ to 9 terms. $\qquad$ 4. $5\frac{2}{3}, 3\frac{2}{5}, 2\frac{3}{7}, \cdots$ to 8 terms.

Insert the number of harmonic means as indicated:

5. Two, between $-\frac{2}{3}$ and $\frac{2}{9}$. $\qquad$ 6. Three, between $3\frac{3}{4}$ and 15.
7. Four, between $\frac{3}{4}$ and 3. $\qquad$ 8. Five, between $-\frac{3}{7}$ and $\frac{3}{5}$.

9. Determine x so that $(x - 2)$, x, and $(x + 4)$ forms an H. P.

10. Derive a formula for the harmonic mean between a and b.

11. Find the 3rd and 4th terms of an H. P. whose first 2 terms are p and q respectively.

12. Find the necessary condition so that A, B, and C will form an H. P.

85. Problems Involving Progressions. Arithmetic and geometric progressions occur in the solution of many practical problems. The following examples illustrate some of the methods used:

Example 1. Three numbers whose sum is 24 form an A. P. If they are increased by 3, 4, and 7 respectively, the resulting numbers will form a G. P. Find the original numbers.

Analysis: Let $(a - d)$, a, and $(a + d)$ represent any three numbers in A. P. Since the sum of these numbers is $3a$, it is evident that the middle number is always equal to one-third the sum of the numbers. Hence, in this example, the three numbers may be represented by $(8 - d)$, 8, and $(8 + d)$.

Solution: Increasing these numbers by 3, 4, and 7 respectively, we have $(11 - d)$, 12, and $(15 + d)$. Applying the condition, $B^2 = AC$, we obtain

$$12^2 = (11 - d)(15 + d).$$

Solving, $d = 3$ or -7.

Answer: The numbers are 5, 8, and 11, or 15, 8, and 1.

Example 2. At the end of each year the value of a certain machine decreases 30% of what its value was at the beginning of the year. If the machine costs $5000, find its value after five years.

Analysis: Let V represent the initial value of the machine. At the end of one year, the machine is worth 70% of its initial value, or $(.70)V$. At the end of the next year, it retains 70% of this new value, or 70% of $(.70)V = (.70)^2V$.

Thus, the terms of the geometric progression

$$(.70)V, \ (.70)^2V, \ (.70)^3V, \ (.70)^4V, \ \cdots$$

represent the values of the machine at the end of each succeeding year.

Solution: When $V = \$5000$, the value at the end of the fifth year is given by

$$(.70)^5 \times 5000 = (.16807) \times 5000 = 840.35.$$

Answer: Its value after five years is $840.35.

EXERCISE 58

1. In boring a well 225 feet deep the cost is 28¢ for the first foot and an additional cent for each subsequent foot. What is the cost of boring the entire well?

2. An automobile is sold by selling tickets marked from 1 to 500. The tickets are sealed and drawn from a box, the price in cents per draw being equal to the number drawn. How much money is received from the sale?

3. If the present value of an automobile is 60% of its value the preceding year, what is the value at the end of six years of a car whose cost is $900?

4. At each stroke of an air pump one-half of the air remaining in a container is removed. What percentage of the original quantity of air remains in the container after the 7th stroke?

5. How many integers are there between 200 and 900 which are multiples of 7?

6. A ball rolls down an inclined plane 3.7 feet the first second, and in each succeeding second 7.4 feet more than in the preceding second. How far will it roll in 10 seconds?

7. A man borrows $400 and agrees to pay back at the end of each month one-half of the amount still due. How long will it be until he owes less than one dollar?

8. The numbers from 1 to 75 are drawn by students for a school party, the fee paid being equal in cents to the number drawn. The fee was returned to the holders of four consecutive numbers chosen by lot, and the net receipts were $25.72. Which were the lucky numbers?

9. A certain Christmas Club fund collects 3 cents the first week, 6 cents the second week, and so on, increasing by 3 cents each week for 50 weeks. How much is in the fund at the end of that time?

10. A used-car dealer offered to sell a car for $300 cash or on the following terms: 1 cent the first day, 2 cents the second day, 4 cents the third day, and so on for 15 days, the amount paid each day being twice that paid on the previous day. Which is the better proposition for the dealer?

11. Find the non-trivial A. P. whose 1st term is 3 and whose 1st, 3rd, and 7th terms form a G. P.

12. In a potato race, a basket and 10 potatoes are arranged in a line at intervals of 5 feet. A contestant starts at the basket, picks up the potatoes, and carries them one at a time to the basket. How far must he run?

13. If the sum of 6 terms of an A. P. is 57 and the sum of 10 terms is 155, find the sum of 15 terms of the progression.

14. The arithmetic mean of two numbers is 13 and their geometric mean is 12. What are the numbers?

15. In a certain auditorium the first row contains 18 seats, the second row 20 seats, the third row 22 seats, and so on for the first 12 rows. The thirteenth row has 41 seats, the fourteenth row 42 seats, and so on for the remainder of the rows. If there are 30 rows in all, find the seating capacity.

16. A vessel contains 100% acid solution. One-third is drawn off and replaced by water; then one-third of the mixture is drawn off and replaced by water. After five such operations, what is the percentage of the acid solution remaining?

17. Derive a formula for the value of an insurance policy n years after January 1, 1940, from the following data: $(n > 5)$.
(1) On January 1, 1940, its value is $5000.
(2) At the end of each year after January 1, 1945, its value is increased $25, $50, $75, etc., according to the number of years elapsed.

18. A carpenter wishes to obtain a pole of sufficient length to make 20 rungs for a ladder. If the rungs diminish uniformly from

24 inches at the base to 16 inches at the top, what length will be needed?

19. A and B start together, traveling in the same direction. A goes 2 miles the first hour, $2\frac{1}{2}$ miles the next, 3 miles the next, and so on. B goes 3 miles the first hour, $3\frac{1}{4}$ miles the next, $3\frac{1}{2}$ miles the next, and so on. In how many hours will they be together again, and how far will each have traveled?

20. The sum of 3 numbers in A. P. is 48. If 1 is taken from the 2nd number and 2 is added to the 3rd number, the resulting numbers will form a G. P. What are the numbers?

21. A company offers a clerk a job, starting at an annual salary of $1200, with a 10% rise in salary each year for ten years. How much will he receive during his sixth year of service?

22. A contractor who fails to complete a building in a certain specified time is compelled to forfeit $100 a day for the first 6 days of extra time required, and for each additional day thereafter the forfeit is increased by $10 each day. If he loses $2580, by how many days did he overrun the contract time?

23. An A. P. and a G. P. each have the same 1st term, 6, and their 3rd terms are also equal. Find the two progressions, if the 2nd term of the G. P. is 3 less than the 2nd term of the A. P.

24. An industrial firm offers an engineer a choice of two contracts. He could start at $2000 and receive an annual increase of $200 thereafter, or he could start at the same rate and receive a semi-annual increase of $50. Which contract offers more money?

25. A man arranges to pay off a debt of $3600 by 20 annual payments which form an A. P. When 15 of the payments are paid, he dies, leaving one-third of the debt unpaid. Find the value of the first payment.

26. Find 3 numbers in A. P. such that their sum is 21 and the product of the first and third is 17 more than the second.

27. Insert two numbers between 3 and 8 so that the first three numbers form an A. P. and the last three numbers form a G. P.

28. The width, the length, and the area of a rectangle form a G. P. If the perimeter of the rectangle is 60, find its dimensions.

29. Two cyclists 94 miles apart start toward each other. One travels 5 miles the first hour, $5\frac{1}{2}$ miles the next, 6 miles the next, and so on, while the other travels at a constant rate of 5 miles per hour. In how many hours will they meet?

30. Find an infinite G. P. whose sum is 3 and such that each term is twice the sum of all the terms which follow it.

31. The sum of three numbers in A. P. is 3 and the squares of the numbers form a G. P. What are the numbers?

32. The sum of three terms in A. P. beginning with $\frac{2}{3}$ is equal to the sum of three terms in G. P. beginning with $\frac{2}{3}$. What are the two progressions, if the common difference of the A. P. equals the common ratio of the G. P.?

33. Find the sum of all positive integers less than 100 which are not multiples of either 2 or 3.

34. The set of positive integers is divided into groups as follows: 1; $(2, 3)$; $(4, 5, 6)$; $(7, 8, 9, 10)$; and so on. Find the sum of the integers in the 30th group.

35. If the sides of a right triangle are in A. P., show that the sides must be in the ratio 3 : 4 : 5.

36. A man was offered one of two propositions. He was to receive either (a) 1 cent for the first month of his age, 2 cents for the second month, 3 cents for the next month, and so on, or (b) \$1.40 for the first year of his age, \$2.80 for the second year, \$4.20 for the next year, and so on. The man figured that in either case he would receive the same amount of money. What was his age?

37. Find the common ratio for which the sides of a right triangle are in G. P.

38. If a, b, c form an A. P. and a, c, b form a G. P., show that c, a, b form an H. P.

39. What number must be added to each of the numbers a, b, and c so that the resulting numbers will form a G. P.?

40. If the sum of p terms of an A. P. is q and the sum of q terms is p, find the sum of $(p + q)$ terms when $p \neq q$.

CHAPTER 12

Mathematical Induction and the Binomial Theorem

86. Mathematical Induction. In the chapter on progressions, we learned by a method of reasoning called **deduction** that

$$2 + 4 + 6 + \cdots + 2n = n(n + 1), \tag{1}$$

where n is any positive integer. The fact that (1) is true for *all* positive integers n may be verified by a different method of reasoning known as **mathematical induction.**

An inductive proof consists of two parts, as illustrated in the following examples:

Example 1. Prove by mathematical induction that

$$2 + 4 + 6 + \cdots + 2n = n(n + 1). \tag{1}$$

Proof: Part I. Verification. The proposition is easily seen to be true for a few particular values of n.

For $n = 1$, $2 = 1(1 + 1)$, or $2 = 2$.
For $n = 2$, $2 + 4 = 2(2 + 1)$, or $6 = 6$.
For $n = 3$, $2 + 4 + 6 = 3(3 + 1)$, or $12 = 12$.

Part II. Step Proof. Now let us assume that the given proposition is true for some general value of n, say $n = k$. That is, we make the **assumption** that

$$2 + 4 + 6 + \cdots + 2k = k(k + 1). \tag{2}$$

As a result of this assumption, we wish to demonstrate that (1) is true when $(k + 1)$ is substituted for n. To do this we add the $(k + 1)$st term, $2(k + 1)$, to both sides of (2); thus

$$2 + 4 + 6 + \cdots + 2k + 2(k + 1) = k(k + 1) + 2(k + 1),$$
$$= (k + 1)(k + 2). \tag{3}$$

Since $(k + 1)(k + 2)$ is the value of $n(n + 1)$ when $n = k + 1$, the result (3) shows that if the proposition *is* true for $n = k$, **then** it *must* also be true for $n = k + 1$. We know, however, from Part I that the proposition is true for $n = 1, 2$, and 3. Therefore, since it *is* true for $n = 3$, it *must* be true for $n = 4$; then since it *is* true for $n = 4$, it *must* be true for $n = 5$, and so on for *all positive integral values of n.*

Note. In Part I, only one verification is necessary to the proof and it should be for the *smallest* positive integral value of n for which the proposition is to hold.

The reasoning of mathematical induction is applicable to any proposition depending on a variable, such as n, which assumes only *positive integral* values. A valid proof *must* contain the two parts:

Part I. Verification *of the proposition for the smallest integral value of **n** for which the proposition is to hold.*

Part II. Step Proof. *Demonstration that if the proposition is true for **n** = **k**, then it must also be true for **n** = **k** + **1**.*

Both parts of the above proof are necessary.

Illustration 1. Suppose that we try to prove that

$$2 + 4 + 6 + \cdots + 2n = n(n + 1) + (n - 1)(n - 2).$$

By substitution we see that the proposition is true for $n = 1$ and $n = 2$. However, taking $n = k$ and adding $2(k + 1)$ to both sides reduces the right side to

$$[k(k+1)+(k-1)(k-2)]+2(k+1)=(k+1)(k+2)+(k-1)(k-2),$$

whereas it should reduce to $(k + 1)(k + 2) + k(k - 1)$ in order to be satisfactory. Hence, Part II fails and the induction is incomplete.

Illustration 2. Suppose that we try to prove that

$$2 + 4 + 6 + \cdots + 2n = n(n + 1) + 2.$$

Taking $n = k$ and adding $2(k + 1)$ to both sides reduces the right side to

$$[k(k + 1) + 2] + 2(k + 1) = (k + 1)(k + 2) + 2.$$

Hence, if the proposition is true for any integral value of n, then it will be true for subsequent integral values. However, no positive integral value can be found which will start the stepping process. Therefore Part I fails, and the induction is incomplete.

Example 2. Prove by mathematical induction that the product $n(n + 1)(n + 2)$ is a multiple of 3 for all positive integral values of n.

Proof: Part I. For $n = 1$, we have $1 \cdot 2 \cdot 3 = 6$, which is a multiple of 3.

Part II. For $n = k$, we assume that $k(k + 1)(k + 2)$ is a multiple of 3, and as a result we wish to show that the product with $n = k + 1$ is also a multiple of 3.

Consider the identity

$$(k + 1)(k + 2)(k + 3) = k(k + 1)(k + 2) + 3(k + 1)(k + 2).$$

By *hypothesis* the first term on the right side is a multiple of 3, and the second term on the right side is an obvious multiple of 3. Hence, the left side of the equation must be a multiple of 3. This completes the proof.

EXERCISE 59

By use of mathematical induction, prove that the following equations, or statements, are true for all positive integral values of n. Do not use direct proofs.

1. $1 + 2 + 3 + \cdots + n = \frac{1}{2} n(n + 1)$.
2. $1 \cdot 2 + 2 \cdot 3 + 3 \cdot 4 + \cdots + n(n + 1) = \frac{1}{3} n(n + 1)(n + 2)$.
3. $2 + 2^2 + 2^3 + \cdots + 2^n = 2^{n+1} - 2$.
4. $1^2 + 2^2 + 3^2 + \cdots + n^2 = \frac{1}{6} n(n + 1)(2 n + 1)$.
5. $1 + 3 + 5 + \cdots + (2 n - 1) = n^2$.
6. $n^2 + n$ is a multiple of 2.
7. $n^3 - n$ is a multiple of 3.
8. $2^{2n} - 1$ is a multiple of 3.
9. $3^{2n} - 1$ is a multiple of 8.
10. $2 n^3 + 3 n^2 + n$ is a multiple of 6.
11. $1^3 + 2^3 + 3^3 + \cdots + n^3 = \frac{1}{4} n^2(n + 1)^2$.
12. $\dfrac{1}{1 \cdot 2} + \dfrac{1}{2 \cdot 3} + \dfrac{1}{3 \cdot 4} + \cdots + \dfrac{1}{n(n + 1)} = \dfrac{n}{n + 1}$.
13. $\dfrac{1}{1 \cdot 3} + \dfrac{1}{2 \cdot 4} + \dfrac{1}{3 \cdot 5} + \cdots + \dfrac{1}{n(n + 2)} = \dfrac{n(3 n + 5)}{4(n + 1)(n + 2)}$.
14. $n(n+1)(n+2)$ is a multiple of 6. Hint: Prove that $(k+1)(k+2)$ is a multiple of 2.
15. $1 \cdot 2 + 2 \cdot 2^2 + 3 \cdot 2^3 + \cdots + n \cdot 2^n = (n - 1)2^{n+1} + 2$.
16. $\dfrac{5}{1 \cdot 2} \cdot \dfrac{1}{3} + \dfrac{7}{2 \cdot 3} \cdot \dfrac{1}{3^2} + \cdots + \dfrac{2 n + 3}{n(n + 1)} \cdot \dfrac{1}{3^n} = 1 - \dfrac{1}{(n + 1)} \cdot \dfrac{1}{3^n}$.
17. $\dfrac{1}{n + 1} + \dfrac{1}{n + 2} + \cdots + \dfrac{1}{2 n + 1} \leq \dfrac{5}{6}$.
18. If n is a positive integer, prove that $(x^n - y^n)$ contains the factor $(x - y)$. Hint: $x^{k+1} - y^{k+1} = x(x^k - y^k) + y^k(x - y)$.
19. If n is a positive integer, prove that $(x^{2n-1} + y^{2n-1})$ contains the factor $(x + y)$. Hint: $x^{2k+1}+y^{2k+1}=x^2(x^{2k-1}+y^{2k-1})-y^{2k-1}(x^2-y^2)$.

20. Show that $U_n = (1 + i)^n + (1 - i)^n$, where $i = \sqrt{-1}$, is always a real number. Hint: Verify the proposition for $n = 1$ and $n = 2$. Then show that $U_{n+2} = 2\,U_{n+1} - 2\,U_n$.

87. The Factorial Symbol. *The symbol* **n!** *is read* **n** **factorial** *or* **factorial** **n** *and is defined as representing the product of all the positive integers from 1 to* **n** *inclusive. Symbolically,*

$$n! = 1 \cdot 2 \cdot 3 \cdots n.$$

The definition of a factorial is sometimes expressed by the functional relationship, $n! = n \cdot (n - 1)!$, for all positive integers greater than 1. Thus, $6! = 6 \cdot 5!$. If n is taken to be 1, we have $1! = 1 \cdot 0!$ or $0! = 1$. For this reason we make the additional *definition* that 0! equals 1.

Illustration.

$$5! \times 0! = 1 \cdot 2 \cdot 3 \cdot 4 \cdot 5 \times 1 = 120,$$
$$7! - 5! = 7 \cdot 6 \cdot 5! - 5! = (42 - 1)5! = 41 \cdot 5!,$$
$$\frac{9!}{7!} = \frac{1 \cdot 2 \cdot 3 \cdot 4 \cdot 5 \cdot 6 \cdot 7 \cdot 8 \cdot 9}{1 \cdot 2 \cdot 3 \cdot 4 \cdot 5 \cdot 6 \cdot 7} = 8 \cdot 9 = 72.$$

88. The Binomial Theorem. In multiplying the binomial $(A + B)$ by itself successively we obtain

$$(A + B)^1 = A + B,$$
$$(A + B)^2 = A^2 + 2\,AB + B^2,$$
$$(A + B)^3 = A^3 + 3\,A^2B + 3\,AB^2 + B^3,$$
$$(A + B)^4 = A^4 + 4\,A^3B + 6\,A^2B^2 + 4\,AB^3 + B^4.$$

We observe in each of the above examples that the expansion of the expression $(A + B)^n$ for $n = 1, 2, 3$, and 4 can be obtained from the following rule:

1. The first term is A^n.

2. The exponent of A decreases by 1 in each successive term and the exponent of B increases by 1.

3. If the coefficient of any term is multiplied by the exponent of A in that term and divided by 1 more than the exponent of B, the result is the coefficient of the next term.

The above rule is a consequence of the following theorem, which is proved in Article 90:

Binomial Theorem. *The binomial formula*

$$(A + B)^n = A^n + nA^{n-1}B + \frac{n(n-1)}{1 \cdot 2} A^{n-2}B^2$$

$$+ \frac{n(n-1)(n-2)}{1 \cdot 2 \cdot 3} A^{n-3}B^3 + \cdots + B^n.$$

is true for all positive integral values of n.

The coefficients of the terms in the expansion of $(A + B)^n$ are called the **binomial coefficients.** These coefficients may be represented in an interesting array known as

PASCAL'S TRIANGLE

$n = 0$						1				
$n = 1$					1		1			
$n = 2$				1		2		1		
$n = 3$			1		3		3		1	
$n = 4$		1		4		6		4		1
$n = 5$	1		5		10		10		5		1
$\cdot\ \cdot\ \cdot$										

This triangular array may be formed numerically by observing that the border elements are always 1, and that every other element is equal to the sum of the two adjacent numbers in the row just above it.

Example 1. Write the first four terms in the expansion of $\left(2x - \frac{x^2}{2}\right)^8$.

Solution: Taking $A = 2x$, $B = -\frac{x^2}{2}$, and $n = 8$, we have

$$\left(2x - \frac{x^2}{2}\right)^8 = (2x)^8 + 8(2x)^7\left(-\frac{x^2}{2}\right) + \frac{8 \cdot 7}{1 \cdot 2}(2x)^6\left(-\frac{x^2}{2}\right)^2$$

$$+ \frac{8 \cdot 7 \cdot 6}{1 \cdot 2 \cdot 3}(2x)^5\left(-\frac{x^2}{2}\right)^3 + \cdots$$

$$= 256x^8 - 512x^9 + 448x^{10} - 224x^{11} + \cdots.$$

NOTE. For increased accuracy it is recommended that the above operation be made in two distinct steps: (*1*) substitution for A, B, and n, and (*2*) simplification of terms.

EXERCISE 60

Evaluate each of the following expressions:

1. $\dfrac{6!}{4!}$.   **2.** $\dfrac{8!}{5!}$.   **3.** $\dfrac{3!6!}{4!5!}$.   **4.** $\dfrac{10!12!}{(11!)^2}$.

5. $\dfrac{100!}{98!}$.   **6.** $\dfrac{87!}{89!}$.   **7.** $\dfrac{102!+101!}{100!}$.   **8.** $\dfrac{100!}{101!-99!}$.

9. Show that $\dfrac{100 \cdot 99 \cdot 98 \cdot 97 \cdot 96}{1 \cdot 2 \cdot 3 \cdot 4 \cdot 5} = \dfrac{100!}{5!95!}$.

Expand each of the following by the Binomial Theorem:

10. $(a + x)^5$.   **11.** $(2x - a)^6$.   **12.** $(x - 2y)^4$.

13. $(ax - b)^8$.   **14.** $(2x + 3)^5$.   **15.** $(x^2 + 2)^6$.

16. $(2a - \frac{1}{2}b)^7$.   **17.** $(y^2 - 2y^{-1})^4$.   **18.** $(\frac{2}{3}x - \frac{3}{2})^5$.

Write and simplify the first four terms in the expansion of each of the following:

19. $(x - 2y)^{10}$.   **20.** $(a + \frac{1}{2})^{16}$.   **21.** $(1 - \frac{1}{3}x)^{27}$.

22. $\left(\dfrac{a}{2} - \dfrac{b}{3}\right)^{12}$.   **23.** $\left(2x + \dfrac{1}{x}\right)^8$.   **24.** $(m^{-1} - 3)^{11}$.

25. $(2x^{\frac{1}{2}} - y)^9$.   **26.** $(a - \frac{1}{2}\sqrt{x})^{13}$.   **27.** $(x^{-1} - \frac{2}{3}\sqrt{x})^{10}$.

Evaluate each of the following by the Binomial Theorem:

28. $(100 + 2)^4$.   **29.** $(1 + .01)^3$.   **30.** $(1 - .02)^4$.

31. $(1 + \sqrt{2})^3$.   **32.** $(\sqrt{3} - 1)^4$.   **33.** $(\sqrt{3} - \sqrt{2})^3$.

Evaluate the following correct to four decimal places:

34. $(1.01)^{20}$.   **35.** $(1.02)^{16}$.   **36.** $(.98)^{15}$.

89. The General Term of the Binomial Formula.

An examination of each term in the binomial formula indicates that (1) the sum of the exponents of A and B is always n and (2) the number of numerical factors in both the numerator and denominator of the coefficient is the same as the exponent of B. Thus, the term involving B^r is

$$(r + 1)\text{st term} = \frac{n(n - 1)(n - 2) \cdots (n - r + 1)}{1 \cdot 2 \cdot 3 \cdots r} A^{n-r}B^r.$$

Multiplying the numerator and the denominator of the above coefficient by $(n - r)(n - r - 1) \cdots 2 \cdot 1$, we have the more compact representation

$$(r + 1)\text{st term} = \frac{n!}{r!(n - r)!} A^{n-r}B^r.$$

Illustration. The fifth term of $(x + y)^{12}$ is

$$\frac{12!}{4!\,8!}\,x^8y^4 = 495\,x^8y^4.$$

90. Proof of the Binomial Theorem for Positive Integral n. We shall prove this theorem by mathematical induction.

Part I. We have already verified the validity of the formula for $n = 1, 2, 3,$ and 4.

Part II. We now assume the truth of the formula for some general value of n, say $n = k$; then

$$\left. \begin{array}{l} (A + B)^k = A^k + kA^{k-1}B + \cdots \\ \qquad\qquad + \dfrac{k!}{(r - 1)!(k - r + 1)!}\,A^{k-r+1}B^{r-1} \\ \qquad\qquad + \dfrac{k!}{r!(k - r)!}\,A^{k-r}B^r + \cdots + kAB^{k-1} + B^k \end{array} \right\} \quad (1)$$

Equation (1) multiplied by A combined with (1) multiplied by B gives

$$A(A + B)^k + B(A + B)^k = (A + B)^{k+1}$$
$$= A^{k+1} + kA^kB + \cdots + \frac{k!}{r!(k - r)}\,A^{k-r+1}B^r + \cdots$$
$$\qquad + A^kB + \cdots + \frac{k!}{(r-1)!(k-r+1)!}\,A^{k-r+1}B^r + \cdots + B^{k+1}.$$

The details in the simplification of the coefficient of $A^{k-r+1}B^r$ are as follows:

$$\frac{k!}{r!(k - r)!} + \frac{k!}{(r - 1)!(k - r + 1)!}$$
$$= (k - r + 1) \cdot \frac{k!}{r!(k - r + 1)!} + r \cdot \frac{k!}{r!(k - r + 1)!}$$
$$= [(k - r + 1) + r]\,\frac{k!}{r!(k - r + 1)!} = \frac{(k + 1)!}{r!(k - r + 1)!}.$$

We observe that the above expression for $(A + B)^{k+1}$ is precisely what we should obtain from the binomial formula by taking $n = k + 1$.

This completes the proof and establishes the validity of the binomial formula for all *positive integral exponents*.

91. The Binomial Series. If in the binomial formula we take $A = 1$ and $B = x$, we obtain the **binomial series**

$$(1+x)^n = 1 + nx + \frac{n(n-1)}{1 \cdot 2}x^2 + \cdots + \frac{n(n-1)\cdots(n-r+1)}{r!}x^r + \cdots.$$

If n is a positive integer, this series terminates with the term x^n and we have merely an alternate form of the binomial formula. However, if n is taken to be any other positive or negative number, the terms of the series continue indefinitely. When n is a rational number and x is numerically less than 1, it is shown in Article 178 that the binomial series is valid in the sense that if more and more terms are added on the right, the result approaches the value given by $(1 + x)^n$.

Illustration. Setting $n = -1$ in the binomial series, we have

$$(1 + x)^{-1} = 1 - x + x^2 - x^3 + x^4 - x^5 + \cdots.$$

If $x = \frac{1}{4}$, the successive sums on the right are 1, 0.7500, 0.8125, 0.7969, 0.8008, 0.7999. Setting $x = \frac{1}{4}$ on the left, we have the **true** value $(1 + \frac{1}{4})^{-1} = (\frac{5}{4})^{-1} = \frac{4}{5} = 0.8000$.

Example 1. Find the cube root of 7, using the binomial series.
Solution: Write 7 as a sum, the first number being a cube and the second number being less than the first.

$$\sqrt[3]{7} = (8 - 1)^{\frac{1}{3}} = [8(1 - \frac{1}{8})]^{\frac{1}{3}} = 2(1 - \frac{1}{8})^{\frac{1}{3}}$$
$$= 2\left[1 + \frac{1}{3}(-\frac{1}{8}) + \frac{\frac{1}{3}(-\frac{2}{3})}{1 \cdot 2}(-\frac{1}{8})^2 + \cdots\right] = 1.913.$$

For fractional and negative values of n, the expansion formula for $(A + B)^n$ may be used. In order that the series thus obtained be valid it is necessary that $|A| > |B|$.

Example 2. Find the first four terms in the expansion of $(a^2 - 2x^2)^{-\frac{1}{2}}$ and simplify each term.
Solution:

$$(a^2 - 2x^2)^{-\frac{1}{2}} = (a^2)^{-\frac{1}{2}} + (-\frac{1}{2})(a^2)^{-\frac{3}{2}}(-2x^2) + \frac{(-\frac{1}{2})(-\frac{3}{2})}{1 \cdot 2}(a^2)^{-\frac{5}{2}}(-2x^2)^2$$
$$+ \frac{(-\frac{1}{2})(-\frac{3}{2})(-\frac{5}{2})}{1 \cdot 2 \cdot 3}(a^2)^{-\frac{7}{2}}(-2x^2)^3 + \cdots$$
$$= a^{-1} + a^{-3}x^2 + \frac{3}{2}a^{-5}x^4 + \frac{5}{2}a^{-7}x^6 + \cdots.$$

EXERCISE 61

Find and simplify the term indicated in the expansion of the following:

1. 5th term of $(2\,x^2 - y^3)^{10}$.

2. 6th term of $\left(x^2 + \dfrac{1}{x}\right)^{12}$.

3. 9th term of $(a - 2\sqrt{x})^{11}$.

4. 5th term of $(2\,x - \sqrt{x})^{15}$.

5. Middle term of $(x^{\frac{3}{2}} + x^{\frac{2}{3}})^{12}$.

6. Middle term of $(1 + 2\,x)^{10}$.

Find and simplify the term in the expansion of the following which contains the expression indicated:

7. $(\frac{1}{2} - x)^{12}$; x^5.

8. $(x + 2)^{15}$; x^9.

9. $(2 - \sqrt{y})^{10}$; $y^{\frac{7}{2}}$.

10. $(z - z^{-1})^{15}$; z^7.

11. $\left(x^2 - \dfrac{2}{x}\right)^{16}$; x^{11}.

12. $(y^2 - y^{-1})^{12}$; y^0.

Write and simplify the first four terms in the expansion of the following:

13. $(1 - x)^{-1}$.

14. $(1 - x)^{-2}$.

15. $(1 - x)^{-3}$.

16. $(1 + x^2)^{\frac{1}{2}}$.

17. $(1 - x)^{-\frac{1}{2}}$.

18. $(1 - x^2)^{\frac{3}{2}}$.

19. $(a^3 + x^3)^{\frac{1}{3}}$.

20. $(x^2 - y^2)^{\frac{1}{2}}$.

21. $(8 - z)^{\frac{4}{3}}$.

22. $(a^4 + b^4)^{\frac{1}{4}}$.

23. $(4 - x^2)^{-\frac{1}{2}}$.

24. $(x^3 + 2\,x)^{\frac{2}{3}}$.

Use the binomial series to find the value of each of the following, correct to four significant figures:

25. $\sqrt{98}$.

26. $\sqrt[3]{30}$.

27. $\sqrt[5]{36}$.

28. $\sqrt[3]{1.15}$.

29. $4^{-\frac{1}{3}}$.

30. $5^{\frac{3}{2}}$.

31. $(1.04)^{-10}$.

32. $(1.03)^{-8}$.

CHAPTER 13

Inequalities

92. Definitions. An expression indicating that one number is *greater* or *less* than another number is called an **inequality.** In particular, if a and b are real numbers, the relation " a is greater than b " means that $(a - b)$ is a positive number, and we write $a > b$. Similarly, the relation " c is less than d " means that $(c - d)$ is a negative number, and we write $c < d$. Each of the numbers is called a **member** or **side** of the inequality and both must be *real numbers.*

If the real numbers are represented graphically in their *normal order*, it is clear that an inequality, such as $5 > 2\frac{1}{2}$, can be inter-

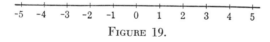

FIGURE 19.

preted as meaning that 5 is to the right of $2\frac{1}{2}$, and $-4 < -1.8$ means that -4 is to the left of -1.8.

NOTE 1. Observe in an inequality that the symbols point toward the smaller number.

NOTE 2. The expression $a \geqq b$ is read " a is greater than or equal to b." Likewise $c \leqq d$ means that c is less than or equal to d.

Two inequalities are said to be of the **same sense** or **same order** if their symbols point in the same direction; otherwise they are said to be of **opposite sense** or **unlike order.** Thus,

$a > b$ and $c > d$ have the same order, whereas $a > b$ and $d < c$ have opposite order.

As with equalities, inequalities may be divided into two classes defined as follows:

Absolute Inequality. *If the sense of an inequality is the same for all values for which its members are defined, it is said to be an absolute or unconditional inequality.*

Illustration 1. $-4 < -\frac{3}{2}$, $\frac{22}{7} > \pi$, $a^2 \geqq 0$ are absolute inequalities.

Conditional Inequality. *If the sense of an inequality is true only for certain values for which its members are defined, it is said to be a conditional inequality.*

Illustration 2. The following are conditional inequalities:

$$x + 3 < 7, \text{ true only if } x < 4;$$
$$x^2 - 2 < x, \text{ true only if } x > -1 \text{ and } x < 2.$$

Note 3. A set of inequalities such as $x > -1$ and $x < 2$ is usually written in the form $-1 < x < 2$. Graphically this means that x lies in the interval from -1 to 2.

93. Properties of Inequalities. In many respects the properties of equalities and inequalities are similar. There are some important exceptions, however, and they should be carefully noted. In the following list of properties, a proof is given for the first property only. The others are proved in like manner.

Property I. *The sense of an inequality is not changed if the same number is added or subtracted from both sides; symbolically,*

$$\text{if } a > b, \text{ then } a \pm c > b \pm c.$$

Proof. By definition, $a > b$ means that $a - b = p$, where p is positive.

Since
$$(a + c) - (b + c) = a - b = p,$$

it follows, by the definition again, that $a + c > b + c$.

Similarly, it can be shown that $a - c > b - c$.

Note 1. Because of Property I, it is evident that a term on one side of an inequality may be **transposed** to the other side with its sign changed.

Property II. *The sense of an inequality is not changed if both sides are multiplied or divided by the same* **positive** *number; symbolically,*

if $a > b$, then $Pa > Pb$ and $a/P > b/P$, where $P > 0$.

Property III. *The sense of an inequality is* **reversed** *if both sides are multiplied or divided by the same* **negative** *number; symbolically,*

if $a > b$, then $Na < Nb$ and $a/N < b/N$, where $N < 0$.

Note 2. Because of Property III, it is evident that changing the signs of both sides of an inequality **reverses** the sense of the inequality. Thus, for $-3 < 2$, by changing signs we have $3 > -2$.

Property IV. *For positive members the sense of an inequality is not changed by taking the same positive integral powers, or roots, of both sides; symbolically,*

if $a > b > 0$, then $a^n > b^n$ and $\sqrt[n]{a} > \sqrt[n]{b}$, where $n > 0$.

Property V. *If two inequalities with* **positive** *members exist in the same sense, the corresponding sides may be added or multiplied together, and the results will be unequal in the same sense; symbolically,*

if $a > b$ and $c > d$, then $a + c > b + d$ and $ac > bd$.

Note 3. In considering the inequalities $6 > 3$ and $5 > 1$ it is evident that the *subtraction* of corresponding sides $1 > 2$ is **not** valid; also *division* $\frac{6}{5} > 3$ is **not** valid.

94. Conditional Inequalities. To solve a conditional inequality means to find the **range of values** which the variable may assume while satisfying the given inequality. The following example illustrates the standard procedure for solving *linear inequalities:*

    Example 1. Solve $\frac{1}{3}x - 1 > x + \frac{1}{3}$.
    Solution: Multiply by 3: $\quad x - 3 > 3x + 1$.
Transpose -3 and $3x$: $\qquad -2x > 4$.
Divide by -2: $\qquad\qquad x < -2$.

A product of linear factors, such as $x(x - 1)(2x - 5)$, will be positive or negative depending on the signs of the factors.

Since a factor changes sign only when its value passes through zero, the sign of a product may (at most) change sign as each factor passes through zero.

Example 2. Solve $x(x - 1)(2x - 5) > 0$.

Solution: Let $f(x) = x(x - 1)(2x - 5)$. Since the factors are zero for $x = 0$, $x = 1$, and $x = \frac{5}{2}$, it follows that $f(x)$ is wholly positive or wholly negative in each of the four intervals

$$(1)\ x < 0,\ (2)\ 0 < x < 1,\ (3)\ 1 < x < \tfrac{5}{2},\ (4)\ \tfrac{5}{2} < x.$$

Choosing *any* value of x in each interval, we find

$$(1)\ f(-1) = -14,\ (2)\ f(\tfrac{1}{2}) = +1,\ (3)\ f(2) = -2,\ (4)\ f(3) = +6.$$

Thus, $f(x) > 0$ when $0 < x < 1$ or $x > \frac{5}{2}$.

NOTE 1. If a quadratic $(ax^2 + bx + c)$ cannot be factored into two *real* linear factors, then it has the same sign for all values of x.

Since a fraction may change sign when its denominator changes sign, the method may be extended.

Example 3. Solve $\quad \dfrac{2x}{x^2 - x - 2} < \dfrac{1}{x}$.

Solution: Transposing and combining, we obtain

$$\frac{x^2 + x + 2}{(x + 1)x(x - 2)} < 0.$$

Since $x^2+x+2 = 0$ has imaginary roots, the expression (x^2+x+2) has the same sign for all x. Thus, the sign of the fraction can change only at $x = -1$, $x = 0$, and $x = 2$. Hence, testing at $x = -2$, $-\frac{1}{2}$, 1, and 3, we find the signs of the factors as

$$\frac{+}{-\ -\ -},\qquad \frac{+}{+\ -\ -},\qquad \frac{+}{+\ +\ -},\qquad \frac{+}{+\ +\ +}.$$

Thus x has the range $x < -1$ and $0 < x < 2$. Graphically, the range is illustrated as shown in Figure 20.

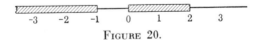

FIGURE 20.

NOTE 2. Unless a graph of the function is desired, the trial computations in each interval may be confined to the signs only, as is illustrated in the above example.

EXERCISE 62

Solve the following inequalities:

1. $2x + 8 < 0$.
2. $3x - 6 > 0$.
3. $4x < 10 - x$.

4. $7x + 10 > 11x + 2$.
5. $1 - x < 2 - 3x$.
6. $4(x-5) > 5(x-2)$.

7. $\frac{2}{3}x - 1 < x + \frac{1}{6}$.
8. $(x-1)^2 > (x+2)^2$.
9. $(x+1)(2x-1) > 0$.

10. $x^2 < 10 - 3x$.
11. $x + 5 < 4x^2$.
12. $x(6x - 1) > 35$.

13. $2x^2 + 10 > 9x$.
14. $(x+1)(x+5) < 45$.
15. $x(3x+2) > (x+2)^2$.

16. $x^2 + 4 < 0$.
17. $x^2 + 2x + 2 > 0$.
18. $2x^2 + 5 < 6x$.

19. $(x + 2)(x - 1)(x - 5) > 0$.
20. $(x - 2)^2(x - 4) < 0$.

21. $x^3 - 4x > 0$.
22. $2x^3 + 5x^2 - 3x > 0$.

23. $3x^4 < 2x^3 + 5x^2$.
24. $(x^2 - 1)(x^2 - 4) > 0$.

25. $(x^2 + 1)(2x - 3) < 0$.
26. $(2x + 1)^2(x^2 + 3) > 0$.

27. $\dfrac{x - 1}{x - 2} > 0$.
28. $\dfrac{x - 5}{x + 3} < 0$.
29. $\dfrac{x}{1 - x} < 0$.

30. $\dfrac{5}{(x-1)(x+3)} > 0$.
31. $\dfrac{5}{(x-1)} > (x+3)$.
32. $\dfrac{2}{x - 2} < \dfrac{1}{x + 1}$.

33. $\dfrac{2x}{3x + 1} < \dfrac{x - 2}{2x - 1}$.
34. $\dfrac{1}{x} - \dfrac{1}{6} > \dfrac{1}{x + 1}$.

35. $\dfrac{x}{2} + \dfrac{2}{x} > 2$.
36. $\dfrac{3}{x + 1} + \dfrac{2}{2x - 1} < \dfrac{13}{18}$.

Find the values of x for which the following radicals are real:

37. $\sqrt{x^2 - 4}$.
38. $\sqrt{3x^2 - 2x - 8}$.
39. $\sqrt{6 + x - x^2}$.

Find the values of k for which the roots of the following equations are real (Discriminant $\geqq 0$):

40. $kx^2 - 4x + 6 = 0$.
41. $kx^2 + 4x - 9 = 2kx$.
42. $x^2 = kx - 1$.

Find the values of k for which the graphs of the following equations (a) are tangent; (b) meet in two points; (c) meet in no points:

43. $\begin{cases} y^2 = 4x, \\ y = x + k. \end{cases}$
44. $\begin{cases} 4x^2 + y^2 = 2, \\ y = kx + 2. \end{cases}$

45. $\begin{cases} x^2 + y^2 = 25, \\ 3x - 4y = k. \end{cases}$
46. $\begin{cases} x^2 - 4y = 4, \\ y + 4 = k(x + 2). \end{cases}$

95. Absolute Inequalities. From our study of real numbers, we know that the square of any non-zero real number is positive. This property of real numbers combined with the general properties of inequalities leads to many interesting inequalities.

Example 1. If a, b, c represent unequal positive numbers, show that

$$a^2 + b^2 + c^2 > ab + bc + ca.$$

Solution: Since $a - b \neq 0$, $b - c \neq 0$, and $c - a \neq 0$, we have

$$(a - b)^2 > 0,\ (b - c)^2 > 0,\ (c - a)^2 > 0,$$

or

$$a^2 + b^2 > 2\,ab,\ b^2 + c^2 > 2\,bc,\ c^2 + a^2 > 2\,ca.$$

Adding corresponding members and dividing by 2 gives

$$a^2 + b^2 + c^2 > ab + bc + ca.$$

Example 2. Show that $\sqrt{6} > 1 + \sqrt{2}$.

Solution: Since both members of the given inequality are positive, by use of Property IV we may write

$$(\sqrt{6})^2 > (1 + \sqrt{2})^2 \quad \text{or} \quad 3 > 2\sqrt{2}.$$

Again by squaring, we have $(3)^2 > (2\sqrt{2})^2$ or $9 > 8$. Since this latter inequality is obviously true, retracing our steps makes it evident that the original inequality is also true.

EXERCISE 63

If the letters represent unequal positive numbers, prove that:

1. $x^2 + 1 > 2\,x$.

2. $\dfrac{a}{b} + \dfrac{b}{a} > 2$.

3. $(x + 1)^2 > x^2 + 1$.

4. $\frac{1}{2}(x + y) > \sqrt{xy}$.

5. $a^2b + ab^2 < a^3 + b^3$.

6. $\dfrac{2\,xy}{x + y} < \sqrt{xy}$.

7. $\sqrt{x} + \sqrt{y} > \sqrt{x + y}$.

8. $a + b > \sqrt{a^2 + b^2}$.

9. $a^2 + b^2 + c^2 < (a + b + c)^2$.

10. $a^4 + b^4 > a^3b + ab^3$.

11. $(a^2 + b^2)^2 < (a + b)(a^3 + b^3)$.

12. $(a + b)(a + 3\,b) < (a + 2\,b)^2$.

Show without decimal substitution that the following inequalities are correct:

13. $\sqrt{13} < 1 + \sqrt{7}$.

14. $\sqrt{5} + \sqrt{6} > \sqrt{3} + \sqrt{8}$.

15. $\sqrt{3} + \sqrt{19} > 6$.

16. $3\sqrt{5} + 5\sqrt{3} < 3\sqrt{3} + 5\sqrt{5}$.

17. $\sqrt{5} > \sqrt[3]{11}$.

18. $\sqrt{7} - \sqrt{13} > \sqrt{5} - \sqrt{11}$.

CHAPTER 14

Complex Numbers

96. Imaginary and Complex Numbers. In Article 51 we defined the **imaginary unit** i to represent the symbol $\sqrt{-1}$ and to have the property that $i^2 = -1$. Assuming that the laws of algebra apply to i as a literal number, it follows from the definition that the successive integral powers of i can be reduced to one of the four values $i, -1, -i, +1$.

Illustration 1. $i^3 = i^2 \cdot i = (-1)i = -i$; $i^4 = (i^2)^2 = (-1)^2 = 1$.

If a and b are real numbers, then $(a + bi)$ is called a **complex number** whose *real* part is a and whose *imaginary* part is bi, b being the coefficient of the imaginary part. If $b \neq 0$, the complex number is also called an **imaginary number,** and if $a = 0$ when $b \neq 0$, it is called a **pure imaginary number.** When $b = 0$, the complex number reduces to the real number a.

Illustration 2. $(3 + 2i)$ and $(5 - i\sqrt{2})$ are imaginary numbers; $-3i$ and $\sqrt{-5}$ are pure imaginary numbers; $\frac{1}{2}$ and $-\sqrt{2}$ are real numbers; and all of these are complex numbers.

Definition. *Two complex numbers $(a + bi)$ and $(c + di)$ are called equal if and only if $a = c$ and $b = d$.*

As an immediate result of this definition, it follows that

$$\textit{if } a + bi = 0, \textit{ then } a = 0 \textit{ and } b = 0.$$

Example. Find x and y, if $x - y + 2\ ix = 3 - 4\ i$.

Solution: Equating real and imaginary parts, we have $x - y = 3$ and $2\ x = -4$; hence $x = -2$ and $y = -5$.

If two complex numbers differ only in the sign of their imaginary parts, they are called **conjugate complex numbers,** and either is called the conjugate of the other.

Illustration 3. $(a + bi)$ is the conjugate of $(a - bi)$, bi is the conjugate of $-bi$, and a real number is its own conjugate.

97. Fundamental Operations with Complex Numbers.

The four fundamental operations of addition, subtraction, multiplication, and division as applied to complex numbers are defined as follows:

I, II. Addition and Subtraction. *To express the sum (or difference) of two complex numbers, as a complex number, add (or subtract) the real and imaginary parts separately. Thus,*

$$(a + bi) + (c + di) = (a + c) + (b + d)i,$$
$$(a + bi) - (c + di) = (a - c) + (b - d)i.$$

Illustration 1. Combining the real and imaginary parts, we have

$$(2 + 3\ i) + (1 - 4\ i) - (-2 - 2\ i) = 5 + i.$$

III. Multiplication. *To express the product of two complex numbers, as a complex number, multiply them according to the rules of algebra and substitute -1 for i^2. Thus,*

$$(a + bi)(c + di) = ac + adi + bci + bdi^2,$$
$$(a + bi)(c + di) = (ac - bd) + (ad + bc)i.$$

Illustration 2. Using the binomial formula, we have

$$(-1+i)^3=(-1)^3+3(-1)^2i+3(-1)i^2+i^3 = -1+3\ i+3-i= 2+2\ i.$$

IV. Division. *To express the quotient of two complex numbers, as a complex number, multiply both numerator and denominator of the indicated quotient by the conjugate of the denominator. Thus,*

$$\frac{a + bi}{c + di} = \frac{a + bi}{c + di} \cdot \frac{c - di}{c - di}$$
$$= \frac{ac - adi + bci - bdi^2}{c^2 - d^2i^2}$$

$$= \frac{(ac + bd) + (bc - ad)i}{c^2 + d^2}$$

$$\frac{a + bi}{c + di} = \frac{ac + bd}{c^2 + d^2} + \frac{bc - ad}{c^2 + d^2}i, \ c + di \neq 0.$$

Illustration 3. Dividing $(- 4 + 7\,i)$ by $(2 - i)$, we have

$$\frac{- 4 + 7\,i}{2 - i} = \frac{- 4 + 7\,i}{2 - i} \cdot \frac{2 + i}{2 + i} = \frac{- 8 - 4\,i + 14\,i + 7\,i^2}{4 - i^2}$$

$$= \frac{- 15 + 10\,i}{5} = - 3 + 2\,i.$$

NOTE. In all problems involving imaginary numbers the given quantity should be expressed in terms of the imaginary unit i before any operations are performed.

Example. Reduce $\dfrac{1 + \sqrt{- 4}}{\sqrt{- 1} - 1} - \dfrac{1 + \sqrt{- 1}}{\sqrt{- 1}}$ to the form $(a + bi)$.

Solution: Writing this in terms of i and combining fractions, we obtain

$$\frac{1 + 2\,i}{i - 1} - \frac{1 + i}{i} = \frac{(i + 2\,i^2) - (i^2 - 1)}{i^2 - i} = \frac{i}{- 1 - i}$$

$$= \frac{i}{- 1 - i} \cdot \frac{- 1 + i}{- 1 + i} = \frac{- i - 1}{2} = - \tfrac{1}{2} - \tfrac{1}{2}\,i.$$

EXERCISE 64

If letters represent positive numbers, express each of the following in terms of i, and simplify:

1. $\sqrt{- 4}$.   **2.** $\sqrt{- a^2 b^4}$.   **3.** $-\sqrt{- 25\,c^2}$.

4. $\sqrt{- \tfrac{9}{16}} + \sqrt{36}$.   **5.** $\sqrt{- a^2} - \sqrt{a^2}$.   **6.** $\tfrac{1}{2}(5 - \sqrt{- 12})$.

Find x and y:

7. $x + iy = 2 - 3\,i$.   **8.** $1 + ix = y - 5\,i$.   **9.** $x - 2\,iy = 7$.

10. $(x - 3) = 2(y + 1)i$.   **11.** $x + y - iy = 1 + i$.   **12.** $2\,x - ix = y + 2\,i$.

Perform the indicated operations and reduce to the form $(a + bi)$:

13. $\sqrt{- 9} - 2\sqrt{4} + \sqrt{- 16}$.   **14.** $2\sqrt{- 25} + \sqrt{- 64} - 3\sqrt{36}$.

15. $2\,i - i^2 - 3\,i^3$.   **16.** $i^4 - 2\,i^2 + 5\,i - 1$.

17. $(2\,i)^4 - (i^3)^3$.   **18.** $(3\,i)^3 - (- 2\,i)^2$.

19. $i^{-3} + (2\,i)^{-1}$.   **20.** $3\,i^{-2} - (- i)^{-1}$.

21. $(4 + 3\,i) + (- 2 + i)$.   **22.** $2 - (5 - 2\,i)$.

23. $(2 - 5\,i) - (3 - 3\,i)$.   **24.** $(- 6 - 2\,i) + (4 - 7\,i)$.

25. $\sqrt{- 10}\sqrt{- 15}\sqrt{- 24}$.   **26.** $\sqrt{- 12}(2\sqrt{3} - 5\sqrt{- 3})$.

27. $(3 + 2\,i)(2 + 3\,i)$.   **28.** $(5 - 3\,i)(- 2 + i)$.

29. $(3 - \sqrt{-2})^2$.

30. $(\frac{1}{2} - \frac{1}{3}i)(\frac{1}{2} + \frac{2}{3}i)$.

31. $(-4 + 7i) \div (2 - i)$.

32. $15i \div (1 + 2i)$.

33. $(45 + i\sqrt{3}) \div (7 - i\sqrt{3})$.

34. $(-2 + 11i) \div (3 - 4i)$.

35. $(8 - 5i) \div (2i)$.

36. $(18 - i) \div (3i - 2)$.

37. $(3 + 2i)^3$.

38. $(1 - i)^2(4 + 3i)$.

39. $(2 - i) - 2(2 - i)^2$.

40. $(-3 - 5i)^2 - 4$.

41. $(3 - 2i) \div (1 + i)^2$.

42. $(1 - 2i)^{-1}$.

43. $(2 + 3i - 4i^2 + i^3)^2$.

44. $(2 + 2i^2 - 3i^3)^3$.

45. $\dfrac{1}{i} + \dfrac{1}{i+1}$.

46. $\dfrac{i}{1-i} + \dfrac{1-i}{i}$.

47. $\left(1 - \dfrac{1}{i}\right)^2$.

48. $\dfrac{i^3 + 8}{i + 2} + 2i$.

49. $(\sqrt{-18} - 2)^{-2}$.

50. $(2 + i)^4 - (2 - i)^4$.

Evaluate each of the following for the value indicated:

51. $x^2 + 7$, $x = 3 - 4i$.

52. $2x^2 - 2x + 1$, $x = 1 - i$.

53. $x + \dfrac{1}{x}$, $x = \frac{4}{5} + \frac{3}{5}i$.

54. $\dfrac{x^2}{x-1}$, $x = 2 + i$.

55. $2x^3 + 3x + 5$, $x = \frac{1}{2} - \frac{3}{2}i$.

56. $x^3 - 2x^2 + 5x$, $x = 1 + 2i$.

Solve for x:

57. $(1 + i)x = 2 - i$.

58. $ix + 3 - 2i = (1 - 2i)x - i$.

59. $\dfrac{x}{i} + \dfrac{x}{i+1} = \dfrac{5}{i+2}$.

60. $\dfrac{x}{1+i} + i = \dfrac{x}{1-i} - i$.

98. Graphic Representation of Complex Numbers. A complex number $(x + yi)$ may be represented graphically as a point in a plane whose coordinates are (x, y).

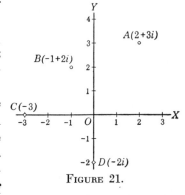

Illustration. In Figure 21, A represents $(2 + 3i)$; B, $(-1 + 2i)$; C, $(-3 + 0i)$ or -3; and D, $(0 - 2i)$ or $-2i$.

FIGURE 21.

When complex numbers are represented as the points of a plane the x-axis is called the **axis of real numbers,** the y-axis the **axis of imaginary numbers,** and the plane itself is called the **complex plane.** A complex number written as $(x + yi)$ is said to be in **rectangular** or **Cartesian** form.

99. Graphic Addition of Complex Numbers. Let the points P_1 and P_2 represent the complex numbers $(x_1 + y_1 i)$ and $(x_2 + y_2 i)$ respectively. Draw the lines OP_1 and OP_2, and complete the parallelogram with OP_1 and OP_2 as sides. The fourth vertex R represents the sum $(x_1 + y_1 i) + (x_2 + y_2 i)$.

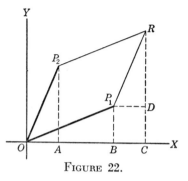
FIGURE 22.

Proof: In Figure 22, if we construct $P_2 A$, $P_1 B$, and RC parallel to OY and $P_1 D$ parallel to OX, the right triangles OAP_2 and $P_1 DR$ will be congruent. Hence, $P_1 D = OA$ and $DR = AP_2$. Therefore, we have

$$OC = OB + BC = OB + P_1 D = OB + OA = x_1 + x_2$$
and
$$CR = CD + DR = BP_1 + AP_2 = y_1 + y_2.$$

NOTE 1. Observe that the **parallelogram rule** for the addition of complex numbers is the same as that for adding vectors. For this reason many vector problems can be solved by using imaginary numbers to represent the vectors.

NOTE 2. To subtract $(x_2 + y_2 i)$ from $(x_1 + y_1 i)$ graphically, we add $(-x_2 - y_2 i)$ and $(x_1 + y_1 i)$.

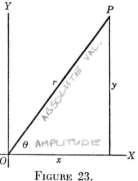
FIGURE 23.

100. Polar Form of a Complex Number.* Let the point P represent the complex number $(x + yi)$ in Figure 23. Let r be the length OP and θ the angle XOP; then

$$x = r \cos \theta, \quad y = r \sin \theta \tag{1}$$
and
$$r = \sqrt{x^2 + y^2}, \quad \tan \theta = \frac{y}{x}. \tag{2}$$

Hence, the complex number may be written

$$x + iy = r(\cos \theta + i \sin \theta). \tag{3}$$

---

* Some knowledge of trigonometry is needed for the remainder of the chapter.

The latter form, which is often abbreviated as **r cis θ,** is called the **polar** or **trigonometric form** of the number. The angle θ is called the **amplitude** or **argument**, and the positive length r is called the **modulus** or **absolute value** of the number.

Illustration. Plotting the three complex numbers $3\,i$, $-\frac{3}{2}$, and $(\sqrt{2} + i\sqrt{2})$ in Figure 24, we find their respective polar forms as

$$3\,i = 3(\cos 90° + i \sin 90°) = 3 \text{ cis } 90°,$$
$$-\tfrac{3}{2} = \tfrac{3}{2} \text{ cis } 180°, \quad \sqrt{2} + i\sqrt{2} = 2 \text{ cis } 45°.$$

NOTE 1. When a complex number is expressed in polar form, observe that the amplitude is not uniquely determined. Thus, if $\theta = 45°$, we could use $\theta = 405°$, or $\theta = -315°$, etc. To avoid this indefiniteness, θ is usually taken in the range $0° \leqq \theta < 360°$.

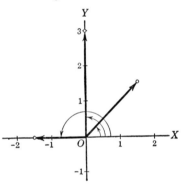

FIGURE 24.

NOTE 2. The absolute value of $(x + yi)$ is often written as $|\,x + yi\,|$; hence $|\,x + yi\,| = r = \sqrt{x^2 + y^2}$. Thus,

$$|-3| = |-3 + 0\,i| = \sqrt{(-3)^2 + 0^2} = 3$$
and $\quad |-3 + 4\,i| = \sqrt{(-3)^2 + (4)^2} = 5.$

The polar form of $(x + yi)$ may be found by:

1. *Plotting the point* $(x + yi)$ *to determine the quadrant angle,*
2. *Finding r from* $r = \sqrt{x^2 + y^2}$,
3. *Determining* θ *by inspection, or from* $\tan \theta = y/x$ *and a table of tangents.*

Example 1. Find the polar form of $(4 - 5\,i)$.
Solution: *1.* The point lies in the fourth quadrant (Figure 25).

2. $r = \sqrt{(4)^2 + (-5)^2} = \sqrt{41}$.

3. $\tan \theta = -\frac{5}{4} = -1.250$. From Table II, when $\tan \alpha = 1.250$, we find that $\alpha = 51.3°$. Hence $\theta = 360° - 51.3° = 308.7°$. Therefore, $(4 - 5\,i) = \sqrt{41}(\cos 308.7° + i \sin 308.7°)$.

Example 2. Represent $4(\cos 120° + i \sin 120°)$ graphically, and find its rectangular form.

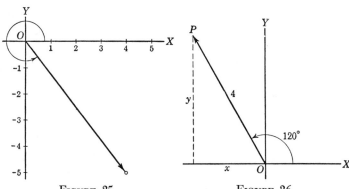

FIGURE 25.   FIGURE 26.

Solution: In Figure 26 lay off $\theta = 120°$ and determine the point P four units from the origin.

Since $\sin 120° = \sin 60° = \frac{1}{2}\sqrt{3}$ and $\cos 120° = -\cos 60° = -\frac{1}{2}$, we have $4(\cos 120° + i \sin 120°) = 4(-\frac{1}{2} + \frac{1}{2}\,i\sqrt{3}) = -2 + 2\,i\sqrt{3}$.

NOTE 3. Trigonometric functions of certain elementary angles are given in the accompanying table.

θ	0°	30°	45°	60°	90°
$\sin \theta$	0	$\frac{1}{2}$	$\frac{1}{2}\sqrt{2}$	$\frac{1}{2}\sqrt{3}$	1
$\cos \theta$	1	$\frac{1}{2}\sqrt{3}$	$\frac{1}{2}\sqrt{2}$	$\frac{1}{2}$	0
$\tan \theta$	0	$\frac{1}{3}\sqrt{3}$	1	$\sqrt{3}$	∞

EXERCISE 65

Represent each complex number graphically and give its absolute value:

1. $5 + 12\,i$.

2. $-\sqrt{2} + i$.

3. $\sqrt{-25}$.

4. $3 - \sqrt{-4}$.

5. -8.

6. $i\sqrt{3} - 3$.

Represent each complex number, its conjugate, and its negative on the same complex plane:

7. $4 - 3\,i.$ **8.** $6.$ **9.** $2(1 - i\sqrt{2}).$

10. $\frac{1}{2}(1 - i\sqrt{3}).$ **11.** $-2 - 2\,i\sqrt{3}.$ **12.** $-7\,i.$

Find each sum graphically, and check results algebraically:

13. $(2 + i) + (3 + 2\,i).$ **14.** $(5 - i) + (2 + 4\,i).$

15. $(-2 + 3\,i) + 4\,i.$ **16.** $7 + (3 + 4\,i).$

17. $(2 + 2\,i) - (3 - 4\,i).$ **18.** $(-2 + 5\,i) - (-1 - i).$

19. $(i - 3) + (4\,i + 1).$ **20.** $(2\,i + 3) - (3\,i - 2).$

Write the given complex number in its polar form:

21. $3 + 3\,i.$ **22.** $2 - 2\,i\sqrt{3}.$ **23.** $-5.$

24. $4\,i.$ **25.** $5 - 5\,i.$ **26.** $3\,i - \sqrt{3}.$

27. $3 - 4\,i.$ **28.** $-12 - 5\,i.$ **29.** $2 + i\sqrt{2}.$

30. $8.$ **31.** $-6\,i.$ **32.** $2\,i\sqrt{2} - 4.$

Graph each of the following complex numbers, and write each number in its rectangular form:

33. $4(\cos 45° + i \sin 45°).$ **34.** $2(\cos 60° + i \sin 60°).$

35. $5(\cos 150° + i \sin 150°).$ **36.** $3(\cos 180° + i \sin 180°).$

37. $2 \operatorname{cis} 270°.$ **38.** $2\sqrt{2} \operatorname{cis} 225°.$ **39.** $5 \operatorname{cis} 50°.$ **40.** $3 \operatorname{cis} 200°.$

Reduce the following complex numbers to rectangular form and then write in polar form:

41. $2(\cos 135° + i \sin 45°).$ **42.** $3(\cos 45° - i \sin 45°).$

43. $\sqrt{2}(\cos 90° + i \sin 45°).$ **44.** $5(\sin 30° + i \cos 30°).$

45. If $z_1 = x_1 + y_1 i$ and $z_2 = x_2 + y_2 i$, prove graphically that $|z_1 + z_2| \leqq |z_1| + |z_2|.$

101. Products and Quotients in Polar Form.

Given two complex numbers in polar form, consider the product

$r_1(\cos \theta_1 + i \sin \theta_1) \cdot r_2(\cos \theta_2 + i \sin \theta_2)$

$\quad = r_1 r_2[\cos \theta_1 \cos \theta_2 + i \cos \theta_1 \sin \theta_2 + i \sin \theta_1 \cos \theta_2 + i^2 \sin \theta_1 \sin \theta_2]$

$\quad = r_1 r_2[(\cos \theta_1 \cos \theta_2 - \sin \theta_1 \sin \theta_2) + i(\sin \theta_1 \cos \theta_2 + \cos \theta_1 \sin \theta_2)]$

$\quad = r_1 r_2[\cos (\theta_1 + \theta_2) + i \sin (\theta_1 + \theta_2)].$

Products of three or more complex numbers may be found by repeated use of the above procedure; and by induction we can establish the following theorem:

Theorem 1. *The absolute value of a product of complex num-*

bers is the product of their absolute values, and the amplitude of the product is the sum of their amplitudes. Thus,

$$r_1 \text{ cis } \theta_1 \cdot r_2 \text{ cis } \theta_2 \cdots = (r_1 r_2 \cdots) \text{ cis } (\theta_1 + \theta_2 + \cdots).$$

Illustration 1. $2(\cos 20° + i \sin 20°) \cdot 3(\cos 130° + i \sin 130°)$
$$= 6(\cos 150° + i \sin 150°) = -3\sqrt{3} + 3\,i.$$

Similarly, for the quotient of two complex numbers, we have

$$\frac{r_1(\cos \theta_1 + i \sin \theta_1)}{r_2(\cos \theta_2 + i \sin \theta_2)} = \frac{r_1}{r_2}\left[\frac{(\cos \theta_1 + i \sin \theta_1)}{(\cos \theta_2 + i \sin \theta_2)} \cdot \frac{(\cos \theta_2 - i \sin \theta_2)}{(\cos \theta_2 - i \sin \theta_2)}\right]$$

$$= \frac{r_1}{r_2}\left[\frac{(\cos \theta_1 \cos \theta_2 + \sin \theta_1 \sin \theta_2) + i(\sin \theta_1 \cos \theta_2 - \cos \theta_1 \sin \theta_2)}{\cos^2 \theta_2 + \sin^2 \theta_2}\right]$$

$$= \frac{r_1}{r_2}[\cos (\theta_1 - \theta_2) + i \sin (\theta_1 - \theta_2)].$$

Theorem 2. *The absolute value of a quotient of two complex numbers is the quotient of their absolute values, and the amplitude of the quotient is the amplitude of the dividend minus the amplitude of the divisor.* Thus,

$$r_1 \text{ cis } \theta_1 / r_2 \text{ cis } \theta_2 = (r_1/r_2) \text{ cis } (\theta_1 - \theta_2), \text{ if } r_2 \neq 0.$$

Illustration 2. $\dfrac{6(\cos 160° + i \sin 160°)}{3(\cos 70° + i \sin 70°)} = 2(\cos 90° + i \sin 90°)$
$$= 2\,i.$$

102. De Moivre's Theorem. *If n is any positive integer,* then

$$[r(\cos \theta + i \sin \theta)]^n = r^n(\cos n\theta + i \sin n\theta). \quad = r^n \text{ cis } n\theta.$$

This theorem follows as a corollary of Theorem 1, Article 101.

Illustration. $[2(\cos 30° + i \sin 30°)]^6 = 2^6(\cos 180° + i \sin 180°)$
$$= -64.$$

NOTE. It can be shown that De Moivre's Theorem is also true when n is any positive or negative rational number. Thus, for example, when $n = -1$, we have

$$[r(\cos \theta + i \sin \theta)]^{-1} = \frac{1}{r(\cos \theta + i \sin \theta)} = \frac{1(\cos 0° + i \sin 0°)}{r(\cos \theta + i \sin \theta)}$$

$$= \frac{1}{r}[\cos (0° - \theta) + i \sin (0° - \theta)]$$

$$= r^{-1}[\cos (-\theta) + i \sin (-\theta)].$$

Example. Evaluate $(i - 1)^4$, using De Moivre's Theorem.

Solution: Plotting the complex number $(i - 1)$, we find that $r = \sqrt{2}$ and $\theta = 135°$; hence

$$(i - 1)^4 = [\sqrt{2}(\cos 135° + i \sin 135°)]^4 = (\sqrt{2})^4(\cos 540° + i \sin 540°)$$
$$= 4(\cos 180° + i \sin 180°) = -4.$$

This result may be verified by expanding $(i - 1)^4$.

103. Roots of Complex Numbers. Let $\rho(\cos \alpha + i \sin \alpha)$ be any nth root of the complex number $r(\cos \theta + i \sin \theta)$. Then

$$r(\cos \theta + i \sin \theta) = [\rho(\cos \alpha + i \sin \alpha)]^n$$
$$= \rho^n(\cos n\alpha + i \sin n\alpha). \tag{1}$$

If two complex numbers are equal, their absolute values must be equal, but their amplitudes may differ by some integral multiple of 360°. Hence, from (1) we have

$$\left.\begin{array}{ll} \rho^n = r & \text{or} \quad \rho = \sqrt[n]{r}, \\ n\alpha = \theta + k \cdot 360° & \text{or} \quad \alpha = \dfrac{\theta}{n} + k \cdot \dfrac{360°}{n}, \end{array}\right\} \tag{2}$$

where k is any integer. If we take $k = 0, 1, 2, \cdots, (n - 1)$ in (2), we obtain n distinct values of α, all less than 360°. Corresponding to these amplitudes we obtain n distinct roots.

Theorem. *Any complex number $x + yi = r(\cos \theta + i \sin \theta)$ has n distinct nth roots given by the formula*

$$\sqrt[n]{r}\left[\cos\left(\frac{\theta}{n} + k \cdot \frac{360°}{n}\right) + i \sin\left(\frac{\theta}{n} + k \cdot \frac{360°}{n}\right)\right],$$

where k assumes the values $0, 1, 2, \cdots, (n - 1)$.

Illustration. The cube roots of $8(\cos 120° + i \sin 120°)$ are

$$\sqrt[3]{8}\left[\cos\left(\frac{120°}{3} + 0 \cdot \frac{360°}{3}\right) + i \sin\left(\frac{120°}{3} + 0 \cdot \frac{360°}{3}\right)\right]$$
$$= 2(\cos 40° + i \sin 40°),$$

$$\sqrt[3]{8}\left[\cos\left(\frac{120°}{3} + 1 \cdot \frac{360°}{3}\right) + i \sin\left(\frac{120°}{3} + 1 \cdot \frac{360°}{3}\right)\right]$$
$$= 2(\cos 160° + i \sin 160°),$$

$$\sqrt[3]{8}\left[\cos\left(\frac{120°}{3} + 2 \cdot \frac{360°}{3}\right) + i \sin\left(\frac{120°}{3} + 2 \cdot \frac{360°}{3}\right)\right]$$
$$= 2(\cos 280° + i \sin 280°).$$

NOTE. The cube roots of the above illustration are plotted in Figure 27. Observe that these points all lie on a circle of radius 2 and that they divide the circumference into three equal parts.

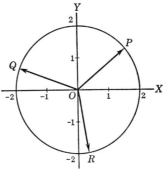

FIGURE 27.

Example. Find all solutions of the equation $x^5 + 32 = 0$.

Solution. Since $x^5 = -32$ and $x = \sqrt[5]{-32}$, it is evident that the required solutions are the five fifth roots of -32. Hence, writing -32 in its polar form $32(\cos 180° + i \sin 180°)$, and noting that the amplitude increment is $360°/5 = 72°$, we obtain the five roots 2 cis 36°, 2 cis 108°, 2 cis 180°, 2 cis 252°, and 2 cis 324°. Observe that the third of these roots reduces to -2.

104. Square Roots in Rectangular Form. Let $(p + qi)$ represent a square root of the complex number $(x + yi)$. Then, in the relation

$$x + yi = (p + qi)^2 = p^2 - q^2 + 2\,pqi,$$

by equating real and imaginary parts, we have

$$p^2 - q^2 = x \quad \text{and} \quad 2\,pq = y.$$

Taking $q = y/2\,p$, we have

$$p^2 - \frac{y^2}{4\,p^2} = x \quad \text{or} \quad 4\,p^4 - 4\,xp^2 - y^2 = 0.$$

Solving, we obtain

$$p^2 = \frac{4\,x \pm \sqrt{16\,x^2 + 16\,y^2}}{8} = \frac{x \pm r}{2}, \text{ where } r = \sqrt{x^2 + y^2}.$$

Since p is real, p^2 must equal $(x + r)/2$, and we may write

$$p = \pm \frac{r + x}{\sqrt{2(r + x)}}, q = \pm \frac{y}{\sqrt{2(r + x)}}.$$

Therefore the square roots are given by the formula*

$$\sqrt{x + yi} = \pm \frac{(r + x + yi)}{\sqrt{2(r + x)}}, r + x \neq 0$$

where $r = \sqrt{x^2 + y^2}$.

*When $r + x = 0$, we have $y = 0$ and the square roots are $\pm i\sqrt{-x}$.

Illustration. For $(3 + 4 i)$, $r = 5$; hence the square roots are

$$\pm \frac{(5 + 3 + 4 i)}{\sqrt{2(5 + 3)}} = \pm (2 + i).$$

Example. Solve $x^2 - 8 x + 1 + 8 i = 0$.

Solution: Using the quadratic formula, we obtain

$$x = \frac{8 \pm \sqrt{64 - 4(1 + 8 i)}}{2} = 4 \pm \sqrt{15 - 8 i}.$$

Since $r = 17$, $\sqrt{15 - 8 i} = \pm (4 - i)$; hence $x = 4 \pm (4 - i) = 8 - i$
or i.

EXERCISE 66

Perform the indicated operations and express the results in rectangular form:

1. $3(\cos 17° + i \sin 17°) \cdot 2(\cos 28° + i \sin 28°)$.
2. $2(\cos 70° + i \sin 70°) \cdot 5(\cos 50° + i \sin 50°)$.
3. $3 \text{ cis } 111° \cdot 3 \text{ cis } 159°$.   4. $\frac{1}{2} \text{ cis } 157° \cdot 6 \text{ cis } 83°$.
5. $\frac{6(\cos 100° + i \sin 100°)}{3(\cos 40° + i \sin 40°)}$.   6. $\frac{5(\cos 15° + i \sin 15°)}{20(\cos 165° + i \sin 165°)}$.
7. $8 \text{ cis } 308°/2 \text{ cis } 173°$.   8. $15 \text{ cis } 325°/5 \text{ cis } 145°$.

Express in polar form and perform the indicated operations:

9. $(1 + i)(2 i - 2)$.   10. $(-1 + i\sqrt{3})(3\sqrt{3} + 3 i)$.
11. $(-3\sqrt{3} - 3 i)/(2 + 2 i\sqrt{3})$.   12. $(-5 + 5 i)/(2 - 2 i)$.
13. $(2 + 2 i)(-3 + 3 i)(-1 - i)$.
14. $(-2\sqrt{3} + 2 i)(1 - i\sqrt{3})/(3\sqrt{3} + 3 i)$.

Find the following powers and roots, and express answers in rectangular form if the table on page 151 applies:

15. $[2(\cos 150° + i \sin 150°)]^5$.   16. $[3(\cos 112\frac{1}{2}° + i \sin 112\frac{1}{2}°)]^4$.
17. $[\frac{1}{2}(\cos 58° + i \sin 58°)]^3$.   18. $[2(\cos 240° + i \sin 240°)]^6$.
19. $(1 + i)^{10}$.   20. $(\frac{1}{2} - \frac{1}{2} i\sqrt{3})^8$.   21. $(-\sqrt{3} - i)^7$.
22. $(2 - 2 i)^5$.   23. $(i - 1)^{-3}$.   24. $(\sqrt{3} - 3 i)^{-2}$.
25. $\sqrt{25(\cos 240° + i \sin 240°)}$.   26. $\sqrt[3]{\frac{1}{8}(\cos 270° + i \sin 270°)}$.
27. $\sqrt[5]{32(\cos 30° + i \sin 30°)}$.   28. $\sqrt[4]{81(\cos 180° + i \sin 180°)}$.
29. $\sqrt[3]{-2 + 2 i}$.   30. $\sqrt[6]{-64}$.   31. $\sqrt[4]{-\frac{1}{2}(1 + i\sqrt{3})}$.
32. $(8 i)^{\frac{1}{3}}$.   33. $(4 - 4 i)^{\frac{1}{5}}$.   34. $(-\frac{1}{2} + \frac{1}{2} i\sqrt{3})^{\frac{1}{4}}$.

Find all roots of the following equations:

35. $x^3 + 8 = 0$.   36. $x^4 - 1 = 0$.   37. $x^6 = 729$.
38. $x^2 - 1 = i\sqrt{3}$.   39. $x^3 = i$.   40. $i x^3 - 1 = 0$.

Find the square roots of the following complex numbers, using the formula in Article 104:

41. $4 - 3i$.   **42.** $5 + 12i$.   **43.** $-8 + 15i$.

44. $40 - 9i$.   **45.** i.   **46.** $1 + i$.

Find all roots of the following equations:

47. $x^2 - (1 - 2i)x = (\frac{1}{2} + i)$.   **48.** $x^2 - 7 = 4i(x - 1)$.

49. $ix^2 + 2x - 2i = 0$.   **50.** $(x + i)^{-1} - x^{-1} = \frac{1}{2}i$.

51. If $\sqrt[3]{N}$ is any cube root of the complex number N, show that the other two cube roots are given by $\omega\sqrt[3]{N}$ and $\omega^2\sqrt[3]{N}$, where $\omega = -\frac{1}{2} + \frac{1}{2}i\sqrt{3}$. Hint: Each cube root must satisfy $x^3 = N$.

51.

IST METHOD   Solve equation $z^3 = N = a^3$, $z^3 - a^3 = 0$

$$(z - a)(z^2 + az + a^2) = 0$$

solutions   1. $z = a$

2. $z = \dfrac{-a \pm \sqrt{a^2 - 4a^2}}{2}$

$= \dfrac{-a \pm a\sqrt{-3}}{2}$

$= a\left(\dfrac{-1 \pm i\sqrt{3}}{2}\right)$

ie. $a\left(\dfrac{-1 + i\sqrt{3}}{2}\right)$

$a\left(\dfrac{-1 - i\sqrt{3}}{2}\right)$

2ND $z = r \operatorname{Cis}\theta$, $r^3 \operatorname{Cis} 3\theta = N = n\operatorname{Cis}\alpha$

$r^3 = n$, $3\theta = \alpha$

$r = \sqrt[3]{n}$ $\theta = \alpha/3$

$z = \sqrt[3]{n} \operatorname{Cis}\left(\dfrac{\alpha}{3} + \dfrac{2\pi K}{3}\right)$ $K = 0, 1, 2;$

1   $z_0 = \sqrt[3]{n} \operatorname{Cis} \dfrac{\alpha}{3}$

2   $z_1 = \sqrt[3]{n} \operatorname{Cis} \dfrac{\alpha}{3} + \dfrac{2\pi}{3} = \sqrt[3]{n} \operatorname{Cis}\dfrac{\alpha}{3} \times \operatorname{Cis}\dfrac{2\pi}{3}$

3. $z_2 = \sqrt[3]{n} \operatorname{Cis} \dfrac{\alpha}{3} + \dfrac{4\pi}{3} = \sqrt[3]{n} \operatorname{Cis}\dfrac{\alpha}{3} \times \operatorname{Cis}\dfrac{4\pi}{3}$

Put $\sqrt[3]{n} \operatorname{Cis} \dfrac{\alpha}{3} = a$ $\left(\operatorname{Cis}\dfrac{2\pi}{3}\right)^2$

$\operatorname{Cis} \dfrac{2\pi}{3} = \omega$

THEN. $z_0 = a$

$z_1 = a\omega$

$z_2 = a\omega^2$

$\omega = \operatorname{Cis}\dfrac{2\pi}{3} = \operatorname{Cis} 125° + i\operatorname{Sin} 125°$

$= -\dfrac{1}{2} + i\sqrt{3}/2.$

CHAPTER 15

Polynomials and Equations

105. Definitions. A function $f(x)$ having the form

$$f(x) = a_0 x^n + a_1 x^{n-1} + a_2 x^{n-2} + \cdots + a_{n-1} x + a_n, \qquad (1)$$

where n is a positive integer and $a_0, a_1, a_2, \cdots, a_{n-1}, a_n$ are constants with $a_0 \neq 0$, is called a **polynomial** of the nth degree in x.

The equation formed in taking $f(x) = 0$ is called an **integral rational equation** or **general equation** of the nth degree in x. Such equations of the first, second, third, fourth, and fifth degrees are called **linear, quadratic, cubic, quartic** (or **biquadratic**), and **quintic** equations respectively.

NOTE. A root of the equation $f(x) = 0$ is called a **zero** of the function $f(x)$.   ie $y = 0$. at that print.

In this chapter any functional notation, such as $f(x)$, $Q(x)$, and so on, will be understood to represent a polynomial in x. Furthermore, we shall restrict our discussion to polynomials and integral rational equations with real coefficients, even though in general the coefficients of (1) are real or imaginary numbers. Nevertheless, the statements and the proofs of the theorems presented are valid for complex coefficients unless otherwise stated.

106. Remainder Theorem. *If a polynomial $f(x)$ is divided by $(x - r)$ until a constant remainder is obtained, this remainder is equal to $f(r)$.*

$R = f(r)$

Proof: Let $Q(x)$ be the quotient and R the constant remainder obtained when $f(x)$ is divided by $(x - r)$. In accordance with the definition of division,

$$dividend = quotient \times divisor + remainder,$$

we have

$$f(x) = (x - r)Q(x) + R, \tag{1}$$

where $Q(x)$ is a polynomial whose degree is 1 less than that of $f(x)$. Since (1) is valid for all values of x, we obtain for $x = r$

$$f(r) = (r - r)Q(r) + R \quad \text{or} \quad R = f(r).$$

Illustration. If $f(x) = x^3 - x + 1$ is divided by $(x + 2)$, we obtain the quotient $Q(x) = x^2 - 2x + 3$, and the remainder $R = -5$. Also, from $(x - r) = (x + 2)$, we have $r = -2$. Thus, $f(-2) = (-2)^3 - (-2) + 1 = -5$, which agrees with the remainder theorem.

Example. Find the value of m for which $x^3 - mx^2 - 6$ is divisible by $(x - 3)$; that is, $R = 0$.

Solution: Since $r = 3$ and $R = 0$, on substituting in $f(r) = R$, we obtain

$$(3)^3 - m(3)^2 - 6 = 0.$$

Hence,

$$27 - 9m - 6 = 0 \quad \text{or} \quad m = \tfrac{7}{3}.$$

107. Factor Theorem. *If r is a zero of $f(x)$, then $(x - r)$ is a factor of $f(x)$.*

Proof: By hypothesis $f(r) = 0$ and by the remainder theorem $R = f(r) = 0$; hence

$$f(x) = (x - r)Q(x) + R$$

reduces to $f(x) = (x - r)Q(x)$, in which $(x - r)$ is a factor of $f(x)$.

Converse of the Factor Theorem. *If $(x - r)$ is a factor of $f(x)$, then r is a zero of $f(x)$.*

Proof: By hypothesis, $f(x) = (x - r)Q(x)$. Therefore, $f(r) = (0)Q(r) = 0$, or r is a zero of $f(x)$.

Example. Show that $(x + 1)$ is a factor of $x^9 + 1$.

Solution: From $x - r = x + 1$, we find $r = -1$. Since (-1) is a zero of $x^9 + 1$, that is, $(-1)^9 + 1 = 0$, it follows by the factor theorem that $(x + 1)$ is a factor of $x^9 + 1$.

108. Synthetic Division. The division of a polynomial $f(x)$ by a binomial of the form $(x - r)$ may be simplified by a process known as **synthetic division.** The development of this process is shown in the following illustration:

Illustration. Divide $(2 x^3 - 3 x^2 - 5 x + 8)$ by $(x - 2)$.
By ordinary long division, we have

$$
\begin{array}{l}
2 x^3 - 3 x^2 - 5 x + 8 \;\underline{|\,x - 2} \text{ (divisor)} \\
\underline{2 x^3 - 4 x^2} \qquad\qquad 2 x^2 + x - 3 \text{ (quotient)} \\
\qquad\quad x^2 - 5 x \\
\qquad\quad \underline{x^2 - 2 x} \\
\qquad\qquad\; - 3 x + 8 \\
\qquad\qquad\; \underline{- 3 x + 6} \\
\qquad\qquad\qquad\qquad 2 \text{ (remainder)}
\end{array}
$$

In the above we omit the first term of each partial product and the second term of each remainder, since they are repetitions of terms already written. Thus,

$$
\begin{array}{l}
2 x^3 - 3 x^2 - 5 x + 8 \;\underline{|\,x - 2} \\
\qquad\quad\underline{- 4 x^2} \qquad\qquad 2 x^2 + x - 3 \\
\qquad\qquad x^2 \\
\qquad\qquad\quad \underline{- 2 x} \\
\qquad\qquad\quad\; - 3 x \\
\qquad\qquad\qquad\quad \underline{+ 6} \\
\qquad\qquad\qquad\qquad 2
\end{array}
$$

Next we write only the coefficients and arrange them in a more compact form. The quotient is omitted since its coefficients are repetitions of the numbers in the third line (when the first number of the dividend is repeated in the third line). Thus,

$$
\begin{array}{rrrr|r}
2 & -3 & -5 & +8 & \underline{\;1 - 2} \\
 & -4 & -2 & +6 & \\
\hline
2 & +1 & -3 & +2 &
\end{array}
$$

For convenience, to replace subtraction by addition, we change the -2 in the divisor to $+2$ and omit the 1. Thus,

$$
\begin{array}{rrrr|r}
2 & -3 & -5 & +8 & \underline{\;+2} \\
 & +4 & +2 & -6 & \\
\hline
2 & +1 & -3 & +2 &
\end{array}
$$

Quotient $= 2 x^2 + x - 3.$ *Remainder* $= 2.$

Rule for Synthetic Division. *To divide a polynomial $f(x)$ by $(x - r)$, arrange $f(x)$ in descending powers of x, writing the coefficient zero for missing powers.*

1. Write the coefficients a_0, a_1, a_2, $\cdots$, a_n (zeros included) in the first line, and place r at the right.

2. Write a_0 in the first place in the third line.

3. Multiply a_0 by r, write the product in the second line under a_1, and their sum in the third line; multiply this sum by r, add to a_2, and write the sum in the third line; and so on, until finally a product has been added to a_n.

4. The last number in the third line is the remainder, and the other numbers in the third line are the coefficients of the powers of x in the quotient, arranged in descending order.

Example. Divide $(2 x^4 - 3 x^2 - x)$ by $(x + 3)$.
Solution: Since $x - r = x + 3$, we have $r = -3$; hence

$$
\begin{array}{rrrrr|r}
2 & 0 & -3 & -1 & 0 & \underline{-3} \\
  & -6 & +18 & -45 & +138 & \\
\hline
2 & -6 & +15 & -46 & +138 &
\end{array}
$$

Quotient $= 2 x^3 - 6 x^2 + 15 x - 46$. *Remainder* $= 138$.

NOTE 1. Synthetic division may be used to find the value of a polynomial $f(x)$ when $x = r$, since the remainder obtained is equal to $f(r)$. Thus, in the above example, 138 is also the value of $2(-3)^4 - 3(-3)^2 - (-3)$. *SUBS-TITUTION*

NOTE 2. Synthetic division is valid only for divisors of the form $(x - r)$. Division by a binomial such as $(2 x - 1) = 2(x - \frac{1}{2})$ can be performed by dividing synthetically by $(x - \frac{1}{2})$, and then dividing the coefficients of the quotient by 2.

EXERCISE 67

Using the remainder theorem, find the remainders when

- **1.** $2 x^3 - x^2 + 2 x + 3$ is divided by $(x - 2)$. *19*
- **2.** $3 x^4 + x^3 - 2 x - 7$ is divided by $(x + 3)$. *200*
- **3.** $x^5 - 2 x^2 - x + 5$ is divided by $(x + 1)$. *3*
- **4.** $4 x^4 - 3 x^3 + 2 x^2 - x$ is divided by $(x - 1)$. *2*

Find the value of m so that

- **5.** $x^3 - mx^2 + 2$ divided by $(x - 1)$ has remainder 3. *0*
- **6.** $2 x^4 - 3 x^3 - mx$ divided by $(x - 2)$ has remainder -4. *6*

7. $mx^3 + 5x - m$ divided by $(x + 3)$ has remainder 13.

8. $3x^3 - 2mx + 4$ divided by $(x + 1)$ has remainder 0.

Determine by the factor theorem whether

9. $(x - 1)$ is a factor of $3x^3 - 4x^2 - 5x + 6$.

10. $(x + 2)$ is a factor of $x^4 + 5x - 6$.

11. $(x + 1)$ is a factor of $x^{10} - 3x^7 + 5x^3 + 1$.

12. $(x - 3)$ is a factor of $2x^3 - 4x^2 - 7x + 2$.

Determine m so that

13. $(x + 3)$ is a factor of $2x^3 - 3x^2 + mx + 6$.

14. $(x - 2)$ is a factor of $mx^4 - 5x^3 + 2x + 2m$.

15. $(x + 2)$ is a factor of $mx^3 - (2m - 1)x - 10$.

16. $(x - \frac{1}{2})$ is a factor of $4x^3 - 6x^2 + 3m$.

By synthetic division, find the quotient and the remainder in each of the following:

17. $(x^3 - 3x^2 - 2x + 5) \div (x - 3)$.

18. $(-2x^4 + 4x^3 + 55x + 7) \div (x - 4)$.

19. $(x^5 + 2x^3 - 7x + 15) \div (x + 2)$.

20. $(3x^4 + 2x^3 + 4x^2 - x) \div (x + 3)$.

21. $(2x^3 - 0.2x^2 - 1.74x + 0.24) \div (x - 0.2)$.

22. $(x^4 + 2.2x^3 + 1.2x^2 + 4) \div (x + 1.2)$.

23. $(3x^3 - 4x^2 - x + 2) \div (x - \frac{1}{3})$.

24. $(4x^3 + 6x^2 - 6x - 7) \div (2x - 1)$. See Note 2.

25. $(x^3 - 3ax^2 - 4a^2x + 9a^3) \div (x - a)$.

26. $(2x^3 + 3x^2y - 12xy^2 - 2y^3) \div (x - 2y)$.

Solve, using synthetic division:

27. If $f(x) = x^3 - 5x^2 + 7$, find $f(2)$ and $f(-3)$.

28. If $f(x) = 2x^4 - 3x^2 + x + 2$, find $f(3)$ and $f(-2)$.

29. If $f(x) = x^4 + 2x^3 - 3x^2 - x$, find $f(1)$ and $f(-5)$.

30. If $f(x) = 3x^3 - 5x^2 - 14x + 2$, find $f(4)$ and $f(-4)$.

31. If $f(x) = x^3 - 2x^2 - 3x - 5$, find $f(-\frac{1}{2})$ and $f(0.2)$.

32. If $f(x) = 9x^4 - 4x^2 - 2$, find $f(\frac{1}{3})$ and $f(0.7)$.

33. If $f(x) = x^3 + 4ax^2 - 7a^2x - a^3$, find $f(a)$ and $f(-2a)$.

34. If $f(x) = x^4 - 2x^2y^2 + 3xy^3 - y^4$, find $f(-y)$ and $f(2y)$.

35. Find m so that 2 is a zero of $x^3 - 2x^2 + mx - 1$.

36. Find m so that -3 is a zero of $2x^4 - mx^2 + 44x - m$.

If n is a positive integer, show by the factor theorem that

37. $(x - 1)$ is always a factor of $x^n - 1$.

38. $(x - 1)$ is never a factor of $x^n + 1$.

39. $(x + 1)$ is a factor of $x^n - 1$, if n is even.

40. $(x + 1)$ is a factor of $x^n + 1$, if n is odd.

109. Graphs of Polynomials. In graphing a polynomial $f(x)$, either synthetic division or direct substitution may be used in computing the values of $f(x)$.

Example. Graph $f(x) = 2x^3 - 3x^2 - 12x + 5$.

Solution: For $x = 0, 1$, and -1, the values of $f(x)$ are easily determined by substitution. Using synthetic division, we can evaluate $f(x)$ for other values of x. For example,

$$\begin{array}{rrrr|r} 2 & -3 & -12 & +5 & \underline{-2.5} \\ & -5 & +20 & -20 & \\ \hline 2 & -8 & +8 & -15 & \end{array} \qquad \begin{array}{rrrr|r} 2 & -3 & -12 & +5 & \underline{+3.5} \\ & +7 & +14 & +7 & \\ \hline 2 & +4 & +2 & +12 & \end{array}$$

x	-2.5	-2	-1	0	1	2	3	3.5
$f(x)$	-15	1	12	5	-8	-15	-4	12

NOTE 1. For future reference, observe that if _r is positive_ and the numbers of the third line in synthetic division have the same sign, all real zeros of $f(x)$ are less than r; also if _r is negative_ and the numbers of the third line alternate in sign, all real zeros of $f(x)$ are greater than r.

+ r
= SIGN.
$0^S < r$

$-r$
ALT. SIGN
$0^S > r$

If we plot these points and draw a smooth curve through them, we have the graph shown in Figure 28. We observe that

the graph crosses the x-axis at three points. The abscissas of these points are the real zeros of $f(x)$. Thus the roots of $f(x) = 0$ are approximately $x = -2.1, 0.4$, and 3.1. Point A on the graph where $f(x)$ reaches a peak and then decreases is called a **maximum** point of the graph; similarly, point B is called a **minimum** point. It is shown in more advanced mathematics that a cubic function can have no

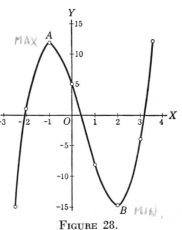

FIGURE 28.

more than two maxima and minima points. Cubic functions which have no maxima and minima points are shown in Figure 29.

The example above illustrates the following graphic **properties of polynomials** which are stated without proof:

1. Single-Valued. For each x, there is one and only one value for $f(x)$.

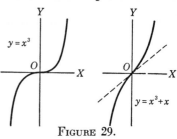

FIGURE 29.

2. Continuous. There is one connected curve with no breaks or sharp turns.

3. Maxima and Minima Points. A polynomial of the nth degree has *at most* $(n - 1)$ maxima and minima points.

4. Zeros. If $f(a)$ and $f(b)$ have opposite signs, then $f(x)$ is zero for at least one value of x between a and b.

NOTE 2. When a polynomial is expressed as a product of linear factors such as $f(x) = a_0(x - r_1)(x - r_2)^2(x - r_3)^3$, its graph may be easily sketched in accordance with the following rule: *If the exponent of a linear factor is* (a) **one,** *the graph crosses the axis at an angle;* (b) **even,** *the graph is tangent to the axis and does not cross it;* (c) **odd** > 1, *the graph is tangent to the axis and crosses it.*

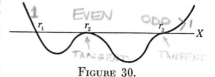

FIGURE 30.

Thus, the graph of $f(x)$ will appear as in Figure 30.

EXERCISE 68

Graph the following polynomials:

1. $x^3 - x^2 - 4x + 4$.
2. $2x^3 - 3x^2 - 9x$.
3. $2x^3 - 3x^2 + 9x - 5$.
4. $x^3 - 3x^2 + 3x + 1$.
5. $x^4 - 20x^2 + 64$.
6. $x^4 - 4x^3 + 2x^2 - 12x$.
7. $x^4 - 2x^3 - 8$.
8. $2x^4 - x^3 + x^2 - x - 3$.

Graph and estimate the real roots correct to one decimal place:

9. $x^3 - 5x - 3 = 0$.
10. $2x^3 - 5x^2 - 4x + 6 = 0$.
11. $x^4 - 9x^2 + 3x + 4 = 0$.
12. $x^4 - x^3 - 5x^2 + 2x + 6 = 0$.

Without expanding, sketch the following polynomials. Determine a few points on the curve.

13. $(x + 3)^2(x + 1)(x - 2)$.
14. $(x + 2)(x - 1)^3$.
15. $3(x + 1)^2(x - 3)^2$.
16. $(x + 3)^3(x - 2)^4$.

17. $(x + 3)^3(x + 1)(x - 1)$.　　**18.** $2x^2(x - 1)(x - 3)^3$.

19. $-(x + 2)^2(x - 1)(x - 3)^2$.　　**20.** $x^2(x - 2)^2(x - 4)^2(x - 6)^2$.

110. Fundamental Theorem of Algebra. *Every integral rational equation in a single variable has at least one root.*

The validity of this theorem will be assumed since the proof is beyond the scope of this book.

Corollary 1. *Every polynomial $f(x)$ of the nth degree in x can be expressed as a product of n linear factors.*

Proof: By the fundamental theorem $f(x) = 0$ has at least one root; denote it by r_1. Then, by the factor theorem, $(x - r_1)$ is a factor of $f(x)$, and we have

$$f(x) = (x - r_1)Q_1(x),$$

where $Q_1(x)$ is a polynomial having a_0x^{n-1} as its term of highest degree.

Again, by the fundamental theorem, $Q_1(x)$ has at least one zero, say r_2, and hence contains the factor $(x - r_2)$. Thus, $Q_1(x) = (x - r_2)Q_2(x)$, and

$$f(x) = (x - r_1)(x - r_2)Q_2(x),$$

where $Q_2(x)$ is a polynomial having a_0x^{n-2} as its term of highest degree.

Continuing this process n times, we obtain

$$f(x) = (x - r_1)(x - r_2) \cdots (x - r_n)Q_n(x),$$

where $Q_n(x)$ is a polynomial having a_0x^{n-n} or a_0 as its term of highest degree. Therefore we have

$$f(x) = a_0(x - r_1)(x - r_2) \cdots (x - r_n). \tag{1}$$

NOTE 1. The above numbers $r_1, r_2, \cdots, r_n$ are not necessarily distinct, and some or all may be imaginary.

Corollary 2. *Every equation $f(x) = 0$ of degree n in x can have no more than n distinct roots.*

Proof: Let c be an arbitrary number. Then, by Corollary 1, we have

$$f(c) = a_0(c - r_1)(c - r_2) \cdots (c - r_n).$$

If c is different from the n numbers $r_1, r_2, \cdots, r_n$, then no factor of $f(c)$ is zero and hence $f(c) \neq 0$. Thus, c is not a root of $f(x) = 0$, and $f(x) = 0$ has no roots other than the numbers $r_1, r_2, \cdots, r_n$.

If, among $r_1, r_2, \cdots, r_n$, a root r occurs only once, then r is called a **simple root**. If r occurs exactly m times $(m > 1)$, then r is called a **multiple root of order m** or a **root of multiplicity m**. Roots of multiplicities 2 and 3 are also called **double roots** and **triple roots** respectively.

Note 2. If a root of multiplicity m is counted as m roots, then an equation of the nth degree has exactly n roots.

Corollary 3. _If two polynomials in x, each of degree not greater than n, are equal in value for more than n distinct values of x, then the polynomials are identical._

Proof: Let $a_0x^n + a_1x^{n-1} + \cdots + a_n$ and $b_0x^n + b_1x^{n-1} + \cdots + b_n$ represent the polynomials. Then, by hypothesis, the equation

$$(a_0 - b_0)x^n + (a_1 - b_1)x^{n-1} + \cdots + (a_n - b_n) = 0 \qquad (2)$$

has more than n distinct roots. If any one of the coefficients $(a_0 - b_0), (a_1 - b_1), \cdots, (a_n - b_n)$ in (2) were not zero, we would have an equation of degree n or less, having more than n distinct roots. This contradicts Corollary 2; hence all the coefficients of (2) must be zero. Thus, $a_0 = b_0, a_1 = b_1, \cdots, a_n = b_n$, and the polynomials are identical.

Note 3. Likewise, if two polynomials are identical, then the coefficients of corresponding powers must be equal. Thus, if $2x-5 \equiv Ax+B$, then $A = 2$ and $B = -5$.

Example. Find an equation of lowest degree having the five roots: $\frac{1}{2}$, double root -1, i, and $-i$.
Solution: If $a_0 \neq 0$, any equation of the form

$$a_0(x - \tfrac{1}{2})(x + 1)^2(x - i)(x + i) = 0$$

has the given roots. If $a_0 = 2$, this equation may be written with integral coefficients. Thus

$$(2x - 1)(x^2 + 2x + 1)(x^2 + 1) = 0,$$
or $\qquad 2x^5 + 3x^4 + 2x^3 + 2x^2 - 1 = 0.$

111. Theorem on Imaginary Roots. _If an imaginary number $(a + bi)$ is a root of an equation $f(x) = 0$ with real_ *coefficients, the conjugate imaginary number* $(a - bi)$ *is also a root.*

Proof: Since $(a + bi)$ is a root of $f(x) = 0$, then $[x - (a + bi)]$ is a factor of $f(x)$. We proceed to show that $[x - (a - bi)]$ is also a factor of $f(x)$, by showing that the product

$$[x - (a + bi)][x - (a - bi)] \quad \text{or} \quad x^2 - 2ax + (a^2 + b^2)$$

is a factor of $f(x)$.

Let $f(x)$ be divided by $[x^2 - 2ax + (a^2 + b^2)]$. Denote the quotient by $Q(x)$, and the remainder, if any, by $Rx + R'$. Thus,

$$f(x) = [x^2 - 2ax + (a^2 + b^2)]Q(x) + Rx + R'.$$

By hypothesis, $f(a + bi) = 0$. Hence, on substituting $(a + bi)$ for x, we obtain

$$0 = [0]Q(a + bi) + R(a + bi) + R'.$$

Hence, $(Ra + R') + (Rb)i = 0$; and equating to zero the real and imaginary parts (Article 96), we obtain

$$Ra + R' = 0, \; Rb = 0.$$

By hypothesis $b \neq 0$; hence $R = 0$ and $R' = 0$. Therefore, since $[x - (a + bi)][x - (a - bi)]$ is a factor of $f(x)$, it follows that $(a - bi)$ is a root of $f(x) = 0$.

NOTE. Since imaginary roots occur in conjugate pairs, an equation $f(x) = 0$ of odd degree with real coefficients must have at least one real root.   N.B.

If the coefficients of $f(x)$ are *rational*, a similar theorem may be proved in much the same way for quadratic surds.

Theorem on Quadratic Surds. *If a quadratic surd* $(a + \sqrt{b})$, *where* a *and* b *are rational and* $\sqrt{b}$ *is irrational, is a root of an equation* $f(x) = 0$ *with* **rational** *coefficients, then the conjugate surd* $(a - \sqrt{b})$ *is also a root.*

Example. Solve the equation $x^4 - 4x^3 + 3x^2 + 8x - 10 = 0$, if one of its roots is $(2 + i)$.

Solution: Since $(2 + i)$ is a root, $(2 - i)$ is also a root. Therefore, the expression

$$[x - (2 + i)][x - (2 - i)] = x^2 - 4x + 5$$

is a factor of the given equation. By division, we find the other factor to be $(x^2 - 2)$. Hence, the roots of the given equation are $x = 2 \pm i$, $\pm\sqrt{2}$.

EXERCISE 69

Find an equation with integral coefficients having only the following numbers as roots:

1. $1, -2, 3$.   **2.** $-\frac{2}{3}, -1, \frac{1}{2}$.   **3.** $\frac{3}{2}, -2, \pm\sqrt{3}$.

4. $2, 2, \pm\frac{1}{2}i$.   **5.** $-4, (3 \pm 2i)$.   **6.** $(3 \pm\sqrt{2}), \pm i$.

7. $\frac{1}{2}, \frac{1}{2}, -2, -2$.   **8.** $(2 \pm i\sqrt{3}), -\frac{1}{3}$.   **9.** $0, \pm 2, \pm i\sqrt{2}$.

10. $\frac{1}{2}(3 \pm\sqrt{5}), \pm 3$.   **11.** $2, 2, 2, 3, 3$.   **12.** $\pm i, \pm 2i, \pm 3i$.

Find all roots of the following equations:

13. $(x - 3)(x + 4)(2x + 1) = 0$.   **14.** $(x - 1)(2x - 5)(x^2 + 1) = 0$.

15. $(x - 4)(2x^2 + x - 3) = 0$.   **16.** $(x^2 - 2x)(x^2 - 4x + 2) = 0$.

17. $(x^2 - 8)(x^2 - 2x + 2) = 0$.   **18.** $(2x^2+9)(4x^2-4x-1)=0$.

Find a cubic equation with integral coefficients having the following numbers as roots:

19. $-3, (1 + i\sqrt{2})$.   **20.** $\frac{2}{3}, (4 -\sqrt{3})$.   **21.** $\frac{1}{2}, \frac{1}{2}(3 - 2i\sqrt{2})$.

Find a quartic equation with integral coefficients having the following numbers as roots:

22. $2, -\frac{1}{2}, (5 - 2i)$.   **23.** $\sqrt{2}, -\sqrt{3}$.   **24.** $\frac{1}{2}(1 -\sqrt{3}), i\sqrt{2}$.

Given the roots as indicated, find the other roots:

25. $2x^3 - 6x^2 + 5x - 2 = 0; r_1 = 2$.

26. $2x^3 - x^2 - 6x + 3 = 0; r_1 = -\sqrt{3}$.

27. $x^3 - 5x^2 + 7x + 13 = 0; r_1 = 3 - 2i$.

28. $x^4 - 5x^3 + 10x + 4 = 0; r_1 = -1, r_2 = 2$.

29. $x^4 - 3x^3 + 3x^2 - 6x + 2 = 0; r_1 = i\sqrt{2}$.

30. $4x^4 - 24x + 7 = 0; r_1 = 1 + \frac{1}{2}\sqrt{2}$.

31. Show that $x^5 - 3x^4 + 16x - 16 = 0$ has 2 as a double root.

32. Show that $x^4 - 2x^3 + 2x - 1 = 0$ has 1 as a triple root.

Find the values of A and B in the following identities:

33. $3x - 7 \equiv Ax + B(x + 1)$.   **34.** $5x + 8 \equiv A(x - 2) + 3B$.

35. Prove the Theorem on Quadratic Surds.

112. Rational Roots. If an equation $f(x) = 0$ has integral coefficients, then all rational roots can be determined as follows:

Theorem. *If a rational number p/q, reduced to lowest terms, is a root of an equation*

$$a_0 x^n + a_1 x^{n-1} + \cdots + a_{n-1} x + a_n = 0 \qquad (1)$$

with integral coefficients, then p *is a factor of* a_n *and* q *is a factor of* a_0.

Proof: Since p/q is a root of equation (1), we have

$$a_0 \frac{p^n}{q^n} + a_1 \frac{p^{n-1}}{q^{n-1}} + \cdots + a_{n-1} \frac{p}{q} + a_n = 0. \qquad (2)$$

Multiplying both sides of (2) by q^n, we obtain

$$a_0 p^n + a_1 p^{n-1} q + \cdots + a_{n-1} p q^{n-1} + a_n q^n = 0. \qquad (3)$$

Transposing the term $a_n q^n$ and factoring p from the left member gives

$$p(a_0 p^{n-1} + a_1 p^{n-2} q + \cdots + a_{n-1} q^{n-1}) = -a_n q^n. \qquad (4)$$

From the hypotheses it is evident that both members of (4) are integers; and since p is an obvious factor of the left member, it must also be a factor of $-a_n q^n$. However, p has no factor in common with q except ± 1; hence p must be a factor of a_n.

By similar reasoning, we have

$$q(a_1 p^{n-1} + \cdots + a_{n-1} p q^{n-2} + a_n q^{n-1}) = -a_0 p^n,$$

and hence it is clear that q must be a factor of a_0.

Illustration. For the equation $2 x^5 - 5 x^2 + 3 = 0$, p must be a factor of 3, hence ± 1, ± 3; q must be a factor of 2, hence ± 1, ± 2. Thus the only possible rational roots are ± 1, ± 3, $\pm \frac{1}{2}$, $\pm \frac{3}{2}$. If none of these numbers is a root, the equation has **no** *rational* roots.

Corollary. *Any rational root of an equation*

$$x^n + b_1 x^{n-1} + \cdots + b_{n-1} x + b_n = 0 \qquad (5)$$

with integral coefficients is an integer which is a factor of b_n.

NOTE 1. In testing for rational roots, if a root is found, the factor corresponding to the root should be divided out of the equation. The quotient remaining is called the **depressed equation**.

Example 1. Solve $f(x) = 2 x^4 - 9 x^3 + 3 x^2 + 16 x + 6 = 0$.
Solution: By the above theorem, the possible rational roots are ± 1, ± 2, ± 3, ± 6, $\pm \frac{1}{2}$, $\pm \frac{3}{2}$.
Testing 1 and -1 by direct substitution, we have

$$f(1) = 2 - 9 + 3 + 16 + 6 = 18, \text{ hence 1 is not a root;}$$
$$f(-1) = 2 + 9 + 3 - 16 + 6 = 4, \text{ hence } -1 \text{ is not a root.}$$

Testing 2, by synthetic division, we find $f(2) = 10$; hence 2 is not a root.

$$\begin{array}{r} 2 - 9 + 3 + 16 + 6 \underline{\,|+2} \\ + 4 - 10 - 14 + 4 \\ \hline 2 - 5 - 7 + 2 + 10 \end{array}$$

Testing -2, we find that -2 is not a root. Furthermore, since the numbers in the third line alternate in sign, there can be no root less than -2 (NOTE 1, Article 109).

$$\begin{array}{r} 2 - 9 + 3 + 16 + 6 \underline{\,|-2} \\ - 4 + 26 - 58 + 76 \\ \hline 2 - 13 + 29 - 38 + 82 \end{array}$$

Testing 3, we find $f(3) = 0$; hence 3 is a root and $(x - 3)$ is a factor of $f(x)$.

$$\begin{array}{r} 2 - 9 + 3 + 16 + 6 \underline{\,|+3} \\ + 6 - 9 - 18 - 6 \\ \hline 2 - 3 - 6 - 2 \quad 0 \end{array}$$

The possible rational roots of the depressed equation

$$f'(x) = 2x^3 - 3x^2 - 6x - 2 = 0$$

are ± 1, ± 2, $\pm \frac{1}{2}$. Since ± 1 and ± 2 were not roots of $f(x) = 0$, they cannot be roots of $f'(x) = 0$. Hence, testing $-\frac{1}{2}$, we find $f'(-\frac{1}{2}) = 0$. Thus, $-\frac{1}{2}$ is a root of $f'(x) = 0$ and hence of $f(x) = 0$.

$$\begin{array}{r} 2 - 3 - 6 - 2 \underline{\,|-\tfrac{1}{2}} \\ - 1 + 2 + 2 \\ \hline 2 - 4 - 4 \quad 0 \end{array}$$

The remaining roots of $f(x) = 0$ are the roots of the second depressed equation $x^2 - 2x - 2 = 0$. Solving by the quadratic formula, we obtain $x = 1 \pm \sqrt{3}$.

Thus the roots of the given equation are 3, $-\frac{1}{2}$, $(1 + \sqrt{3})$, and $(1 - \sqrt{3})$.

NOTE 2. If r is a multiple root of $f(x) = 0$ then r is also a root of the depressed equation $f'(x) = 0$.

EXERCISE 70

In each of the following equations, find the rational roots and, when possible, the remaining roots:

1. $x^3 + x^2 - 4x - 4 = 0$. **2.** $x^3 - 2x^2 - 9x + 18 = 0$.

3. $x^3 - 2x^2 - 2x - 3 = 0$. **4.** $x^3 + x + 10 = 0$.

5. $2x^3 + x^2 - 7x - 6 = 0$. **6.** $4x^3 + 12x^2 - 15x + 4 = 0$.

7. $3x^3 - 2x^2 + 15x - 10 = 0$. **8.** $8x^3 - 28x^2 + 18x + 5 = 0$.

9. $x^4 - 15x^2 + 10x + 24 = 0$. **10.** $x^4 - 8x^2 - 3x = 0$.

11. $x^4 - x^3 + 2x^2 - 4x = 8$. **12.** $x^4 + 7x^2 + 8x = 6x^3 + 6$.

13. $4x^4 + 2x^3 + x - 1 = 0$. **14.** $6x^4 - 10x^3 + 5x^2 - 15x = 6$.

15. $2x^4 + 2x^3 - 9x^2 = 8x - 4$. **16.** $4x^4 - 19x^2 + 9 = 9x$.

17. $x^5 - 2x^4 - 15x^3 + 40x^2 + 4x - 48 = 0$.

18. $6x^5 - 7x^4 - 30x^3 + 18x^2 + 3x - 2 = 0$.

19. $(x - 4)^3 = x^2$. **20.** $x(x + 1)(x + 2) = 2730$.

21. $\dfrac{2}{x^2} + \dfrac{6}{x + 1} = 5$. **22.** $\dfrac{2}{x + 1} - \dfrac{1}{x - 1} = \dfrac{20x}{3}$.

23. $7 + \sqrt{49 - 24x} = 2x^2$. **24.** $\sqrt[3]{3x - 4} = x - 2$.

Factor each of the following polynomials:

25. $x^3 - x^2 - 5x - 3$. **26.** $x^3 + 2x^2 - 2x + 3$.
27. $4x^3 - 13x^2 - x + 1$. **28.** $2x^3 + 5x^2 - x - 1$.
29. $x^4 - 8x^2 + 5x + 6$. **30.** $x^4 - 5x^3 + 20x - 16$.

Solve the following systems of equations algebraically:

31. $\begin{cases} y = x^3, \\ y = 7x - 6. \end{cases}$ **32.** $\begin{cases} y = x^4, \\ y = 2x - x^3. \end{cases}$

33. $\begin{cases} x^2 y = 4, \\ y = (x - 1)^2. \end{cases}$ **34.** $\begin{cases} y^2 - xy = x + 1, \\ xy + y = 4x^2. \end{cases}$

35. The sum of two numbers is 4 and the sum of their cubes is 19. Find the numbers.

36. The length of a rectangular box is 1 foot more than twice the width, and the height is one-half the width. Find the dimensions, if the volume is 72 cubic feet.

37. The sum of the reciprocals of three consecutive integers is $\frac{47}{60}$. Find the integers.

38. The dimensions of a rectangular box are 4 feet by 9 feet by 4 feet. If all dimensions are decreased by the same amount, the volume obtained will be one-half the original volume. Find the new dimensions.

39. The hypotenuse of a right triangle is 1 foot longer than a side, and the area of the triangle is 30 square feet. Find the sides of the triangle.

40. The product of two integers is 48, and the sum of their squares is ten times their sum. Find the integers.

113. Irrational Roots Determined by Linear Interpolation.
Approximate values for the irrational roots of an integral rational equation with real coefficients may be determined to any degree of accuracy by a method of successive interpolations, as is illustrated in the example below.

NOTE 1. Before determining irrational roots, an equation should be depressed by removing all linear factors corresponding to rational roots.

Example. Solve $f(x) \equiv x^3 - 3x^2 + x - 7 = 0$. (1)

Solution: (a) The irrational roots are first located approximately by graphing $y = x^3 - 3x^2 + x - 7$ (Figure 31). From the graph we see that there is only one real root whose value is approximately 3.3.

(b) To locate the root between successive tenths we compute, by synthetic division, $f(3.3) = -0.433$ and $f(3.4) = 1.024$. Therefore the root is between 3.3 and 3.4 (Article 109).

(c) To determine the hundredths digit h, we use the method of linear interpolation (Article 128), in which h is determined by the proportion $\dfrac{h}{0.10} = \dfrac{0.433}{1.457}$.

x		$f(x)$		
$0.10\begin{bmatrix} h\begin{bmatrix} 3.30 \\ ? \\ 3.40 \end{bmatrix}\end{bmatrix}$		$\begin{bmatrix}\begin{bmatrix} -0.433 \\ 0.000 \\ 1.024 \end{bmatrix} 0.433\end{bmatrix} 1.457$		

Thus, $h = 0.0297$ or 0.03, and the root of (1) correct to two decimal places is 3.33.

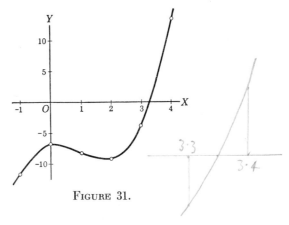

FIGURE 31.

NOTE 2. To justify this conclusion completely, it should be shown that the values $f(3.325)$ and $f(3.335)$ have a different sign.

To determine the root more accurately, we repeat steps (b) and (c) for each succeeding digit.

NOTE 3. The approximate determination of real roots by the method of linear interpolation is applicable to any equation involving real quantities only.

EXERCISE 71

Each of the following equations has one irrational root. Find it correct to two decimal places.

1. $x^3 + 3x - 10 = 0$.
2. $x^3 + x^2 + 3x + 7 = 0$.
3. $x^4 - 2x + 1 = 0$.
4. $x^4 - 4x^2 - 5x + 10 = 0$.
5. $x^3 + 1.1x + 0.5 = 0$.
6. $x^4 - 0.2x^3 - 7x + 1.4 = 0$.

Each of the following equations has two irrational roots. Find them correct to two decimal places.

7. $x^4 + x - 6 = 0$.

8. $x^4 + x^3 - 2x - 3 = 0$.

9. $2x^4 + 4x^3 + 1 = 0$.

10. $x^5 - x^3 + x^2 - 2x + 1 = 0$.

11. $x^5 - 20x + 8 = 0$.

12. $x^5 - 2x^3 - 8x^2 + 16 = 0$.

The positive root of $x^4 = 5$ is the value of $\sqrt[4]{5}$; find the following roots correct to two decimal places:

13. $\sqrt[4]{5}$.

14. $\sqrt[3]{-17}$.

15. $\sqrt[5]{237}$.

Solve, obtaining x correct to two decimal places:

16. $x\sqrt{x} = x + 5$.

17. $\sqrt{x} = \sqrt[3]{x + 1}$.

18. $(1 + x)^3 = 1.3$.

19. Find the number whose square is 1 more than its reciprocal. Express the answer correct to three decimal places.

20. Find, correct to three decimal places, the radius of a sphere whose volume is doubled when the radius is increased 1 foot.

21. The dimensions of a rectangular box are 4 feet by 5 feet by 6 feet. Find, correct to two decimal places, the equal amount that must be added to each dimension in order to double the volume.

22. The depth to which a sphere of radius r and density d will sink in water is given by a *positive* root of the equation $x^3 - 3rx^2 + 4r^3d = 0$. Find the depth in feet, correct to two decimal places, to which a cork (density 0.24) sphere 1 foot in diameter will sink.

23. A box is to be made from a rectangular piece of cardboard 10 inches by 12 inches by cutting equal squares from the corners and turning up the sides. Find the side of these squares, correct to two decimal places, if the box is to contain 84 cubic inches.

24. The area of an isosceles triangle inscribed in a circle of radius r is given by the formula $A = b\sqrt{r^2 - b^2} + br$, where b is one-half the base of the triangle. Find the base of the triangle, correct to two decimal places, when $r = 5$ and $A = 20$.

CHAPTER 16

Theory of Equations

114. Descartes's Rule of Signs. If a polynomial $f(x)$ with real coefficients is arranged in descending powers of x, there is said to be a **variation in sign** wherever two successive terms differ in sign.

Illustration 1. In the polynomial $x^5 - x^3 - 2x + 6$, there are two variations in sign, one from x^5 to $-x^3$ and another from $-2x$ to 6. Observe that zero terms are disregarded in counting variations in sign.

Lemma. If $f(x)$ is a polynomial with real coefficients having $(x - r)$ as a factor, where r is a positive number, then the quotient $Q(x) = f(x)/(x - r)$ has at least one less variation in sign than $f(x)$.

Illustration 2. Dividing $f(x) = x^5 + 2x^4 - 2x^3 - 5x^2 + 4$ by $(x - 1)$, we obtain the quotient
$Q(x) = x^4 + 3x^3 + x^2 - 4x - 4$.
We observe that $f(x)$ has two variations in sign and $Q(x)$ has one.

$$\begin{array}{rrrrrr} 1 & +2 & -2 & -5 & 0 & +4 \ \underline{\lfloor 1} \\ & +1 & +3 & +1 & -4 & -4 \\ \hline 1 & +3 & +1 & -4 & -4 & 0 \end{array}$$

Proof: We assume that the leading coefficient of $f(x)$ is positive. Then in finding the quotient $Q(x)$ by synthetic division, it is clear, since $r > 0$, that the coefficients of $Q(x)$ are positive at least until the first negative coefficient of $f(x)$ is reached. If at that time, or subsequently, the sign of a coefficient of $Q(x)$ becomes negative (or zero), then the signs of succeeding coefficients of $Q(x)$ will also be negative, at least until the next positive coefficient of $f(x)$ is reached, and so on. Hence, *no variation in sign can occur in $Q(x)$ until there has been a corresponding variation in sign in $f(x)$.*

174

However, since the remainder is zero, the sign of the last coefficient in $Q(x)$ must be opposite to the sign of the last coefficient in $f(x)$; and thus, certainly the last variation in sign in $f(x)$ does not occur in $Q(x)$. Therefore $Q(x)$ will have *at least* one less variation in sign than $f(x)$.

NOTE 1. Since the sign of the last coefficient in $Q(x)$ is opposite to the sign of the last coefficient in $f(x)$, the variations in sign in $Q(x)$ are actually less than those of $f(x)$ by an **odd** number.

Descartes's Rule of Signs. *The number of positive roots of an equation $f(x) = 0$ with real coefficients cannot exceed the number of variations in sign in $f(x)$, and the number of negative roots cannot exceed the number of variations in sign in $f(-x)$.*

Proof: Let r_1, r_2, $\cdots$, r_k be the positive roots of $f(x) = 0$; then

$$f(x) = (x - r_1)(x - r_2) \cdots (x - r_k)Q_k(x).$$

Dividing $f(x)$ by $(x - r_1)$, we obtain a quotient $Q_1(x)$. Dividing $Q_1(x)$ by $(x - r_2)$, we obtain a quotient $Q_2(x)$. Continuing this process k times we finally obtain the quotient $Q_k(x)$.

By the above lemma, each polynomial in the sequence $f(x)$, $Q_1(x)$, $Q_2(x)$, $\cdots$, $Q_k(x)$ has at least one less variation in sign than the preceding polynomial. Hence, $Q_k(x)$ has at least k fewer variations in sign than there are in $f(x)$. $Q_k(x)$, however, cannot have less than zero variations in sign, and hence $f(x)$ must have at least k variations in sign. That is, the number k of positive roots cannot exceed the number of variations in sign in $f(x)$.

Since the roots of $f(-x) = 0$ are opposite in sign to the roots of $f(x) = 0$ (Article 116), it follows that the negative roots of $f(x) = 0$ are the positive roots of $f(-x) = 0$. Hence, by the proof already given, the number of negative roots of $f(x) = 0$ cannot exceed the number of variations in sign in $f(-x)$.

NOTE 2. It follows from NOTE 1 that if the number of positive roots of $f(x) = 0$ is less than the number of variations in sign in $f(x)$, it is less by an even number. Thus, if $f(x)$ has five variations in sign, then $f(x) = 0$ has 5, 3, or 1 positive roots, *never* 4 or 2.

Illustration 3. The equation $f(x) = x^5 - x - 5 = 0$ has five roots: (*a*) there *is* one positive root, since $f(x)$ has one variation in sign; (*b*) there are two or no negative roots, since $f(-x) = -x^5 + x - 5$ has two variations in sign; and hence, (*c*) there are *at least* two imaginary roots.

EXERCISE 72

Using Descartes's Rule of Signs, discuss the nature of the roots of the following equations and list the possibilities which exist:

1. $x^3 - 2x^2 + 4x - 1 = 0$.
2. $2x^3 + x^2 + 2x + 3 = 0$.
3. $x^3 + 5x^2 - 2x - 4 = 0$.
4. $x^3 + 4x^2 - x + 2 = 0$.
5. $x^3 + 5x - 7 = 0$.
6. $3x^3 - 2x^2 - 4 = 0$.
7. $x^4 + x^3 - x^2 - 2x + 1 = 0$.
8. $x^4 - 3x^3 + 2x - 5 = 0$.
9. $2x^4 - x^3 + 3x - 2 = x^2$.
10. $x^4 + x^3 + x^2 + x = 1$.
11. $x^5 - 4x^3 + 2x + 3 = 0$.
12. $x^5 + 2x^4 - 3x^3 - x = 5$.
13. $x^7 + x^5 - x^3 = x^2 + 4$.
14. $x^6 - 2x^4 - 3x^3 - 2x = 3$.

Give the exact number of imaginary roots in each of the following:

15. $x^4 + 3x^3 + x - 2 = 0$.
16. $3x^4 + 5x^2 + 2 = 0$.
17. $2x^6 - 3x^4 - 7 = 0$.
18. $x^{10} + 1 = 0$.
19. $x^{12} - 4 = 0$.
20. $x^6 - 3x^3 - 4 = 0$.

115. Relation Between the Roots and Coefficients.

If the equation

$$a_0x^n + a_1x^{n-1} + a_2x^{n-2} + \cdots + a_n = 0, \ a_0 \neq 0, \quad (1)$$

or the equivalent equation

$$x^n + \frac{a_1}{a_0}x^{n-1} + \frac{a_2}{a_0}x^{n-2} + \cdots + \frac{a_n}{a_0} = 0, \quad (2)$$

has the numbers $r_1, r_2, \cdots, r_n$ as roots, Equation (2) is identically equal to the product

$$(x - r_1)(x - r_2) \cdots (x - r_n) = 0. \quad (3)$$

Expanding this product, we obtain

$$x^n - S_1x^{n-1} + S_2x^{n-2} - \cdots + (-1)^nS_n = 0, \quad (4)$$

where

$$\left.\begin{aligned}
S_1 &= r_1 + r_2 + \cdots + r_n, \\
S_2 &= r_1r_2 + r_1r_3 + \cdots + r_{n-1}r_n, \\
S_3 &= r_1r_2r_3 + r_1r_2r_4 + \cdots + r_{n-2}r_{n-1}r_n, \\
&\cdots\cdots\cdots\cdots\cdots\cdots\cdots\cdots\cdots \\
S_n &= r_1r_2 \cdots r_n.
\end{aligned}\right\} \quad (5)$$

Equating corresponding powers of (2) and (4), we may state the results given in (5) in the form:

$\dfrac{a_1}{a_0} = -$ *(the sum of the roots)*,

$\dfrac{a_2}{a_0} = +$ *(the sum of the products of the roots taken two at a time)*,

$\dfrac{a_3}{a_0} = -$ *(the sum of the products of the roots taken three at a time)*,

. . . .

$\dfrac{a_n}{a_0} = (-1)^n$ *(the product of the roots)*.

Illustration 1. If $r_1 = 1, r_2 = 2, r_3 = -3$, then $S_1 = (1) + (2) + (-3) = 0$, $S_2 = (1)(2) + (1)(-3) + (2)(-3) = -7$, and $S_3 = (1)(2)(-3) = -6$. Hence, the equation having $1, 2$, and -3 as roots is $x^3 - (0)x^2 + (-7)x - (-6) = 0$, or $x^3 - 7x + 6 = 0$.

Illustration 2. If r_1, r_2, and r_3 are the three roots of the equation $2x^3 + 3x^2 - 5x - 4 = 0$, then

$$r_1 + r_2 + r_3 = -\tfrac{3}{2}, \quad r_1r_2 + r_1r_3 + r_2r_3 = -\tfrac{5}{2}, \quad r_1r_2r_3 = 2.$$

Example. Solve the equation $3x^3 + x^2 + px - 5 = 0$, if one root is the negative of another.

Solution: Let $a, -a, b$ denote the roots; then

$$(a) + (-a) + (b) = -\tfrac{1}{3} \quad \text{and} \quad (a)(-a)(b) = \tfrac{5}{3}.$$

Hence, the roots are $b = -\tfrac{1}{3}$ and $\pm a = \pm \sqrt{5}$.

EXERCISE 73

1. Expand and express $(x - r_1)(x - r_2)(x - r_3)(x - r_4)$ in powers of x.

Using Equation (4), find the equations whose roots are:

2. $1, -2, 3$.   **3.** $2, 3, -4$.   **4.** $2, \pm i\sqrt{2}$.

5. $-1, (1 \pm \sqrt{2})$.   **6.** $\tfrac{3}{2}, (1 \pm i)$.   **7.** $2, 1, -3, 2$.

Find S_1, S_2, S_3, $\cdots$ for each of the following equations:

8. $x^3 - 4x^2 - 3x + 1 = 0$.   **9.** $2x^3 + x^2 - 2x - 5 = 0$.
10. $2x^4 - 4x^2 - 3x - 5 = 0$.   **11.** $x^5 - 3x^3 - 4x - 7 = 0$.

12. Find the third root of $2x^3 - 3x^2 + px + q = 0$ if 2 and -1 are roots.

If one of the roots is the negative of another, solve:

13. $2x^3 - x^2 + px - 1 = 0$.   **14.** $x^3 - 3x^2 - 5x + p = 0$.

If one of the roots is twice another, solve:

15. $2x^3 - 3x^2 + px + 6 = 0$.   **16.** $4x^3 + 16x^2 + 9x + p = 0$.

If the sum of two of the roots is 3, solve:

17. $2x^3 - 5x^2 - 3x + p = 0.$ **18.** $x^3 - x^2 + px - 2 = 0.$

If the difference of two of the roots is 2, solve:

19. $4x^3 - 4x^2 + px + 10 = 0.$ **20.** $3x^3 - 2x^2 - 3x + p = 0.$

If one of the roots is the reciprocal of another, solve:

21. $4x^3 + px + 10 = 0.$ **22.** $6x^3 - x^2 + px + 12 = 0.$

23. Solve the equation $x^4 + px^2 + 8x - 3 = 0$, if it has a triple root.

24. Solve the equation $x^4 - 2x^3 - 3x^2 + px + q = 0$, if it has two double roots.

If r_1, r_2, and r_3 are the roots of the equation $x^3 - 2x^2 + 3x - 4 = 0$, find the value of the following expressions:

25. $r_1^2 + r_2^2 + r_3^2$. Hint: Find $(r_1 + r_2 + r_3)^2$.

26. $\dfrac{1}{r_1} + \dfrac{1}{r_2} + \dfrac{1}{r_3}.$ **27.** $\dfrac{1}{r_1 r_2} + \dfrac{1}{r_1 r_3} + \dfrac{1}{r_2 r_3}.$ **28.** $r_1^3 + r_2^3 + r_3^3.$

116. Transformation of Equations.

The n roots r_1, r_2, $\cdots$, r_n of the equation

$$f(x) = a_0 x^n + a_1 x^{n-1} + \cdots + a_{n-1}x + a_n = 0 \qquad (1)$$

may often be found more readily by **transforming** the given equation into another equation $g(y) = 0$, whose roots bear a definite relation to those of the given equation.

We shall consider three such transformations.

I. *Transformation to Multiply the Roots.* To form an equation whose roots are m times those of (1), that is, mr_1, mr_2, $\cdots$, mr_n, we let $y = mx$. Thus, substituting $x = y/m$ in (1), we obtain

$$a_0 \frac{y^n}{m^n} + a_1 \frac{y^{n-1}}{m^{n-1}} + \cdots + a_{n-1}\frac{y}{m} + a_n = 0. \qquad (2)$$

Multiplying both sides of (2) by m^n, we have

$$a_0 y^n + a_1 m y^{n-1} + \cdots + a_{n-1}m^{n-1}y + a_n m^n = 0. \qquad (3)$$

Rule 1. *To form an equation whose roots are each m times the corresponding roots of $f(x) = 0$, multiply the second term by m, the third term by m^2, and so on, taking into account all terms whose coefficients are zero.*

Illustration 1. The equation whose roots are twice the corresponding roots of $2x^4 - 3x^3 + x - 5 = 0$ is

$$2y^4 - (2)3y^3 + (2)^3y - (2)^45 = 0 \quad \text{or} \quad y^4 - 3y^3 + 4y - 40 = 0.$$

NOTE 1. By taking $m = a_0$ (often a divisor of a_0 is sufficient), it is clear that an equation can always be transformed into an equation whose leading coefficient is unity. Thus, the problem of finding rational roots in a given equation becomes one of finding integral roots in the new equation.

II. *Transformation to Change the Signs of Roots.* To form an equation whose roots are opposite in sign to those of (1), we let $y = -x$ or $x = -y$. Since $(-y)^k$ equals y^k when k is even and $-y^k$ when k is odd, we have:

Rule 2. *To form an equation whose roots are numerically the same as the corresponding roots of $f(x) = 0$, but opposite in sign, change the signs of the terms of odd degree.*

NOTE 2. Rule 2 is a special case of Rule 1 for $m = -1$. Hence, the required equation can also be obtained by changing the signs of alternate terms, starting with the second, terms with zero coefficients being taken into account.

Illustration 2. The roots of $x^3 - 2x^2 - 5x + 6 = 0$ are 1, -2, and 3, whereas the roots of $x^3 + 2x^2 - 5x - 6 = 0$ are -1, 2, and -3.

III. *Transformation to Diminish the Roots.* To form an equation whose roots are each h less than the corresponding roots of (1), that is, $r_1 - h$, $r_2 - h$, $\cdots$, $r_n - h$, we let $y = x - h$. Thus, substituting $x = y + h$ in (1), we obtain

$$a_0(y + h)^n + a_1(y + h)^{n-1} + \cdots + a_{n-1}(y + h) + a_n = 0, \quad (4)$$

which may be written in the form

$$a_0y^n + A_1y^{n-1} + \cdots + A_{n-1}y + A_n = 0, \quad (5)$$

where the coefficients A_1, $\cdots$, A_{n-1}, A_n are as yet undetermined.

The coefficients of (5) may be determined by expanding the terms of Equation (4) and collecting like powers of y. However, these coefficients can be determined more simply in the following manner. Substituting $y = x - h$ in (5), we obtain the equation

$$a_0(x - h)^n + A_1(x - h)^{n-1} + \cdots + A_{n-1}(x - h) + A_n = 0 \quad (6)$$

which is identically equal to the given equation $f(x) = 0$.

If the left side of Equation (6), which is $f(x)$, is divided by $(x - h)$, the remainder is A_n. If the quotient obtained is divided by $(x - h)$, the remainder is A_{n-1}. This process may be continued until all the coefficients A_n, A_{n-1}, $\cdots$, A_2, A_1 have been determined.

Rule 3. *To form an equation whose roots are each h less than the corresponding roots of $f(x) = 0$, divide $f(x)$ and each successive quotient by $(x - h)$ until a constant quotient is reached. The remainders in the order obtained and lastly the constant quotient are the respective coefficients of 1, y, y^2, $\cdots$, y^n in the new equation.*

Illustration 3. To form an equation whose roots are those of $2x^3 - 7x^2 + 2x + 3 = 0$ each decreased by 2, we divide synthetically by $(x - 2)$ in accordance with Rule 3.

$$
\begin{array}{r}
2 \quad -7 \quad +2 \quad +3 \quad \underline{|2} \\
+4 \quad -6 \quad -8 \\
\end{array}
$$

First quotient: $2x^2 - 3x - 4$ $\quad$ $2 \quad -3 \quad -4 \ | \ -5$ $\qquad A_3 = -5$

$\qquad\qquad\qquad\qquad\qquad +4 \quad +2 \ |$

Second quotient: $2x + 1$ $\qquad$ $2 \quad +1 \ | \ -2$ $\qquad A_2 = -2$

$\qquad\qquad\qquad\qquad\qquad +2 \ |$

Third quotient: 2 $\qquad\qquad\quad$ $2 \quad +3$ $\qquad\qquad A_1 = +3$

The required equation: $\qquad 2y^3 + 3y^2 - 2y - 5 = 0.$

NOTE 3. To form an equation whose roots are each h more than those of $f(x) = 0$, diminish the roots by $-h$.

Example. Transform the equation $2x^3 + 6x^2 + 2x - 5 = 0$ into an equation in which the second-degree term is missing.

Solution: In the expansion of Equation (4), it is evident that $A_1 = na_0h + a_1$. Hence, if $h = -a_1/na_0$, the coefficient of y^{n-1} will be zero.

In this example, $h = -(6)/3(2) = -1$. Hence, by synthetic division, we obtain the equation $2y^3 - 4y - 3 = 0$, whose roots are each 1 *more* than the corresponding roots of the given equation.

$$
\begin{array}{r}
2 \quad +6 \quad +2 \quad -5 \quad \underline{|-1} \\
-2 \quad -4 \quad +2 \\
\hline
2 \quad +4 \quad -2 \ | \ -3 \\
-2 \quad -2 \ | \\
\hline
2 \quad +2 \ | \ -4 \\
-2 \ | \\
\hline
2 \quad +0
\end{array}
$$

EXERCISE 74

Transform, to multiply the roots by the number indicated:

1. $x^3 - 3x^2 + 2x + 5 = 0$; 3. **2.** $2x^3 - x^2 - 3x + 4 = 0$; -2.
3. $x^3 - 5x + 1 = 0$; $\frac{1}{2}$. **4.** $x^4 - 5x^3 - 2x - 3 = 0$; 0.2.
5. $x^4 - 1.2x^3 - 0.0046 = 0$; 10. **6.** $8x^5 - 1 = 0$; -2.

Determine the smallest positive multiplicative factor which will transform the following equations into new equations whose highest powers have coefficients of 1, and find the new equations:

7. $2x^3 - 3x^2 + 2x - 1 = 0$. **8.** $3x^3 + 2x^2 - x - 5 = 0$.
9. $4x^3 - 3x + 2 = 0$. **10.** $12x^4 - x^2 - 2x + 1 = 0$.

Transform, to change the signs of the roots:

11. $2x^3 + 4x^2 + x - 5 = 0$. **12.** $x^4 - 3x^2 + 2x + 7 = 0$.
13. $x^5 + 2x^3 - 3x - 8 = 0$. **14.** $2x^4 - x^3 - 3x - 2 = 0$.

Transform, to diminish the roots by the number indicated:

15. $x^3 - 2x^2 + 5x - 7 = 0$; 1. **16.** $2x^3 + 4x^2 - 3x - 5 = 0$; 2.
17. $3x^3 - 5x + 3 = 0$; -3. **18.** $5x^3 + 2x + 2 = 0$; -1.
19. $x^4 - 2x^3 + 5x - 2 = 0$; $-\frac{1}{2}$. **20.** $2x^4 - 3x^2 + x - 2 = 0$; 3.
21. $2x^3 - 5x^2 - 2x + 1 = 0$; 0.8. **22.** $x^3 - 4x^2 + 2x - 3 = 0$; 0.1.
23. $x^5 - 2x^3 - 2x^2 + 7 = 0$; 1. **24.** $x^6 - 64 = 0$; 2.

Transform, to obtain equations in which the coefficients of the next to the highest power of the variable are zero:

25. $x^3 - 3x^2 + 2x - 5 = 0$. **26.** $2x^3 + 12x^2 - 5x - 7 = 0$.
27. $x^3 - 2x^2 + 3x - 4 = 0$. **28.** $x^4 - 8x^3 + 2x - 3 = 0$.

117. Irrational Roots by Horner's Method.

In Article 113 the irrational roots of an integral rational equation with real coefficients were determined approximately by a method of linear interpolation. An alternate method of approximation, known as Horner's method, is explained in the following example:

Example. Find the real roots of the equation

$$f(x) = x^3 - 3x^2 + x - 7 = 0. \qquad (1)$$

Solution: From the graph of $y = x^3 - 3x^2 + x - 7$ (Figure 31, Article 113), it is evident that Equation (1) has one real root located between $x = 3$ and $x = 4$, and two imaginary roots. To find the real root, we proceed as follows:

(a) *Transform $f(x) = 0$ to decrease the roots by* **3.**

$$
\begin{array}{rrrr|r}
1 & -3 & +1 & -7 & \underline{3} \\
  & +3 & 0 & +3 & \\
\hline
1 & 0 & +1 & -4 & \\
  & +3 & +9 & & \\
\hline
1 & +3 & +10 & & \\
  & +3 & & & \\
\hline
1 & +6 & & &
\end{array}
$$

Hence the transformed equation

$$f_1(x_1) = x_1^3 + 6\,x_1^2 + 10\,x_1 - 4 = 0, \tag{2}$$

has a root between $x_1 = 0$ and $x_1 = 1$ corresponding to the root of (1) between $x = 3$ and $x = 4$. We now locate the root of $f_1(x_1) = 0$ between successive tenths. Since the root of (2) is numerically less than 1, a rough approximation to the root can be obtained from (2) by neglecting all but the last two terms; thus, $10\,x_1 - 4 = 0$. This gives the value $x_1 = 0.4$, which is called a **trial divisor**. In order accurately to locate the root, we compute $f_1(0.3) = -0.433$ and $f_1(0.4) = 1.024$. Hence, the root of (2) lies between 0.3 and 0.4.

(b) *Transform $f_1(x_1) = 0$ to decrease the roots by* **0.3.**

$$
\begin{array}{rrrr|r}
1 & +6.0 & +10.00 & -4.000 & \underline{0.3} \\
  & +0.3 & +1.89 & +3.567 & \\
\hline
1 & +6.3 & +11.89 & -0.433 & \\
  & +0.3 & +1.98 & & \\
\hline
1 & +6.6 & +13.87 & & \\
  & +0.3 & & & \\
\hline
1 & +6.9 & & &
\end{array}
$$

The second transformed equation

$$f_2(x_2) = x_2^3 + 6.9\,x_2^2 + 13.87\,x_2 - 0.433 = 0, \tag{3}$$

has a root between $x_2 = 0$ and $x_2 = 0.1$ corresponding to the root of (2) between $x_1 = 0$ and $x_1 = 1$. The trial divisor of (3) is $x_2 = 0.433/13.87 = 0.03^+$, and we find $f_2(0.03) = -0.010663$ and $f_2(0.04) = 0.132904$. Hence, the root of (3) lies between 0.03 and 0.04.

(c) *Transform $f_2(x_2) = 0$ to decrease the roots by* **0.03.**

$$
\begin{array}{rrrr|r}
1 & +6.90 & +13.8700 & -0.433000 & \underline{0.03} \\
  & +0.03 & +0.2079 & +0.422337 & \\
\hline
1 & +6.93 & +14.0779 & -0.010663 & \\
  & +0.03 & +0.2088 & & \\
\hline
1 & +6.96 & +14.2867 & & \\
  & +0.03 & & & \\
\hline
1 & +6.99 & & &
\end{array}
$$

The third transformed equation

$$f_3(x_3) = x_3^3 + 6.99\,x_3^2 + 14.2867\,x_3 - 0.010663 = 0 \qquad (4)$$

has a root between $x_3 = 0$ and $x_3 = 0.01$ corresponding to the root of (3) between $x_2 = 0$ and $x_2 = 0.1$. The trial divisor of (4) is $x_3 = 0.010663/14.2867 = 0.0007^+$.

Thus far the approximate value of the real root of $f(x) = 0$ has been determined as

$$x = 3 + 0.3 + 0.03 + 0.0007 = 3.3307,$$

which is certainly correct to three decimal places and probably to four. The process can be continued if greater accuracy is desired.

The above computations are usually arranged in the following compact form:

```
1   − 3   +  1   − 7  |3_                        x₀ = 3⁺.
    + 3        0   + 3
1     0   +  1|  − 4
    + 3   +  9|
1   + 3|  + 10
    + 3|
```

$x_0 = 3^+.$

```
1   + 6.0   + 10.00   − 4.000  |0.3             10 x₁ − 4 = 0,
    + 0.3   +  1.89   + 3.567                      x₁ = 0.3⁺.
1   + 6.3   + 11.89|  − 0.433
    + 0.3   +  1.98|
1   + 6.6|  + 13.87
    + 0.3|
```

$10\,x_1 - 4 = 0,\quad x_1 = 0.3^+.$

```
1   + 6.90   + 13.8700 − 0.433000 |0.03         13.87 x₂ − 0.433 = 0,
    + 0.03   +  0.2079 + 0.422337                  x₂ = 0.03⁺.
1   + 6.93   + 14.0779| − 0.010663
    + 0.03   +  0.2088|
1   + 6.96|  + 14.2867
    + 0.03|
```

$13.87\,x_2 - 0.433 = 0,\quad x_2 = 0.03^+.$

```
1   + 6.99 + 14.2867 − 0.010663                  14.2867 x₃ − 0.010663 = 0,
                                                   x₃ = 0.0007⁺.
```

$14.2867\,x_3 - 0.010663 = 0,\quad x_3 = 0.0007^+.$

Required root: $x = 3 + 0.3 + 0.03 + 0.0007 = 3.3307$

NOTE 1. Decimals may be avoided in the above example by multiplying the roots of each transformed equation by 10 before making the next transformation. This additional transformation always keeps the trial divisor as some number between 0 and 10.

NOTE 2. To find a negative root of $f(x) = 0$ by Horner's method, find the corresponding positive root of $f(-x) = 0$ and change its sign.

EXERCISE 75

Each of the following equations has one irrational root; find it by Horner's method, correct to three decimal places:

1. $x^3 + 4x - 7 = 0$.   **2.** $x^3 + 2x^2 + 5x + 1 = 0$.

3. $x^4 - 3x + 2 = 0$.   **4.** $x^4 + 2x^3 - 2x - 4 = 0$.

5. $x^3 - 1.2x + 2.7 = 0$.   **6.** $x^4 - 0.3x^2 + 0.2x - 0.9 = 0$.

Each of the following equations has two irrational roots; find them by Horner's method, correct to two decimal places:

7. $x^4 + 3x - 5 = 0$.   **8.** $x^4 - x^2 + 6x - 9 = 0$.

9. $3x^4 + 5x + 1 = 0$.   **10.** $x^4 - 2x^3 + 3x^2 - 7 = 0$.

11. $x^5 - 2x + 1 = 0$.   **12.** $x^5 - 2x^3 + 3x^2 - 2 = 0$.

Find the following principal roots by Horner's method, correct to three decimal places:

13. $\sqrt[3]{7}$.   **14.** $\sqrt[5]{-5}$.   **15.** $\sqrt[4]{8}$.

16. The approximate formula $\sin x = x - \frac{1}{6}x^3$ is valid for small angles x expressed in radians. Find, to three decimal places, the angle in radians whose sine is 0.0113.

17. Three positive numbers form an arithmetical progression whose common difference is 2. If their geometric mean is 5.5, find the numbers correct to three decimal places. NOTE: The geometric mean of a, b, and c is $\sqrt[3]{abc}$.

18. The volume of a spherical segment is given by the formula, $V = \pi r h^2 - \frac{1}{3}\pi h^3$, where r is the radius of the sphere and h is the height of the segment. Find the height of a segment whose volume is one-third the volume of the sphere.

118. Algebraic Solution of Equations. An integral rational equation

$$f(x) = a_0 x^n + a_1 x^{n-1} + \cdots + a_{n-1}x + a_n = 0, \Big| a_0 \neq 0,$$

is said to have an **algebraic solution** if its roots can be expressed in terms of its coefficients by means of formulas involving only a finite number of additions, subtractions, multiplications, divisions, and extractions of roots.

Theorem 1. *The equation $f(x) = 0$ can be solved algebraically when $n = 1, 2, 3,$ or 4.*

We have already shown how to find the algebraic solution of equations for $n = 1$ and $n = 2$. The proof of Theorem 1 will be completed in the following articles where the cases $n = 3$ and $n = 4$ are discussed.

Theorem 2. *The equation $f(x) = 0$ cannot, in general, be solved algebraically when $n \geq 5$.*

The proof of Theorem 2 is beyond the scope of this book, and hence is omitted.

119. The Cube Roots of Unity. The roots of the equation $x^3 - 1 = 0$ are called the **cube roots of unity.** Clearly $r_1 = 1$ is one of the roots. Dividing by $(x - 1)$ gives the depressed equation $x^2 + x + 1 = 0$; its roots are

$$r_2 = -\tfrac{1}{2} + \tfrac{1}{2} i\sqrt{3} \quad \text{and} \quad r_3 = -\tfrac{1}{2} - \tfrac{1}{2} i\sqrt{3}.$$

The root r_2 is commonly denoted by ω (read omega); and since $(-\tfrac{1}{2} + \tfrac{1}{2} i\sqrt{3})^2 = -\tfrac{1}{2} - \tfrac{1}{2} i\sqrt{3}$, the root r_3 is represented by ω^2. By direct multiplication of ω and ω^2, we obtain the relation $\omega^3 = 1$.

Thus the three cube roots of unity may be written as 1, ω, and ω^2, and similarly the three cube roots of any real number N may be written as $\sqrt[3]{N}$, $\omega\sqrt[3]{N}$, and $\omega^2\sqrt[3]{N}$.

120. Solution of the Cubic Equation. A general cubic equation can be written in the form

$$x^3 + bx^2 + cx + d = 0, \tag{1}$$

and the transformation $x = y - \tfrac{1}{3} b$ reduces Equation (1) to the form

$$y^3 + py + q = 0, \tag{2}$$

where

$$p = c - \tfrac{1}{3} b^2 \quad \text{and} \quad q = d - \tfrac{1}{3} bc + \tfrac{2}{27} b^3. \tag{3}$$

Equation (2) is called the **reduced cubic.**

If in the reduced cubic we put $y = u + v$, we obtain

$$u^3 + v^3 + (3 uv + p)(u + v) + q = 0, \tag{4}$$

and if the new variables are chosen so that

$$3 uv + p = 0 \quad \text{or} \quad v = - p/3 u, \tag{5}$$

we obtain

$$u^3 - \frac{p^3}{27 u^3} + q = 0,$$

or

$$u^6 + qu^3 - \tfrac{1}{27} p^3 = 0. \tag{6}$$

Solving (6) by the quadratic formula for u^3, we obtain

$$u^3 = -\tfrac{1}{2}q \pm \sqrt{R}, \text{ where } R = \tfrac{1}{27}p^3 + \tfrac{1}{4}q^2. \qquad (7)$$

From Equation (4) it follows that $v^3 = -\tfrac{1}{2}q \mp \sqrt{R}$.

If we let

$$A = -\tfrac{1}{2}q + \sqrt{R} \quad \text{and} \quad B = -\tfrac{1}{2}q - \sqrt{R}, \qquad (8)$$

then by Article 119, we have

$$\left. \begin{aligned} u &= \sqrt[3]{A}, \ \omega\sqrt[3]{A}, \ \omega^2\sqrt[3]{A}, \\ v &= \sqrt[3]{B}, \ \omega\sqrt[3]{B}, \ \omega^2\sqrt[3]{B}, \end{aligned} \right\} \qquad (9)$$

where $\quad \omega = -\tfrac{1}{2} + \tfrac{1}{2}i\sqrt{3} \quad$ and $\quad \omega^2 = -\tfrac{1}{2} - \tfrac{1}{2}i\sqrt{3}.$

Choosing values of u and v from (9) which satisfy the condition (5), we obtain the following solutions for the reduced cubic:

$$\left. \begin{aligned} \mathbf{y_1} &= \sqrt[3]{A} + \sqrt[3]{B}, \\ \mathbf{y_2} &= \omega\sqrt[3]{A} + \omega^2\sqrt[3]{B}, \\ \mathbf{y_3} &= \omega^2\sqrt[3]{A} + \omega\sqrt[3]{B}. \end{aligned} \right\} \qquad (10)$$

Since $x = y - \tfrac{1}{3}b$, the three roots of (1) are

$$x_1 = y_1 - \tfrac{1}{3}b, \ x_2 = y_2 - \tfrac{1}{3}b, \ x_3 = y_3 - \tfrac{1}{3}b. \qquad (11)$$

NOTE 1. Since the solutions are symmetric in A and B, it is evident that the definitions in (8) could be interchanged without altering the final result.

It can be shown that Equation (1) with real coefficients has one real root and two conjugate imaginary roots when $\boldsymbol{R > 0}$.

Example 1. Solve $x^3 - 12x^2 + 42x - 49 = 0$.

Solution: Substituting $b = -12$, $c = 42$, and $d = -49$ in (3), we find $p = -6$ and $q = -9$. Hence, by (7), $R = 49/4$.

Thus in (8), $A = 8$ and $B = 1$; hence

$$\begin{aligned} x_1 &= (2) + (1) + 4 = 7, \\ x_2 &= \omega(2) + \omega^2(1) + 4 = \tfrac{5}{2} + \tfrac{1}{2}i\sqrt{3}, \\ x_3 &= \omega^2(2) + \omega(1) + 4 = \tfrac{5}{2} - \tfrac{1}{2}i\sqrt{3}. \end{aligned}$$

NOTE 2. In actual practice the above method of solving cubic equations should be used only when the method described in Article 112 fails.

If $\boldsymbol{R = 0}$, then in (8) we have $A = B = -\tfrac{1}{2}q$; hence in this case the roots of the reduced cubic are respectively $-\sqrt[3]{4q}$, $\tfrac{1}{2}\sqrt[3]{4q}$, and $\tfrac{1}{2}\sqrt[3]{4q}$.

It can be shown that Equation (1) with real coefficients has three real distinct roots when $R < 0$. This is known as the **irreducible case,** since the exact cube roots of imaginary numbers cannot, in general, be determined algebraically. Numerical solutions may, however, be obtained in trigonometric form.

When $R < 0$, express the imaginary numbers A and B in polar form:

$$A = -\tfrac{1}{2} q + \sqrt{R} = r(\cos \theta + i \sin \theta),$$
$$B = -\tfrac{1}{2} q - \sqrt{R} = r(\cos \theta - i \sin \theta).$$

Finding a cube root of each, we have

$$\sqrt[3]{A} = \sqrt[3]{r}(\cos \tfrac{1}{3} \theta + i \sin \tfrac{1}{3} \theta),$$
$$\sqrt[3]{B} = \sqrt[3]{r}(\cos \tfrac{1}{3} \theta - i \sin \tfrac{1}{3} \theta).$$

Since in polar form, $\omega = (\cos 120° + i \sin 120°)$ and $\omega^2 = (\cos 120° - i \sin 120°)$, the solutions in (10) may be written as

$$y_1 = \sqrt[3]{r}[(\cos \tfrac{1}{3} \theta + i \sin \tfrac{1}{3} \theta) + (\cos \tfrac{1}{3} \theta - i \sin \tfrac{1}{3} \theta)],$$
$$y_2 = \sqrt[3]{r}[(\cos \tfrac{1}{3} \theta + i \sin \tfrac{1}{3} \theta)(\cos 120° + i \sin 120°)$$
$$+ (\cos \tfrac{1}{3} \theta - i \sin \tfrac{1}{3} \theta)(\cos 120° - i \sin 120°)],$$
$$y_3 = \sqrt[3]{r}[(\cos \tfrac{1}{3} \theta + i \sin \tfrac{1}{3} \theta)(\cos 120° - i \sin 120°)$$
$$+ (\cos \tfrac{1}{3} \theta - i \sin \tfrac{1}{3} \theta)(\cos 120° + i \sin 120°)],$$

which reduce to

$$\left. \begin{aligned} y_1 &= 2\sqrt[3]{r} \cos \tfrac{1}{3} \theta, \\ y_2 &= 2\sqrt[3]{r} \cos (\tfrac{1}{3} \theta + 120°), \\ y_3 &= 2\sqrt[3]{r} \cos (\tfrac{1}{3} \theta + 240°). \end{aligned} \right\} \tag{12}$$

Example 2. Solve $x^3 - 12x + 8 = 0$.

Solution: Since $p = -12$ and $q = 8$, we have $R = -48$. Writing $A = -\tfrac{1}{2} q + \sqrt{R}$ in polar form, we have

$$A = -4 + 4 i\sqrt{3} = 8(\cos 120° + i \sin 120°).$$

Hence, $r = 8$ and $\theta = 120°$. Substituting in (12), we obtain the required solutions:

$$x_1 = 4 \cos \ 40° = 3.064,$$
$$x_2 = 4 \cos 160° = -3.759,$$
$$x_3 = 4 \cos 280° = 0.694.$$

EXERCISE 76

1. Show by substitution that $\sqrt[3]{2} - \sqrt[3]{4}$ is a root of the equation $x^3 + 6x + 2 = 0$.

2. Show by substitution that $1 + \sqrt[3]{2}$ is a root of the equation $x^3 - 3\sqrt[3]{2}\,x - 3 = 0$.

Show that $R > 0$ in the following equations and solve by the method in Article 120:

3. $x^3 - 6x + 9 = 0$.   **4.** $x^3 + 9x + 26 = 0$.

5. $x^3 - 3x^2 - 6x - 4 = 0$.   **6.** $x^3 - 6x^2 + 18x - 13 = 0$.

Find the roots of the following equations in trigonometric form:

7. $x^3 - 3x - 1 = 0$.   **8.** $x^3 - 24x - 32 = 0$.

9. $x^3 - 3x^2 - 3x + 9 = 0$.   **10.** $x^3 + 3x^2 - 1 = 0$.

Show that $R = 0$ in the following equations and solve by the method in Article 120:

11. $8x^3 + 12x^2 - 18x - 27 = 0$.   **12.** $x^3 - 3\sqrt[3]{9}\,x + 6 = 0$.

13. Given that $(1 \pm \sqrt{3})^3 = 10 \pm 6\sqrt{3}$, solve $x^3 + 6x - 20 = 0$ by the method in Article 120.

14. Given that $(2 \pm \sqrt{3})^3 = 26 \pm 15\sqrt{3}$, solve $x^3 + 6x^2 + 9x - 50 = 0$ by the method in Article 120.

15. Solve the equation in Exercise 1.

16. Solve the equation in Exercise 2.

121. Solution of the Quartic Equation. A general quartic equation may be written in the form

$$x^4 + bx^3 + cx^2 + dx + e = 0. \tag{1}$$

Transposing the last three terms of the left member and adding $\frac{1}{4}b^2x^2$ to both sides, we obtain

$$(x^2 + \tfrac{1}{2}bx)^2 = (\tfrac{1}{4}b^2 - c)x^2 - dx - e. \tag{2}$$

Let u be a number whose value will be determined later. Then, on adding $(x^2 + \tfrac{1}{2}bx)u + \tfrac{1}{4}u^2$ to both sides of (2), we have

$$[(x^2 + \tfrac{1}{2}bx) + \tfrac{1}{2}u]^2 = (\tfrac{1}{4}b^2 - c + u)x^2 + (\tfrac{1}{2}bu - d)x + (\tfrac{1}{4}u^2 - e). \tag{3}$$

The right side of (3) is quadratic in x and will be a perfect square if its discriminant is zero; that is, if

$$(\tfrac{1}{2}bu - d)^2 - 4(\tfrac{1}{4}b^2 - c + u)(\tfrac{1}{4}u^2 - e) = 0. \tag{4}$$

Simplifying Equation (4), we obtain

$$u^3 - cu^2 + (bd - 4e)u + (4ce - b^2e - d^2) = 0. \quad (5)$$

Equation (5) is called the **resolvent cubic** of Equation (1), and can be solved either by trial or by the method in Article 120. Let u_1 be any root of Equation (5); then putting $u = u_1$, we may express the right side of (3) as a perfect square.

$$(Ax + B)^2 = (\tfrac{1}{4}b^2 - c + u_1)x^2 + (\tfrac{1}{2}bu_1 - d)x + (\tfrac{1}{4}u_1^2 - e). \quad (6)$$

The four roots of (1) can then be obtained by solving the quadratic equations

$$x^2 + \tfrac{1}{2}bx + \tfrac{1}{2}u_1 = Ax + B \quad \text{and} \quad x^2 + \tfrac{1}{2}bx + \tfrac{1}{2}u_1 = -Ax - B. \quad (7)$$

Example. Solve $x^4 - 6x^3 + 11x^2 - 2x - 10 = 0$.

Solution: Substituting $b = -6$, $c = 11$, $d = -2$, and $e = -10$ in (5), we obtain the resolvent cubic

$$u^3 - 11u^2 + 52u - 84 = 0.$$

By trial, we find the root $u_1 = 3$. Hence, in (6)

$$(Ax + B)^2 = x^2 - 7x + \tfrac{49}{4} = (x - \tfrac{7}{2})^2.$$

Substituting this expression in (7), we obtain the quadratic equations

$$x^2 - 4x + 5 = 0 \quad \text{and} \quad x^2 - 2x - 2 = 0,$$

whose roots are respectively $x = 2 \pm i$ and $x = 1 \pm \sqrt{3}$.

EXERCISE 77

1. Show by substitution that $1 + \sqrt[4]{5}$ is a root of the equation $x^4 - 4x^3 + 6x^2 - 4x - 4 = 0$.

Solve each of the following equations by the method in Article 121:

2. $x^4 - 3x^3 - 8 = 0$.

3. $x^4 - 2x^3 - 4x^2 - 5x - 2 = 0$.

4. $x^4 - x^3 + 3x - 9 = 0$.

5. $x^4 + 4x^3 + 3x^2 - 8x - 10 = 0$.

6. $x^4 - 15x^2 + 20x - 6 = 0$.

7. $x^4 - 8x^3 + 20x^2 - 16x + 4 = 0$.

Factor each of the following:

8. $x^4 - 3x^3 - 21x^2 + 2$.

9. $2x^4 - 3x^3 + 5x^2 - 5x - 6$.

10. Solve the equation in Exercise 1.

11. Show that the transformation $x = y - \tfrac{1}{4}a$ reduces the quartic equation $x^4 + ax^3 + bx^2 + cx + d = 0$ to the form $y^4 + Ay^2 + B = 0$, provided that $c = \tfrac{1}{8}a(4b - a^2)$.

12. Show that the equation $x^4 + 8x^3 + 18x^2 + 8x - 1 = 0$ satisfies the condition of the preceding exercise. Hence, transform and solve, using the quadratic formula. Express answers correct to two decimal places.

CHAPTER 17

Logarithms

122. Definition of a Logarithm. *If* $N = b^x$, *where* b *is a positive number other than one, the exponent* x *is called the logarithm of* N *to the base* b, *and is written* $x = \log_b N$.

Thus, by definition, the expressions

$$(E) \quad N = b^x \quad \text{and} \quad (L) \quad x = \log_b N$$

represent exactly the same relationship: (E) is called the **exponential form** of the relation, and (L) the **logarithmic form.**

Illustration 1. In the following table the two different forms are given for several relations:

Exponential Form	$3^4 = 81$	$4^{\frac{1}{2}} = 2$	$2^{-3} = \frac{1}{8}$	$5^0 = 1$
Logarithmic Form	$\log_3 81 = 4$	$\log_4 2 = \frac{1}{2}$	$\log_2 \frac{1}{8} = -3$	$\log_5 1 = 0$

NOTE 1. We shall assume without proof the facts (a) that for every two positive numbers N and b ($b \neq 1$) there exists one and only one x such that $N = b^x$; (b) that b^x has meaning when x is an irrational number; and (c) that the laws of exponents are valid for irrational exponents.

NOTE 2. Since $1^x = 1$ for all values of x, it is evident that unity cannot be used as a base for logarithms.

To understand the meaning of any logarithmic expression, such as $\log_2 8$, it is advisable at first to write $x = \log_2 8$ in its equivalent exponential form, $2^x = 8$. In this form we see that $x = 3$; hence $\log_2 8 = 3$.

Illustration 2. To find the value of $\log_9 3$, we write $9^x = 3$. Thus, $x = \frac{1}{2}$, since $9^{\frac{1}{2}} = \sqrt{9} = 3$.

NOTE 3. For any base b, we have $b^0 = 1$ and $b^1 = b$. Hence

$$\log_b 1 = 0 \quad \text{and} \quad \log_b b = 1.$$

Example 1. Find N, if $\log_2 N = 5$.

Solution: Write the given equation in its equivalent exponential form, that is, $N = 2^5$. Evaluating, we have $N = 32$.

Example 2. Find x, if $\log_3 \frac{1}{9} = x$.

Solution: Writing the equation in exponential form, we have $3^x = \frac{1}{9}$. Since by the laws of exponents

$$\frac{1}{9} = \frac{1}{3^2} = 3^{-2},$$

it follows from $3^x = 3^{-2}$ that $x = -2$.

Example 3. Find b, if $\log_b 4 = \frac{2}{3}$.

Solution: Writing the equation in exponential form, we have $b^{\frac{2}{3}} = 4$. Raising both sides to the power $\frac{3}{2}$ and recalling that $b > 0$, we have

$$(b^{\frac{2}{3}})^{\frac{3}{2}} = 4^{\frac{3}{2}}; \text{ hence } b^1 = b = (\sqrt{4})^3 = 8.$$

EXERCISE 78

Express the following equations in logarithmic form:

1. $3^2 = 9$.   **2.** $5^3 = 125$ **3.** $2^4 = 16$.   **4.** $10^3 = 1000$.

5. $4^{-2} = \frac{1}{16}$.   **6.** $25^{\frac{1}{2}} = 5$.   **7.** $32^{\frac{3}{5}} = 8$.   **8.** $8^{-\frac{2}{3}} = \frac{1}{4}$.

Express the following equations in exponential form:

9. $\log_4 16 = 2$.   **10.** $\log_3 27 = 3$.   **11.** $\log_{10} 100 = 2$.

12. $\log_9 3 = \frac{1}{2}$.   **13.** $\log_2 1 = 0$.   **14.** $\log_2 \frac{1}{16} = -4$.

15. $\log_5 5 = 1$.   **16.** $\log_{10} 0.01 = -2$.   **17.** $\log_8 \frac{1}{16} = -\frac{4}{3}$.

18. What are the logarithms of 1, 2, 4, 32, $\frac{1}{8}$, 0.25 (a) to the base 2? (b) to the base 4?

19. For the base 10, what are the logarithms of 100, 10, 1, $\frac{1}{10}$, $\frac{1}{100}$?

20. When the base is 3, what are the numbers whose logarithms are 3, 2, 1, 0, -1, -2, -3?

21. For the base 10, what are the numbers whose logarithms are 0, 1, 5, -1, -3, -6?

Find the value of each of the following logarithms:

22. $\log_2 8$.   **23.** $\log_8 2$.   **24.** $\log_{10} 0.1$.   **25.** $\log_2 64$.

26. $\log_\pi \pi$.   **27.** $\log_{49} 7$.   **28.** $\log_{16} 8$.   **29.** $\log_5 \frac{1}{5}$.

Find the unknown b, x, or N in each of the following:

30. $\log_b 81 = 4$.　　　　**31.** $\log_3 N = -1$.　　　　**32.** $\log_b 16 = \frac{4}{5}$.

33. $\log_5 N = 4$.　　　　**34.** $\log_{0.1} 100 = x$.　　　　**35.** $\log_3 N = 0$.

36. $\log_{\frac{2}{3}} 2\frac{1}{4} = x$.　　　　**37.** $\log_b \frac{1}{27} = -3$.　　　　**38.** $\log_9 \frac{1}{3} = x$.

Evaluate each of the following by finding each logarithm separately and then combining arithmetically:

39. $\log_2 4 - \log_4 2 + \log_3 1$.　　　　**40.** $\log_4 \frac{1}{2} - \log_2 \frac{1}{4} - \log_2 2$.

41. $\log_3 \sqrt{3} + \log_3 \sqrt[3]{3} + \log_3 \sqrt[6]{3}$.　　　　**42.** $\log_{10} 1 - \log_{10} 0.001 + \log_{10} 10$.

123. Laws of Logarithms. Since by definition logarithms are exponents, the rules of operation which apply to exponents also apply to logarithms. These rules, expressed in terms of logarithms, have the following form:

Law I. *The logarithm of a product equals the sum of the logarithms of its factors. In symbols,*

$$\log_b MN = \log_b M + \log_b N.$$

Law II. *The logarithm of a quotient equals the logarithm of the dividend minus the logarithm of the divisor. In symbols,*

$$\log_b \frac{M}{N} = \log_b M - \log_b N.$$

Law III. *The logarithm of a power of a number equals the logarithm of the number multiplied by the exponent of the power. In symbols,*

$$\log_b M^n = n \log_b M.$$

Law IV. *The logarithm of a root of a number equals the logarithm of the number divided by the index of the root. In symbols,*

$$\log_b \sqrt[r]{M} = \frac{\log_b M}{r}.$$

Proof of Law I: Let　　　　$x = \log_b M$ and $y = \log_b N$.

In exponential form,　　　　$M = b^x$ and $N = b^y$.

Multiplying,　　　　$MN = b^x \cdot b^y = b^{x+y}$.

Thus, by definition,　　　　$\log_b MN = x + y$.

Hence, by substitution,　　　　$\log_b MN = \log_b M + \log_b N$.

Proof of Law II: Let　　　　$x = \log_b M$ and $y = \log_b N$.

In exponential form,　　　　$M = b^x$ and $N = b^y$.

Dividing, $$\frac{M}{N} = \frac{b^x}{b^y} = b^{x-y}.$$

Thus, by definition, $$\log_b \frac{M}{N} = x - y.$$

Hence, by substitution $$\log_b \frac{M}{N} = \log_b M - \log_b N.$$

Proof of Law III: Let $x = \log_b M.$

In exponential form, $M = b^x.$

Raising to the nth power, $M^n = (b^x)^n = b^{nx}.$

Thus, by definition, $\log_b M^n = nx.$

Hence, by substitution, $\log_b M^n = n \log_b M.$

Proof of Law IV: By the definition of a fractional exponent, we have $\sqrt[r]{M} = M^{\frac{1}{r}}.$ Hence, using Law III, we have

$$\log_b \sqrt[r]{M} = \log_b M^{\frac{1}{r}} = \frac{1}{r} \log_b M = \frac{\log_b M}{r}.$$

Illustrations. $\log_2 30 = \log_2 2 \cdot 3 \cdot 5 = \log_2 2 + \log_2 3 + \log_2 5,$
$\log_{10} \frac{5}{9} = \log_{10} 5 - \log_{10} 3^2 = \log_{10} 5 - 2 \log_{10} 3.$

Example 1. Express $\frac{1}{2} \log_3 5 - \log_3 7 + 2 \log_3 2$ as a single logarithm.

Solution:

$$\frac{1}{2} \log_3 5 - \log_3 7 + 2 \log_3 2 = \log_3 5^{\frac{1}{2}} - \log_3 7 + \log_3 2^2$$
$$= \log_3 \frac{5^{\frac{1}{2}} \cdot 2^2}{7} = \log_3 \frac{4}{7} \sqrt{5}.$$

Example 2. If $\log_{10} 2 = 0.301$, find $\log_{10} \sqrt[4]{1\frac{1}{4}}$.

Solution: Applying the laws of logarithms, we have

$$\log_{10} \sqrt[4]{1\frac{1}{4}} = \frac{1}{4} \log_{10} \frac{5}{4} = \frac{1}{4} \log_{10} \frac{10}{8} = \frac{1}{4} \log_{10} 10 - \frac{1}{4} \log_{10} 8.$$

Since $\log_{10} 8 = \log_{10} 2^3 = 3 \log_{10} 2$ and $\log_{10} 10 = 1$, we have

$$\log_{10} \sqrt[4]{1\frac{1}{4}} = \frac{1}{4} - \frac{3}{4} \log_{10} 2 = 0.250 - 0.226 = 0.024.$$

EXERCISE 79

Using the laws of logarithms, express each of the following in terms of $\log a$, $\log b$, and $\log c$ (when the same base is used throughout an exercise, the base will not be indicated):

1. $\log abc.$

2. $\log ab^2c^3.$

3. $\log a^2b^{-3}c^{\frac{1}{2}}.$

4. $\log \dfrac{a^2b^5}{\sqrt{c}}.$

5. $\log \dfrac{a^3}{\sqrt[3]{b^2c}}.$

6. $\log \dfrac{a\sqrt{b}}{c^3}.$

7. $\log \sqrt[4]{\dfrac{a^3\sqrt{c}}{b}}.$

8. $\log \sqrt{a\sqrt{b\sqrt{c}}}.$

9. $\log (a^{-1}b)^{-\frac{1}{2}}c^{-\frac{2}{3}}.$

Express each of the following as a single logarithm:

10. $\log a - 2 \log b$.

11. $2 \log a + \frac{2}{3} \log b$.

12. $\log 60 - \log 4$.

13. $\log 10 - \log 6 + \log 33$.

14. $5 \log 2 + 2 \log 5$.

15. $\frac{1}{6} \log 8 - \frac{1}{4} \log 9 + \frac{1}{2} \log 24$.

16. $\log (a + b) + \log (a - b)$.

17. $\log \pi + 2 \log r - \log 2$.

18. $\log 1 + \log 2 + \log 3 + \cdots + \log (n - 1) + \log n$.

19. If $\log_{10} 2 = 0.301$, find the logarithms to the base 10 of (a) 4, (b) 32, (c) $\frac{1}{8}$, (d) 5. Hint: $\log 5 = \log \frac{10}{2}$.

20. If $\log_{10} 3 = 0.477$, find the logarithms to the base 10 of (a) 9, (b) 81, (c) $\frac{1}{27}$, (d) $3\frac{1}{3}$. Hint: $\log 3\frac{1}{3} = \log \frac{10}{3}$.

Given $\log_{10} 2 = 0.301$ and $\log_{10} 3 = 0.477$, find the logarithms of the following numbers to the base 10:

21. 6.

22. 72.

23. 20.

24. $\frac{8}{9}$.

25. $2\frac{1}{4}$.

26. $\sqrt[3]{36}$.

27. $1\frac{2}{3}$.

28. $2\sqrt{3}$.

29. 0.0135.

30. 3×10^4.

31. $\sqrt{2\frac{1}{2}}$.

32. $\left(\frac{1}{6}\right)^{0.6}$.

If $\log 27.8 = 1.444$ and $\log 7.43 = 0.871$, find the following logarithms:

33. $\log (27.8)(7.43)^3$.

34. $\log (7.43)^2 / \sqrt{27.8}$.

35. $\log \sqrt{(27.8)^3} / (7.43)^{\frac{3}{2}}$.

36. $\log (7.43)^{\frac{5}{2}}(27.8)^{-\frac{2}{5}}$.

124. Common Logarithms. The logarithms of all positive numbers, with a given positive base b ($b \neq 1$), are said to constitute a **system of logarithms.** For purposes of computation in our decimal system of numbers, the logarithms having 10 as a base are the most convenient to use.

The system of logarithms having 10 as a base is called the system of **common,** or **Briggsian, logarithms.** In the work that follows, when the base is not explicitly written it is understood to be 10. Thus, $\log N$ means $\log_{10} N$, and the word *logarithm* will mean common logarithm.

'NOTE 1. Another system of logarithms frequently used in advanced mathematics is called the **natural,** or **Naperian,** system of logarithms. This system has for its base the irrational number $e = 2.71828 \cdots$. The natural logarithm of N is commonly written as **ln N.**

The following table lists some of the numbers having integers for logarithms in the common system.

Exponential Form	Logarithmic Form
$10^3 = 1000$	$\log 1000 = 3$
$10^2 = 100$	$\log 100 = 2$
$10^1 = 10$	$\log 10 = 1$
$10^0 = 1$	$\log 1 = 0$
$10^{-1} = 0.1$	$\log 0.1 = -1$
$10^{-2} = 0.01$	$\log 0.01 = -2$
$10^{-3} = 0.001$	$\log 0.001 = -3$

Since, if its base is greater than 1, a logarithm increases as its number increases, any number between 100 and 1000 has a logarithm between 2 and 3. Similarly, a number between 0.001 and 0.01 has a logarithm between -3 and -2.

In general, for any number which is not an exact power of 10, the logarithm consists of a whole-number part (positive or negative) *increased* by a decimal part (less than 1). The integral part is called the **characteristic** of the logarithm, and the decimal part the **mantissa** of the logarithm.

Thus, since 367 is a number between 10^2 and 10^3, we have

$$\log 367 = 2 + \text{a decimal.}$$

Similarly, since 0.0079 is a number between 10^{-3} and 10^{-2}, we have $\qquad \log 0.0079 = -3 + \text{a decimal.}$

NOTE 2. The mantissa of a logarithm is *always* positive, or zero. Thus, if $\log N = -1.6108$, the mantissa is not .6108. Writing -1.6108 with a positive decimal, we have $-2 + .3892$. In this form we see that the mantissa is .3892.

NOTE 3. Logarithms with negative characteristics like $-2 + .3892$ are sometimes written $\bar{2}.3892$, the negative sign being placed above the characteristic. For purposes of computation, however, it is more convenient to write the characteristics in the binomial form, that is,

$$-1 = 9 - 10 \qquad -3 = 7 - 10 \qquad -5 = 5 - 10$$
$$-2 = 8 - 10 \qquad -4 = 6 - 10 \qquad \text{etc.}$$

Thus, to write $\log N = -1.6108$ in the binomial form, we subtract from zero in the following manner:

$$\begin{array}{r} 10.0000 - 10 \\ 1.6108 \\ \hline \log N = \quad 8.3892 - 10 \end{array}$$

Illustration. The following table lists several logarithms and gives the characteristic and mantissa of each:

Logarithm	Characteristic	Mantissa
0.6749	0	.6749
2.0492	2	.0492
9.0000 − 10	− 1	.0000
7.9736 − 10	− 3	.9736
− 0.7582	− 1	.2418

125. Rule for Determining Characteristics. By direct computation we can show that

$$10^{0.25} = 10^{\frac{1}{4}} = \sqrt[4]{10} = \sqrt{\sqrt{10}} = 1.778.$$

On multiplying and dividing this relation successively by 10, we obtain

$$10^{7.2500-10} = 0.001778 \quad \text{hence} \quad \log 0.001778 = 7.2500 - 10$$
$$10^{8.2500-10} = 0.01778 \qquad\qquad \log 0.01778 = 8.2500 - 10$$
$$10^{9.2500-10} = 0.1778 \qquad\qquad \log 0.1778 = 9.2500 - 10$$
$$10^{0.2500} \quad= 1.778 \qquad\qquad \log 1.778 = 0.2500$$
$$10^{1.2500} \quad= 17.78 \qquad\qquad \log 17.78 = 1.2500$$
$$10^{2.2500} \quad= 177.8 \qquad\qquad \log 177.8 = 2.2500$$
$$10^{3.2500} \quad= 1778. \qquad\qquad \log 1778. = 3.2500$$

From the above table it is evident that:

1. The mantissas are the same when the numbers differ only in the position of the decimal point.

2. The characteristic is determined by the position of the decimal point in accordance with the following rule:

Rule for Characteristics

1. *If a number is greater than or equal to one, the characteristic of its logarithm is positive and is 1 LESS than the number of figures to the left of the decimal point.*

2. *If a number is less than one, the characteristic of its logarithm is negative and is 1 MORE than the number of zeros immediately following the decimal point.*

Illustration. The logarithms of the numbers 463.5, 3.064, 0.0004, 17,000, and 0.1008 have the characteristics 2, 0, − 4, 4, and − 1, respectively.

Note. If a number N is written in the form $A \times 10^n$, where $1 \leqq A < 10$, then n is the characteristic of log N. Thus, since 320 = 3.2×10^2 and $0.0067 = 6.7 \times 10^{-3}$, their characteristics are 2 and − 3, respectively.

Example. If log 4.85 = 0.6857, find the logarithms of the numbers 0.485, 485, 0.00485, and 485,000.

Solution: If numbers differ only in the position of their decimal point, their mantissas are the same. Hence the mantissa for each of the given numbers is .6857. By the rule given above, their respective characteristics are − 1, 2, − 3, 5. Thus,

$$\log 0.485 \ \ = 9.6857 - 10, \qquad \log 485 \ \ \ \ \ = 2.6857,$$
$$\log 0.00485 = 7.6857 - 10, \qquad \log 485{,}000 = 5.6857.$$

EXERCISE 80

Write the characteristic and the mantissa for each of the following logarithms:

1. 2.8704.　　　**2.** − 1 + .4669.　　　**3.** 5.7825.
4. − 3 + .4099.　**5.** 0.9961.　　　　**6.** .2833 − 2.
7. 3.6444 − 4.　　**8.** 1.0086.　　　　**9.** 9.9542 − 10.

Find the characteristic and mantissa for each of the following negative logarithms:

10. − 0.1524.　　**11.** − 2.3298.　　**12.** − 3.0246.
13. − 1.5436.　　**14.** − 4.2495.　　**15.** − 0.8356.

Give the characteristics for the logarithms of the following numbers:

16. 64.　　　　**17.** 403.　　　**18.** 7.　　　　**19.** 0.03.
20. 900.　　　**21.** 0.15.　　　**22.** 1.004.　　**23.** 10.01.
24. 400,000.　**25.** 3.1416.　　**26.** 0.00001.　**27.** 0.6×10^{10}.
28. 12345.　　**29.** 5.4×10^{-5}.　**30.** 0.5403.　**31.** 0.00052.

If the logarithm of 544 is 2.7356, write the logarithms of the following numbers:

32. 5.44.　　　**33.** 0.0544.　　**34.** 5440.　　**35.** 0.000544.
36. 0.544.　　**37.** 544,000.　　**38.** 5.44×10^5.　**39.** 54.4×10^{-4}.

Place the decimal point in the sequence of digits 4735 so that the logarithm of the number will have the following characteristics:

40. 3.　　　**41.** − 2.　　**42.** 0.　　　**43.** 5.
44. − 4.　　**45.** 9 − 10.　**46.** 1.　　　**47.** 7 − 10.
48. 5 − 10.　**49.** 2.　　　**50.** 6.　　　**51.** 4.

126. Tables of Logarithms. We have seen that the mantissa of a logarithm depends only on the sequence of figures and not on the position of the decimal point. By methods which are developed in more advanced mathematics, these mantissas can be computed for all numbers to any desired accuracy. These computed values are given in tables of logarithms (actually, tables of mantissas) known as four-place tables, five-place tables, and so on, depending on the number of decimal places to which the mantissas are computed.

On pages 302–303 is a four-place table which contains the mantissas of the logarithms of all the integers from 1 to 1000. Although mantissas are decimals less than 1, they are given in the table without decimal points for convenience in printing. Thus, in Table III, a mantissa of 0253 means .0253.

Illustration. To find the mantissa of log 56.3 we look in Table III for the mantissa of 563. To find this, locate the entry which is in the row headed by 56 and in the column headed by 3. This entry is 7505. Notice that only the last three digits, 505, of the mantissa appear in this column; the first digit, 7, is found in the column headed by 0 either in the same row or in the first row above in which four digits are shown. The required mantissa is thus .7505.

NOTE 1. If a table entry is preceded by an asterisk (*), the first digit of the mantissa is found in the column headed by 0 and in the row directly below. Thus, log 63.6 = 1.8035.

NOTE 2. If a number has less than three figures, add zeros until it has three figures. Thus, to find the mantissa of log 47, locate in the table the mantissa for the number 470; for log 5, find the mantissa for the number 500.

In summary, **to find the logarithm of a number,**

1. Find its characteristic by the rule in Article 125.

2. Find in the table the mantissa corresponding to the given sequence of figures.

Example 1. Find log 6750, log 0.47, and log 0.005.

Solution: (1) By the Rule for Characteristics, the characteristics are 3, − 1, − 3, respectively. (2) In Table III we find the mantissas of 675, 470, and 500 to be .8293, .6721, and .6990, respectively. Hence, log 6750 = 3.8293; log 0.47 = 9.6721 − 10; log 0.005 = 7.6990 − 10.

We reverse the process of finding a logarithm, in order **to find the number corresponding to a given logarithm:**

1. In the table, find the sequence of digits corresponding to the given mantissa.

2. Insert the decimal point in accordance with the value of the characteristic and the rule in Article 125.

NOTE 3. The number thus found is called the **antilogarithm** of the given logarithm. That is, if $\log N = L$, then $N = $ antilog L.

Example 2. Find N, if $\log N = 3.8463$.

Solution: (1) In Table III, corresponding to the mantissa 8463, we find the sequence of digits 702. (2) Since the characteristic is $+3$, we must have four figures to the left of the decimal; thus $N = 7020$.

EXERCISE 81

Using Table III, find the logarithm of each of the following numbers:

1. 288.	**2.** 64.7.	**3.** 0.106.	**4.** 5000.
5. 0.0017.	**6.** 63,800.	**7.** 0.0376.	**8.** 880.
9. 300,000.	**10.** 0.0001.	**11.** 40.5.	**12.** 0.0203.

Using Table III, find the antilogarithm of each of the following logarithms:

13. 0.2833.	**14.** $8.9542-10$.	**15.** 1.0414.	**16.** $9.9961-10$.
17. 2.6990.	**18.** $9.7404-10$.	**19.** 4.5911.	**20.** $6.5502-10$.
21. 5.1106.	**22.** $7.8500-10$.	**23.** 3.9217.	**24.** $8.6191-10$.

127. Significant Digits and Approximations. If a number N is expressed as a decimal, then, reading from left to right, the **significant digits** (or **significant figures**) of N are defined to be the digits beginning with the first non-zero digit and ending with the last digit written.

Illustration 1. The significant digits of 0.02103 and 47.80 are respectively 2, 1, 0, 3, and 4, 7, 8, 0.

NOTE 1. In a number such as 850,000, there is no evident way of determining how many, if any, of the zeros are significant. To give such an indication, the number is usually expressed as a coefficient times a power of 10. Thus, if three figures are significant, we would write 8.50×10^5.

If the number N is an approximation to some true value N', then $(N - N')$ is called the **error** of N, and the significant figures of N indicate the maximum possible error of N. Thus, the approximation 6.4 for $\sqrt{41}$ means that the true value of $\sqrt{41}$ is between 6.35 and 6.45, whereas the approximation 6.40 for $\sqrt{41}$ means that the true value is between 6.395 and 6.405.

Illustration 2. In Table III the mantissas are approximate values expressed to four significant figures. Thus, to say that the mantissa of log 262 is .4183 means that the true mantissa is some number between .41825 and .41835.

We say that a number N is **rounded off** to k figures, if the number written is the closest approximation to N that can be made with k significant figures.

Illustration 3. The approximate value of $\sqrt{3}$ to seven figures is 1.732051. This number rounded off to six figures is 1.73205; to four *decimal* places, 1.7321; to three figures, 1.73; to one figure, 2.

NOTE 2. In rounding off 67.45 to three figures, either 67.4 or 67.5 could be chosen. When such a choice arises, we arbitrarily agree to select the number ending with an even digit. In this case, then, we choose 67.4.

In computations where approximate values are used, the results are usually no more accurate than the least accurate number involved in the computation. Thus, the product $2.4 \times 1.64 = 3.936$ claims false accuracy and should be rounded off to 3.9. Even this result is less accurate than the number 3.9 implies, since the true value of the product lies between $2.35 \times 1.635 = 3.84225$ and $2.45 \times 1.645 = 4.03025$.

NOTE 3. In adding or subtracting approximate numbers, the results should be rounded off in the first digit position where a last significant figure occurs. Thus, adding 3.142 and 0.63, we have 3.77.

In the logarithmic computations in this chapter we shall assume that the accuracy of results is limited only by the use of a four-place logarithm table, and that this restriction insures four-figure accuracy in the results obtained. All given numbers are to be considered as exact numbers.

EXERCISE 82

Give the number of significant figures in each of the following:

1. 272.5.	**2.** 0.0006.	**3.** 27.09.	**4.** 0.2709.
5. 0.6000.	**6.** 1.010.	**7.** 5000.0.	**8.** 32.5.

Express the following numbers in such a way as to indicate accuracy to three significant figures:

9. 27,400,000.   **10.** 900,000.   **11.** 47,350.   **12.** 7,524,500.

For the following approximate numbers, give the values between which the true value is located:

13. 0.200.   **14.** 0.2.   **15.** 1.4157.   **16.** 1.52×10^{-6}.

Round off the following numbers to four significant figures:

17. 0.012344.   **18.** 72.007.   **19.** 23,455.   **20.** 52.5252.

For the following approximate numbers, find (*a*) their sum, (*b*) their product:

21. 26.52 and 3.07.   **22.** 413.2 and 0.255.
23. 0.013045 and 2.94.   **24.** 3.8 and 0.5167.

128. Interpolation. When a number contains four significant figures, the mantissa of its logarithm cannot be found directly in a four-place table. However, by a process known as *linear interpolation*, a close approximation can be obtained for the mantissa in question.

Linear interpolation is based on the assumption that, *for a small change in N, the change in* **log** *N is proportional to the change in N.*

NOTE 1. This principle of *proportional parts* only approximates the true value, but it is sufficiently accurate for all interpolation considered in this book. More refined methods of interpolation are given in advanced works.

Example 1. By interpolation, find log 21.67.
Solution: The required logarithm is 1 + some mantissa.

Number	Mantissa
$10 \begin{bmatrix} 7 \begin{bmatrix} 2160 \\ 2167 \\ 2170 \end{bmatrix} \end{bmatrix}$	$\begin{bmatrix} 3345 \\ ? \\ 3365 \end{bmatrix} x \end{bmatrix} 20$

The number 2167 lies between 2160 and 2170, and the mantissas corresponding to the latter numbers are 3345 and 3365, respectively. Since 2167 is $\frac{7}{10}$ of the way from 2160 to 2170, the corresponding mantissa will be $\frac{7}{10}$ of the way from 3345 to 3365. That is, the amount to be added to 3345 is given by

$$x = \tfrac{7}{10}(3365 - 3345) = 14.$$

Thus, the required logarithm is 1.3359.

This process of interpolation is usually carried through without the decimal points, and in this form the difference (3365 − 3345) is called the **tabular difference.**

NOTE 2. A number with five or more significant figures is rounded off to four figures before interpolating.

NOTE 3. When interpolating in a table, never retain any more significant figures than are given in the table.

The computations required in interpolation are greatly simplified and can be completed *mentally* by using the **tables of proportional parts.** These tables give the various tenth parts of the tabular differences which occur in the table. For example, $\frac{7}{10}$ of a tabular difference of 29 is found in the column headed by 29 and the row headed by 7. This entry is 20.3, or 20 to the nearest integer.

Example 2. By interpolation, find antilog 1.7585.

Solution: The mantissa 7585 is located between the table entries 7582 and 7589; and these mantissas correspond to the numbers 5730 and 5740, respectively. By proportional parts $\frac{x}{10} = \frac{3}{7}$; hence $x = 4\frac{2}{7}$ or 4. Since the characteristic is 1, we have

Number	Mantissa
$10\begin{bmatrix} x\begin{bmatrix}5730\\?\\5740\end{bmatrix}\end{bmatrix}$	$\begin{bmatrix}7582\\7585\\7589\end{bmatrix}3\end{bmatrix}7$

antilog 1.7585 = 57.34.

Observe that the value of x can be determined easily using the proportional parts tables. Thus, for a tabular difference of 7, we find that 2.8 in row 4 is the entry closest to 3; hence $x = 4$.

EXERCISE 83

Find the logarithms of the following numbers:

1. 26.35.	**2.** 4.537.	**3.** 0.9532.	**4.** 200.2.
5. 403.1.	**6.** 0.001073.	**7.** 80,650.	**8.** 499.9.
9. 14.318.	**10.** 684.23.	**11.** 7.505.	**12.** 0.1492.
13. 2.0507.	**14.** 0.06658.	**15.** 729.75.	**16.** 500,370.
17. 0.003005.	**18.** 20.94.	**19.** 0.3458.	**20.** 82.494.

Find the numbers corresponding to the following logarithms:

21. 2.6174.	**22.** 9.2415−10.	**23.** 1.3508.	**24.** 0.9306.
25. 8.8775−10.	**26.** 0.3232.	**27.** 6.6666−10.	**28.** 2.8410.
29. 3.5050.	**30.** 2.9145.	**31.** 9.8019−10.	**32.** 7.2125−10.
33. 9.3553−10.	**34.** 8.7000−10.	**35.** 1.4980.	**36.** 6.5149−10.
37. 0.1234.	**38.** 9.4664−10.	**39.** 3.1416.	**40.** 9.4270.

129. Computation of Products and Quotients. With the Laws of Logarithms I and II, the numerical value of products and quotients may be determined as is illustrated in the examples below. In performing computations with logarithms, it is desirable to make a systematic outline of the details of the entire computation before looking up any mantissas. This procedure insures greater speed and accuracy.

Example 1. Find the product $32.43 \times (- 0.695) \times 0.03025$.

Solution: It is clear the product will be negative; hence let N represent the product $32.43 \times (0.695) \times 0.03025$. By Law I,

$$\log N = \log 32.43 + \log 0.695 + \log 0.03025.$$

For the computation, the outline indicated with bold-face type is written down completely before mantissas are looked up:

$$
\begin{aligned}
\mathbf{log\ 32.43} &= \ \ 1.5109 \\
\mathbf{log\ 0.695} &= \ \ 9.8420 - 10 \\
(+)\ \mathbf{log\ 0.03025} &= \ \ \underline{8.4807 - 10} \\
\mathbf{log\ N} &= 19.8336 - 20 \\
N &= \ \ 0.6817.
\end{aligned}
$$

Adding,

Hence,

Thus, the required product is $- 0.6817$.

Note 1. Since logarithms of negative numbers are not defined, if a negative sign occurs in a computation, *first find the absolute value of the expression by logarithms and then prefix the proper sign*, this sign being determined by inspection.

Note 2. If an error is made in a computation by logarithms, it is likely to have a great effect on the result. An approximate estimate of the result will guard against such errors. Thus, in Example 1, we have the estimate $30 \times 0.7 \times 0.03 = 0.63$.

Example 2. Compute $\dfrac{1.32 \times 0.574}{0.0029 \times 327.6}$.

Solution: Let N be the required number; then by Laws I and II we have

$$\log N = [\log 1.32 + \log 0.574] - [\log 0.0029 + \log 327.6].$$

For the computation:

$$
\begin{aligned}
\log 1.32 &= 0.1206 & \log 0.0029 &= 7.4624 - 10 \\
(+)\ \log 0.574 &= \underline{9.7589 - 10} & (+)\ \log 327.6 &= \underline{2.5153} \\
\log (\text{num.}) &= 9.8795 - 10 & \log (\text{den.}) &= 9.9777 - 10
\end{aligned}
$$

Since the mantissa for the difference $\log$ (num.) $- \log$ (den.) must be positive, we write $\log$ (num.) in the equivalent form $19.8795 - 20$ before subtracting. Thus,

$$\log (\text{num.}) = 19.8795 - 20$$
$$(-) \log (\text{den.}) = \underline{9.9777 - 10}$$

Subtracting, $\qquad \log N = 9.9018 - 10$

Hence, $\qquad\qquad N = 0.7976.$

130. Cologarithms. *The logarithm of the reciprocal of* **N** *is called the* **cologarithm of** *N and is written* **colog** *N.* Thus, since $\log 1 = 0$,

$$\text{colog } N = \log \frac{1}{N} = \log 1 - \log N = -\log N.$$

Illustration. $\quad \text{colog } 0.475 = \log \dfrac{1}{0.475}$; thus

$$\log 1 = 10.0000 - 10$$
$$(-) \log 0.475 = \underline{9.6767 - 10}$$
$$\text{colog } 0.475 = 0.3233.$$

With a little practice this subtraction can be performed mentally as the logarithm is read from the table. In the positive parts of the logarithm and the cologarithm observe that the corresponding digits add to 9, except the last which add to 10.

Example. Evaluate the fraction in Example 2, Article 129, using cologarithms.

Solution:

$$\log 1.32 = 0.1206$$
$$\log 0.574 = 9.7589 - 10$$
$$\text{colog } 0.0029 = 2.5376$$
$$(+) \text{ colog } 327.6 = \underline{7.4847 - 10}$$
$$\log N = 19.9018 - 20$$
$$N = 0.7976.$$

EXERCISE 84

Compute the following by logarithms:

1. $35 \times 23.$
2. $36.7 \times 0.43.$
3. $0.2534 \times 8.29.$
4. $454 \div 61.$
5. $9.13 \div 0.307.$
6. $1.235 \div 7.017.$
7. $433 \times 3.18 \times 0.55.$
8. $(-72.2) \times 0.2075 \times 3.392.$
9. $(-4.135) \times 61.1 \times (-0.17).$
10. $0.465 \times 2.93 \times 52.67.$
11. $\dfrac{8.42 \times 9.355}{3.1416}.$
12. $\dfrac{5555}{269 \times 414}.$
13. $\dfrac{1}{0.718 \times 1.313}.$
14. $\dfrac{173.2 \times 0.483}{26.336}.$
15. $\dfrac{8.45 \times (-0.115)}{0.3195 \times 2005.5}.$
16. $\dfrac{0.217 \times 0.369}{(-0.592) \times 0.0102}.$

17. $\dfrac{25.4 \times (-1.2) \times 0.3147}{(-6.55) \times 0.4444}.$

18. $\dfrac{922 \times 421.4}{3569 \times 1.04 \times 27.3}.$

19. $\dfrac{4 \times 38.7 \times 0.0513}{3 \times 0.622 \times 7.475}.$

20. $\dfrac{81 \times 2.775 \times 0.59}{13 \times (-1.05) \times 3.25}.$

131. Computation of Powers and Roots. With the Laws of Logarithms III and IV, the numerical value of powers and roots may be determined as is illustrated in the following examples:

Example 1. Compute $(0.392)^4$.
Solution: Let $N = (0.392)^4$; then by Law III,

$$\log N = 4 \log 0.392.$$

For the computation:

$$\log 0.392 = \quad 9.5933 - 10$$
$$\underline{\times 4}$$

Multiplying, $\qquad \log N = 38.3732 - 40$

Hence, $\qquad\qquad N = \quad 0.02362.$

NOTE. Law III applies for any positive or negative exponents. Thus, if $N = 25^{-0.3}$, then $\log N = (-0.3) \log 25 = (-0.3)(1.3979) = -0.4194 = 9.5806 - 10$. Hence, $N = 0.3807$.

Example 2. Compute $\sqrt[4]{5.26 \times 0.049}$.

Solution: Let N represent the required root; then by Law IV and Law I,

$$\log N = \tfrac{1}{4} (\log 5.26 + \log 0.049).$$

The computation may be arranged as follows:

$$\log 5.26 = 0.7210$$
$$(+) \log 0.049 = \underline{8.6902 - 10}$$
$$\log \text{(product)} = 9.4112 - 10.$$

In order to avoid decimals in the " minus " term of this logarithm, we change the characteristic $9 - 10$ to the form $39 - 40$ before dividing by 4.

Thus, $\qquad\qquad \log \text{(product)} = 39.4112 - 40$

Dividing by 4, $\qquad\qquad \log N = \quad 9.8538 - 10$

Hence, $\qquad\qquad\qquad N = \quad 0.7142.$

EXERCISE 85

Compute the following by logarithms:

1. 22.4^5. **2.** 0.0638^3. **3.** $(-0.872)^4$. **4.** $(57.5)^{-2}$.

5. $\sqrt{4.97}$. **6.** $\sqrt[3]{-0.525}$. **7.** $\sqrt[6]{319.6}$. **8.** $\sqrt[4]{0.005}$.

9. $(9.616 \times 0.562)^3$.   **10.** $0.77^3 \times 41.69^2$.   **11.** $1.25^4 \div 0.412^2$.

12. $\sqrt[4]{0.32 \times 4.725}$.   **13.** $23.4\sqrt{1.327}$.   **14.** $1/\sqrt[3]{0.5722}$.

15. $\dfrac{65.2^2 \times 1.43}{22.25^3}$.   **16.** $3.95\sqrt{\dfrac{0.251}{4.672}}$.   **17.** $\dfrac{\sqrt[3]{(7.046)^2}}{(0.9125)^3}$.

18. $\dfrac{(22.2)^{\frac{2}{3}}}{(4.6)^{-1} \times (1.6)^{0.2}}$.   **19.** $\sqrt[3]{\dfrac{37\sqrt{0.935}}{(-2.613)^2}}$.   **20.** $\dfrac{(47.3)^{-\frac{1}{2}} \times (109.5)^3}{(0.03287)^{-2}}$.

132. General Computations. In any computation which involves sums or differences, the operations of addition and subtraction are performed arithmetically, as is indicated in the following example:

Example 1. Evaluate $N = \sqrt{(0.2745)^2 + (0.5126)^2}$.
Solution: Evaluating the squares by logarithms, we have

$$\begin{array}{ll} \log 0.2745 = 9.4386 - 10 & \log 0.5126 = \quad 9.7098 - 10 \\ \qquad\qquad\quad \times 2 & \qquad\qquad\qquad \times 2 \\ \log (0.2745)^2 = \overline{18.8772 - 20} & \log (0.5126)^2 = \overline{19.4196 - 20} \end{array}$$

Hence, $(0.2745)^2 = 0.07537$ $(0.5126)^2 = 0.2628$.

Adding, we have $N = \sqrt{0.3382}$; therefore

$$\log N = \tfrac{1}{2} \log 0.3382 = \tfrac{1}{2}(19.5292 - 20) = 9.7646 - 10.$$

Hence, $N = 0.5816$.

NOTE. Occasionally a problem can be simplified by a modification in form. Thus, an expression such as $\sqrt{a^2 - b^2}$ can be written in the form $\sqrt{(a + b)(a - b)}$, which is more suitable for logarithmic computation.

Example 2. The volume of a sphere of radius r is given by the formula $V = \tfrac{4}{3}\pi r^3$. Find the radius of a sphere whose volume is 231.5 cubic inches.

Solution: Solving the formula for r, we have $r = \sqrt[3]{\dfrac{3\,V}{4\,\pi}}$.

For the computation:

$$\begin{array}{ll} \qquad\quad \log 3 = 0.4771 & \qquad\quad \log 4 = 0.6021 \\ (+) \log 231.5 = 2.3646 & (+) \log \pi = 0.4971 \\ \qquad\qquad\quad \overline{2.8417} & \qquad\qquad\quad \overline{1.0992} \\ \qquad\quad (-)\ \underline{1.0992} & \\ \qquad\quad 3\ \overline{\left|\ 1.7425\right.} & \\ \qquad \log r = 0.5808, & \qquad r = 3.809 \text{ inches.} \end{array}$$

Evaluate:

1. $4 + \sqrt[3]{0.172}$.

2. $(23.15)^{\frac{1}{2}} - (3.469)^2$.

3. $(1.6)^{-2} + (0.7)^{\frac{1}{3}}$.

4. $\sqrt{(342)^2 - (295)^2}$.

5. $\sqrt[3]{6 - (1.04)^{10}}$.

6. $\sqrt[5]{(2.17)^2 - (1.95)^2}$.

7. $\dfrac{(1.05)^7 - 1}{(1.05)^{\frac{1}{2}} - 1}$.

8. $\dfrac{4.2 - \sqrt[3]{-106}}{211 + (4.6)^4}$.

9. $\dfrac{12}{3 + (0.7152)^{\frac{3}{4}}}$.

10. $\dfrac{\log 85}{\log 29}$.

11. $\dfrac{2 - \log 3.27}{\log 4.15}$.

12. $\dfrac{67 \log 0.325}{\log 0.9777}$.

13. The volume of a cone of radius r and height h is given by the formula $V = \frac{1}{3}\pi r^2 h$. (a) Find V when $r = 15.4$ and $h = 30.6$; (b) find r when $V = 2467$ and $h = 27.35$.

14. If $S = \frac{1}{2}gt^2$, (a) find S when $g = 980$ and $t = 2.016$; (b) find t when $S = 2115$ and $g = 980$.

15. If the geometric mean of k numbers is the kth root of their product, find the geometric mean of 2.15, 2.21, 2.07, and 2.17.

16. The area of a triangle in terms of its sides a, b, and c is given by the formula $A = \sqrt{s(s-a)(s-b)(s-c)}$ where $s = \frac{1}{2}(a+b+c)$. Find A, when $a = 6.59$, $b = 7.85$, and $c = 5.26$.

17. If $T = 2\pi\sqrt{l/g}$, (a) find T when $l = 2.95$ and $g = 32.2$; (b) find l when $T = 2.565$ and $g = 32.2$.

18. The sides of a rectangle are 2.157 and 3.558 inches, respectively. Find the radius of a circle having the same area.

19. If $a > b$, an approximate value of $\sqrt{a^2 + b^2}$ is given by $0.960\,a + 0.398\,b$. Find the percentage error in this approximation when $a = 6.932$ and $b = 5.167$.

20. If the adiabatic law for the expansion of air is $PV^{1.4} = 986$, where P is the pressure in centimeters of mercury and V is the volume in cubic centimeters, find the volume when the pressure is 132 cm.

133. Exponential and Logarithmic Equations. *An equation in which the unknown occurs in an exponent is called an* **exponential equation.**

Illustration 1. The exponential equation $2^x = 8$ can be solved by inspection since we know that $8 = 2^3$. Thus $2^x = 2^3$, and $x = 3$.

An equation in which the unknown occurs in the logarithm of an expression is called a **logarithmic equation.**

Illustration 2. The logarithmic equation $\log(3x - 2) = 2$ can be solved without tables since we know that $\log 100 = 2$. Thus, $3x - 2 = 100$, and $x = 34$.

Although certain exponential and logarithmic equations can be solved by inspection, the general methods of solving such equations are illustrated in the following examples:

Example 1. Solve $2^x = 5$ for x.

Solution: Taking the logarithms of both members gives $x \log 2 = \log 5$. Solving,

$$x = \frac{\log 5}{\log 2} = \frac{0.6990}{0.3010} = 2.322.$$

Note 1. In evaluating $\log 5/\log 2$, observe that we *actually divide* the value $\log 5$ by the value $\log 2$. This division may be done with logarithms.

Example 2. Solve $\log (x + 1) - \log (x - 1) = 1.5$ for x.

Solution: By use of Law II, we have

$$\log \frac{x + 1}{x - 1} = 1.5.$$

Hence, $\qquad \dfrac{x + 1}{x - 1} = $ antilog $1.5000 = 31.62.$

Solving for x, we obtain $x = 32.62/30.62 = 1.065.$

Note 2. If the logarithms have a base other than 10, write and solve the corresponding exponential equation. Thus, $\log_4 5\, x = 0.7$ means $5\,x = 4^{0.7}$. Hence, to find x, evaluate $4^{0.7}$ and divide by 5.

EXERCISE 87

Solve each of the following (a) by inspection without tables and (b) by the general method with tables:

1. $2^x = 32.$ **2.** $3^{2x} = \frac{1}{81}.$ **3.** $100^x = 1000.$
4. $8^{x+1} = 4.$ **5.** $4^x = \frac{1}{2}.$ **6.** $3^{-x} = 3\sqrt{3}.$

Solve the following exponential and logarithmic equations:

7. $\log (x + 1) = 1.$ **8.** $3^x = 25.$ **9.** $\log 52\, x = 0.7.$
10. $(1.75)^x = 3.27.$ **11.** $(0.8)^x = 0.526.$ **12.** $\log_2 x = 1.4.$
13. $3^{2x+1} = 5^{3x-1}.$ **14.** $\log_3 7\, x = 5.$ **15.** $(1.03)^{-x} = 0.552.$
16. $2^x \cdot 3^{x+1} = 4^{x+2}.$ **17.** $(8.48)^{x+1} = 7^x.$ **18.** $\log x = -\frac{1}{2}.$

19. If $y = 1.32\, e^{0.43x}$, find x when $y = 6.75$. Note: $e = 2.718.$
20. If $y = 6.89\, x^n$, find n when $x = 960$ and $y = 2500.$
21. If $x \log y = 7.78\, x - 1700$, find y when $x = 273.$
22. If $y = (1 + x)^n$, find n when $x = 0.04$ and $y = 2.$
23. If $y = \log \log x$, find x when $y = 0.2553.$
24. If $y = x^{\log n}$, find n when $x = 2.5$ and $y = 3.2.$
25. Solve $l = ar^{n-1}$ for n. **26.** Solve $y = a \log bx$ for x.
27. Solve $A = P(1 + r)^n$ for n. **28.** Solve $y = e^{-kx^2}$ for x.

134. Logarithms to Any Base. If $x = \log_b N$ where b and N are known, x can be found by solving $N = b^x$, using *common* logarithms.

Illustration. To find the value of $\log_7 20$, we solve $7^x = 20$. Thus, taking common logarithms of both sides, we obtain

$$x \log 7 = \log 20; \; x = \frac{\log 20}{\log 7} = \frac{1.3010}{0.8451} = 1.539.$$

The relation in general between systems of logarithms to different bases is expressed in the following theorem:

Theorem. *If a and b are any two bases of logarithms,*

$$\log_b N = \frac{\log_a N}{\log_a b}. \tag{1}$$

Proof: Let $\log_b N = x$; then $N = b^x$. Hence, taking logarithms to the base a, we have

$$\log_a N = \log_a b^x = x \log_a b = (\log_b N)(\log_a b).$$

NOTE. Setting N equal to a in (1), we obtain the relation

$$\log_b a = \frac{1}{\log_a b}. \tag{2}$$

The constant $\log_b a$ is called the **modulus** of the system of logarithms to the base b with respect to the system of logarithms to the base a.

Taking $a = e = 2.718$ and $b = 10$ in (2), we obtain the moduli

$$\log_{10} e = 0.4343 \quad \text{and} \quad \log_e 10 = 2.3026.$$

Thus, to change from natural logarithms to common logarithms, and vice versa, we use the relations

$$\log_{10} N = 0.4343 \log_e N \tag{3}$$

and

$$\log_e N = 2.3026 \log_{10} N. \tag{4}$$

Example. Find the value of ln 27.

Solution: The notation ln N is commonly used to denote the natural logarithm of N; thus, ln 27 means $\log_e 27$.

Substituting in Equation (4), we have

$$\ln 27 = 2.3026 \log 27 = (2.3026)(1.4314) = 3.295.$$

Find the following logarithms:

1. $\log_5 10$.   2. $\ln 162$.   3. $\log_3 30$.   4. $\log_{20} 5$.
5. $\ln\sqrt{2}$.   6. $\ln 0.52$.   7. $\log_{0.1} 7$.   8. $\log_\pi 10$.
9. $\ln 0.01$.   10. $\log_4 12$.   11. $\log_{12} 4$.   12. $\ln 39.5$.

Find N in each of the following:

13. $\ln N = 3.615$.   14. $\log_2 N = 4.106$.   15. $\ln N = 8.932 - 10$.
16. $\ln N = -0.755$.   17. $\ln N = 0.025$.   18. $\log_3 N = 9.407 - 10$.

135. Graphs of Logarithmic Functions. If $y = \log_b x$, then y is called a logarithmic function of x. In Figure 32 the

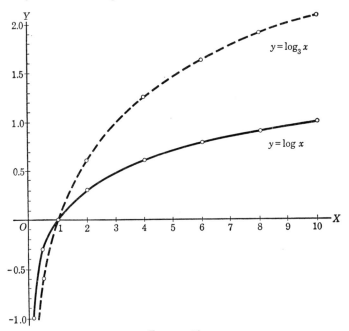

FIGURE 32.

graph of $y = \log x$, or the equivalent relation $x = 10^y$ has been drawn with values obtained from Table III. The graphs of $y = \log_b x$, $b > 1$ have the same general form for all bases b. This is evident since $\log_b x$ equals $\log x$ multiplied by the positive modulus $1/\log b$. Thus, in graphing $y = \log_3 x$, the following relation was used:

$$\log_3 x = \log x/\log 3 = 2.096 \log x.$$

Figure 32 illustrates the following facts about $\log_b x$, $b > 1$:

1. $\log_b x$ is not defined if x is negative.

2. $\log_b 1 = 0$ for all b.

3. $\log_b x$ is negative for $0 < x < 1$; and if x approaches zero, $\log_b x$ decreases without limit.

4. $\log_b x$ is positive for $x > 1$; and if x increases without limit, $\log_b x$ increases without limit.

EXERCISE 89

1. Determine the values of log 3, log 4.5, and log 7 from Figure 32.
2. From Figure 32, determine the values of x for which log x equals 0.7, $\frac{1}{2}$, and -0.25.

Graph the following equations for $0 \leqq x \leqq 10$:

3. $y = \log_2 x$.

4. $y = \ln x$.

5. $y = \log_5 x$.

6. $y = \log (x - 1)$.

7. $y^2 = \log x$.

8. $y = \log \dfrac{1}{x}$.

CHAPTER 18

Interest and Annuities

136. Interest. Money paid for the use of invested capital is called **interest.** The capital invested is called the **principal,** and the sum of the principal and interest is called the **amount.** For a unit of time (one year unless otherwise specified) the ratio of the interest to the principal is called the **rate of interest,** and it is generally quoted in percentage.

Illustration. If a *principal* of $1000 earns $55 *interest* in one year, the *rate of interest* per annum is 55/1000, or .055, or 5.5%. The *amount* at the end of one year is $1000 + $55 = $1055.

137. Simple Interest. If interest is computed on the original principal for the entire time of investment, the interest is called **simple interest** and its magnitude is proportional to the time of investment.

Illustration 1. If $1000 earns interest at the rate of 5% per annum, the *simple interest* at the end of one year is $50, two years is $100, and six months is $25.

If P dollars are invested at simple interest at the rate r, and if I represents the interest and A the amount at the end of t years, then

$$I = \mathbf{Prt} \quad \text{and} \quad A = P + I = P(1 + \mathbf{rt}) \tag{1}$$

212

NOTE 1. In computing **ordinary** *simple interest*, we assume that a month has 30 days and that a year has 360 days.

Example 1. Find the amount of $72 at simple interest for 6 months and 10 days at 6%.

Solution: We have $P = \$72$, $r = 0.06$, and $t = 6\frac{1}{3} \div 12 = 19/36$; hence

$$I = \$72 \cdot 0.06 \cdot \tfrac{19}{36} = \$2.28, \qquad A = \$72 + \$2.28 = \$74.28.$$

The present value of an amount A which is due in t years is the principal P which must be invested now in order to equal A in t years. Solving Equation (1) for P, the present value is given by

$$P = A(1 + rt)^{-1}.$$

To discount A for t years means to find the present value of A. The difference between A and P is called the **discount at** *simple interest* on A.

Example 2. At $4\frac{1}{2}\%$ simple interest, find the present value and discount on a note of $1200 which is due in 16 months.

Solution: We have $A = \$1200$, $r = 0.045$, and $t = \frac{16}{12} = \frac{4}{3}$; hence the present value is

$$P = \$1200(1 + 0.045 \cdot \tfrac{4}{3})^{-1} = \frac{\$1200}{1.06} = \$1132.08,$$

and the discount is $1200 − $1132.08 = $67.92.

NOTE 2. To discount notes of amount A due in t years, use is often made of the formula Adt, where d is the rate of discount per year. Such discounts are called **simple discounts**. Observe that the rate of simple discount d is not the same numerically as the rate of simple interest r.

Illustration 2. At 6% simple discount, the discount on a note of $300 due in 6 months is $300 \cdot 0.06 \cdot \frac{1}{2} = \$9$, and the present value is $291. On the other hand, from $I = Prt$, when $I = \$9$, $P = \$291$, and $t = \frac{1}{2}$, we find that $r = 6.19\%$.

EXERCISE 90

Find the simple interest and the amount of the following:

1. $400 for 3 months at 5%.
2. $650 for 6 months at $4\frac{1}{2}\%$.
3. $21.50 for 2 months and 20 days at 6%.
4. $112.25 for 45 days at $5\frac{1}{2}\%$.

Find the present value and the discount at simple interest of the following:

5. $500 due in 8 months at 6%.

6. $325 due in 5 months at $4\frac{1}{2}\%$.

7. $252.50 due in 4 months and 15 days at 5%.

8. $1015.17 due in 7 months and 10 days at 8%.

9. Discount $1257 for 6 months and 15 days at 6% simple discount.

10. Discount $347.59 for 60 days at $5\frac{1}{2}\%$ simple discount.

11. What interest rate is equivalent to a 6% simple discount rate in discounting an amount due at the end of (*a*) one year, (*b*) three months?

12. What interest rate is equivalent to a 5% simple discount rate in discounting an amount due in 15 years? Note: Simple discount is seldom used when the time interval is more than one year.

13. A man discharges a debt of $257.50 by signing a note for $275 due in 6 months. At what rate is he paying interest?

14. A man borrows $2500 from a bank for 90 days. He pays a simple discount of 5% and a $5 service charge in advance. At what rate is he paying interest?

15. A man borrows $1000, agreeing to pay, at the end of each three-month period, $200 on the principal and the simple interest at 6% on the principal outstanding during that period. Find the total amount that he will pay to discharge the debt.

138. Compound Interest. If the interest due for a given interval of time is added to the principal on which it was computed, and if the interest for each succeeding interval is computed on the new principal so obtained, the sum by which the original principal has been increased, for any length of time, is called the **compound interest** for that time. The amount to which the principal has increased is called the **compound amount,** or the **amount.** The time interval between successive additions of interest is called the **interest period,** or **conversion period.** When the interest period is a year, six months, or three months, the money is said to be **compounded (or converted) annually, semiannually,** or **quarterly,** respectively. Although compound interest is computed for each interest period, the rate of interest is generally quoted on a yearly basis called the **nominal rate.**

Illustration 1. If the *nominal rate* is 6% *compounded quarterly*, then the *interest period* is three months and the rate is 1.5% *per conversion period*.

Let P be the original capital, i the rate per conversion period, n the number of conversion periods, and A the compound amount to which P accumulates by the end of n interest periods. At the end of the first period, the interest due is Pi and the new principal is $P + Pi = P(1 + i)$. Similarly, it is evident that the amount accumulated at the end of any period is $(1 + i)$ times the principal at the beginning of the period. Thus, the amounts at the end of the successive periods are $P(1 + i)$, $P(1 + i)^2$, $P(1 + i)^3$, $\cdots$. Hence, we have the compound interest formula

$$A = P(1 + i)^n. \tag{1}$$

Illustration 2. If the rate is 4% compounded semiannually, the compound amount on $1000 for three years is obtained from (1) with $P = 1000$, $i = 0.02$, and $n = 6$:

$A = 1000(1.02)^6 = 1000(1.1262) = \$1126.20$ (with Table IV)

NOTE 1. Tables IV and V give the values of $(1 + i)^n$ and $(1 + i)^{-n}$ for some of the more common rates of interest. If greater accuracy is needed or other rates are given, it is recommended that the binomial theorem be used. Thus, for the above illustration

$$(1 + .02)^6 = 1 + 6(.02) + \frac{6 \cdot 5}{1 \cdot 2}(.02)^2 + \frac{6 \cdot 5 \cdot 4}{1 \cdot 2 \cdot 3}(.02)^3 + \cdots$$
$$= 1 + 0.12 + 0.006 + 0.00016 + \cdots = 1.12616.$$

When A is given, P is called the **present value** of the amount A. Solving (1) for P, we have the **present value formula**

$$P = A(1 + i)^{-n}. \tag{2}$$

To discount A for n conversion periods means to find the present value of A. The difference $(A - P)$ is called the **compound discount**, or the **discount** on A.

Example. Find the present value and discount on a note for $3000 due in $15\frac{1}{2}$ years, if money is worth 8% compounded quarterly.

Solution: Since $A = 3000$, $i = 0.02$, and $n = 62$, we have

$$P = 3000(1.02)^{-62} = 3000(0.29293) = \$878.79.$$

The discount on the note is ($3000 − $878.79) or $2121.21.

NOTE 2. Since $(1.02)^{-62} = (1.02)^{-50}(1.02)^{-12}$, the value $(1.02)^{-62}$ can be determined from Table V by multiplying $(.37153)$ and $(.78849)$.

139. Nominal and Effective Rates. The rate per year quoted in a given type of compound interest is called the **nominal rate,** whereas the rate per year at which interest is earned for one year is called the **effective rate.** Thus when interest is compounded annually, the nominal and effective rates are the same.

Illustration 1. If $100 is invested for one year at 6% compounded semiannually, 6% is the *nominal rate.* Since the amount at the end of one year is $100(1.03)^2 = 106.09$, the *effective rate* is 6.09%.

Let r represent a nominal rate which is converted m times per year, and let e represent the corresponding effective rate; then for a principal of one dollar the corresponding amounts at the end of one year are respectively $(1 + r/m)^m$ and $(1 + e)$. Equating these amounts, we have the relations

$$\text{EFFECTIVE. } \quad e = \left(1 + \frac{r}{m}\right)^m - 1, \tag{1}$$

and NOMINAL.

$$r = m[(1 + e)^{\frac{1}{m}} - 1]. \tag{2}$$

Illustration 2. To find the nominal rate, compounded quarterly, which is equivalent to an effective rate of 4%, use (2) with $e = 0.04$ and $m = 4$:

$$r = 4[(1.04)^{\frac{1}{4}} - 1] = 4[1.00985 - 1] = 0.0394, \text{ or } 3.94\%,$$

where $(1.04)^{\frac{1}{4}}$ was determined as follows:

$$(1 + .04)^{\frac{1}{4}} = 1 + \tfrac{1}{4}(.04) + \frac{\tfrac{1}{4}(-\tfrac{3}{4})}{2!}(.04)^2 + \cdots = 1.00985.$$

EXERCISE 91

Find the amount and the interest in each of the following:

1. $175 for 3 years at 4% compounded (*a*) annually; (*b*) semiannually; (*c*) quarterly.
2. $550 for 5 years at 6% compounded (*a*) annually; (*b*) semiannually; (*c*) quarterly.
3. $325 for 15 years at 6% compounded quarterly. See Note 2, Article 138.

4. $200 for 6 years at 12% compounded monthly. See Note 2, Article 138.

5. $700 for 2 years at 5% compounded quarterly. Use the binomial theorem.

Find the present value and the discount for the following amounts:

6. $300 due in 5 years at 6% compounded (a) annually; (b) semi-annually; (c) quarterly.

7. $450 due in 4 years at 4% compounded (a) annually; (b) semi-annually; (c) quarterly.

8. $225 due in $14\frac{1}{2}$ years at 4% compounded quarterly. See Note 2, Article 138.

9. $1000 due in 3 years at 6% compounded monthly. Use the binomial theorem.

10. $850 due in 4 years at 3.5% compounded annually. Use the binomial theorem.

11. An insurance firm offers to pay a client $5000 now and $5000 in ten years, or else $10,000 in five years. Which is the better proposition for the client, if money is worth 6% compounded semiannually?

12. Compare the amounts due in two years on $100 at the following rates: (a) 6.3% simple interest; (b) 6% compounded semiannually; (c) 6% compounded quarterly.

13. Find the effective rate when interest is at the rate 8% compounded (a) annually; (b) semiannually; (c) quarterly.

14. Find the effective rate when interest is at the rate 6% compounded (a) semiannually; (b) quarterly; (c) monthly.

15. Find the nominal rate, compounded semiannually, which is equivalent to an effective rate of 5%. Use the binomial theorem.

16. Find the nominal rate, compounded monthly, which is equivalent to an effective rate of 6%. Use the binomial theorem.

17. At what rate, compounded quarterly, will $500 accumulate to $700 in five years? Solve by interpolation in Table IV.

18. At what rate, compounded annually, will money double itself in 15 years? Solve by interpolation in Table IV.

19. How long will it take money to double itself if invested at 6%, compounded semiannually? Solve by interpolation in Table IV.

20. How long will it take $272.18 to accumulate to $318.48 at 3% compounded annually? Solve by interpolation in Table IV.

140. Annuities. A sequence of equal periodic payments is called an **annuity.** The sum of the payments made in one year is called the **annual rent**; the time between successive payments is the **payment interval;** and the time between the beginning of the first payment interval and the end of the last payment interval is called the **term** of an annuity.

Illustration 1. For an annuity of $100 payable each three months for five years, the *payment interval* is three months, the *annual rent* is $400, and the *term* is five years.

Note. Throughout this chapter the discussion will be confined to **ordinary annuities** in which the payments are made at the end of each payment interval.

For a given rate of interest, the **amount of an annuity** is the sum of the compound amounts obtained if each payment, when due, is accumulated at interest until the end of the term. The **present value of an annuity** is the sum of the present values of all payments.

Illustration 2. The amount and present value of an annuity of $100 payable annually for four years, with interest at 5% compounded annually, may be computed in the following tabular form:

Payment Made at End of	Present Value of Payment	Amount of Payment at End of Term
1 year	$100(1.05)^{-1} = 95.24$	$100(1.05)^{3} = 115.76$
2 years	$100(1.05)^{-2} = 90.70$	$100(1.05)^{2} = 110.25$
3 years	$100(1.05)^{-3} = 86.38$	$100(1.05)^{1} = 105.00$
4 years	$100(1.05)^{-4} = 82.27$	$100 = 100.00$
	Present Value $= \$354.59$	Amount $= \$431.01$

141. Annuity Formulas. In financial practice, for any annuity, the conversion period of the interest rate is usually chosen to be the same as the payment interval. We shall restrict the following discussion to such annuities.

Payment Made at End of	Present Value of Payment	Amount of Payment at End of Term
1 period	$(1+i)^{-1}$	$(1+i)^{n-1}$
2 periods	$(1+i)^{-2}$	$(1+i)^{n-2}$
. . . .	. . . .	. . . . .
$(n-1)$ periods	$(1+i)^{-(n-1)}$	$(1+i)$
n periods	$(1+i)^{-n}$	1

The preceding table gives an annuity whose periodic payment is one dollar, payable at the end of each of n periods, and whose interest rate is i per period.

Let $a_{\overline{n}|i}$ (read as a angle n at i) represent the sum of the present values and $s_{\overline{n}|i}$ the sum of the amounts; then

$$a_{\overline{n}|i} = (1 + i)^{-n} + (1 + i)^{-(n-1)} + \cdots + (1 + i)^{-2} + (1 + i)^{-1}.$$

This is a geometric progression with the common ratio $(1 + i)$; hence, by Article 82, we have

$$a_{\overline{n}|i} = \frac{1 - (1 + i)^{-n}}{i}. \tag{1}$$

In like manner we have

$$s_{\overline{n}|i} = 1 + (1 + i) + \cdots + (1 + i)^{n-2} + (1 + i)^{n-1}$$

or

$$s_{\overline{n}|i} = \frac{(1 + i)^n - 1}{i}. \tag{2}$$

NOTE 1. Numerical values for $a_{\overline{n}|i}$ and $s_{\overline{n}|i}$ are given in Tables VI and VII for some values of n and i.

If each payment of an annuity is R dollars, the present value A and the amount S will be, respectively, R times the values obtained in Equations (1) and (2). Thus

$$A = Ra_{\overline{n}|i} \quad \text{and} \quad S = Rs_{\overline{n}|i}. \tag{3}$$

Illustration 1. If an annuity pays \$100 at the end of each three months for five years, and if the rate of interest is 8% compounded quarterly, the present value of the annuity is

$$A = 100\, a_{\overline{20}|.02} = 100(16.3514) = \$1635.14,$$

and the amount of the annuity is

$$S = 100\, s_{\overline{20}|.02} = 100(24.2974) = \$2429.74.$$

To determine the periodic payments R when either A or S is known, we solve the equations in (3):

$$R = A \cdot \frac{1}{a_{\overline{n}|i}} = Aa_{\overline{n}|i}^{-1} \quad \text{or} \quad R = S \cdot \frac{1}{s_{\overline{n}|i}} = Ss_{\overline{n}|i}^{-1}. \tag{4}$$

Numerical values of $a_{\overline{n}|i}^{-1}$ may be obtained in Table VIII for some values of n and i. Since

$$a_{\overline{n}|i}^{-1} = s_{\overline{n}|i}^{-1} + i,$$

values for $s_{\overline{n}|i}^{-1}$ may also be obtained from Table VIII.

NOTE 2. The above relation is proved as follows:

$$a_{\overline{n}|i}^{-1} = \frac{i}{1-(1+i)^{-n}} = \frac{i(1+i)^n}{(1+i)^n-1} = \frac{i(1+i)^n - i + i}{(1+i)^n-1}$$

$$= \frac{i[(1+i)^n-1]}{(1+i)^n-1} + \frac{i}{(1+i)^n-1} = i + s_{\overline{n}|i}^{-1}.$$

Illustration 2. The value of $a_{\overline{24}|.03}^{-1}$ as given in Table VIII is 0.05905, which *decreased* by 0.03 gives $s_{\overline{24}|.03}^{-1} = 0.02905$.

Example. At 6% compounded annually, what equal payments should be made at the end of each year for 15 years to pay for a house whose present value is $12,000?

Solution: From Equation (4), we have

$$R = 12,000 \, a_{\overline{15}|.06}^{-1} = 12,000(0.10296) = \$1235.50.$$

NOTE 3. Since the above tabular value is correct to five significant figures, the answer is valid to no more than five figures.

EXERCISE 92

Find the present value and amount of the following annuities with interest as given:

1. $100 annually for 10 years at 6% compounded annually.
2. $400 quarterly for 6 years at 8% compounded quarterly.
3. $280 semiannually for 15 years at 4% compounded semiannually.
4. $100 quarterly for 10 years at 6% compounded quarterly.
5. What equal payments each year for 10 years will discharge a debt of $10,000, if money is worth 5% compounded annually?
6. If money is worth 12% compounded monthly, what equal payments each month for 2 years will pay for an automobile worth $985?
7. If a savings account earns 4% compounded quarterly, how much should be deposited each quarter in order to accumulate $4000 in 12 years?
8. In order to have a fund of $6500 at the end of 15 years, what equal annual deposits should be made if money earns 5% compounded annually?

Using Tables IV and V, compute the numerical values of the following:

9. (a) $a_{\overline{40}|.03}$,   (b) $s_{\overline{60}|.04}$.   10. (a) $s_{\overline{20}|.05}^{-1}$,   (b) $a_{\overline{55}|.03}^{-1}$.

11. At what rate, compounded quarterly, will quarterly payments of $350 for 12 years discharge a debt of $12,000? Hint: Interpolate in Table VI.

12. At what rate, compounded semiannually, will semiannual payments of $500 accumulate a fund of $15,000 at the end of 10 years? Hint: Interpolate in Table VII.

142. Application of Annuities. The extinction of a debt by any satisfactory set of payments is called the **amortization** of the debt. If the payments are equal and the payment intervals are the same, the debt is said to be **amortized** by an annuity.

Example 1. A debt of $3000, with interest at 6% compounded annually, is amortized by four equal annual payments. Find the annual payment and construct an amortization schedule.

Solution: Since $A = \$3000$, $i = 0.06$, and $n = 4$, we have

$$R = 3000\, a_{\overline{4}|.06}^{-1} = 3000(0.28859) = \$865.77.$$

AMORTIZATION SCHEDULE

Year	Principal at Beginning of Year	Interest Due at End of Year	Annual Payment at End of Year	Principal Repaid at End of Year
1	$3000.00	$180.00	$ 865.77	$ 685.77
2	2314.23	138.85	865.77	726.42
3	1587.31	95.23	865.77	770.54
4	816.77	49.00	865.77	816.77
Totals		$463.08	$3463.08	$3000.00

A fund created to pay an obligation at some future date is called a **sinking fund.** If the fund is accumulated by investing equal amounts at equal intervals, the **amount in the fund** at any time is the amount of the annuity formed by the deposits.

Illustration 1. If a $1000 annual deposit is made in a sinking fund paying 5% per annum, the amount in the fund at the end of 10 years is $1000\, s_{\overline{10}|.05} = \$12,577.90$.

A **bond** is a written contract agreeing (a) to pay a specified **redemption price** on a fixed future date, and (b) to pay equal **dividends,** at a specified rate, at regular intervals until the **redemption date.** The dividend is periodic interest, always computed on the **face value** or **par value** of the bond. A bond is **redeemable at par** or **redeemable at a premium,** if the redemption price is respectively equal to or greater than its face value.

Illustration 2. The statement " A $500, 6% bond with semi-annual dividends, redeemable in 12 years at 105% " means a bond whose face value is $500, whose redemption price in 12 years is 105% of $500 or $525, and which has 24 dividends of $15 payable each six months until and including the redemption date.

When a bond is sold on a dividend date, the purchaser will receive the redemption price when due and the future dividends, which form an annuity. Hence, the price of a bond should be computed as follows:

Price = (present value of redemption price)
+ (present value of dividends)

where the present values are computed at the purchaser's rate.

Example 2. A $1000, 4% bond, with annual dividends is redeemable at par in 12 years. Find the price which will yield an investor 6% compounded annually.

Solution: The redemption price is $1000, the dividends are $40, $n = 12$, and $i = 0.06$; hence

$$P = 1000(1.06)^{-12} + 40\,a_{\overline{12}|.06} = 1000(.49697) + 40(8.3838) = \$832.32.$$

Example 3. If money is worth 5% compounded annually, find the present value of a sequence of annual payments of $300, the first due at the end of 3 years and the last due at the end of 8 years.

FIGURE 33.

Solution: An annuity whose term does not begin for a given length of time is called a **deferred annuity.** This is shown graphically in Figure 33.

The value of the annuity at time B is $300\,a_{\overline{6}|.05} = \$1522.70$. Discounting the value at B for two periods, we obtain the value at time A as $1522.70(1.05)^{-2} = \$1381.10$.

NOTE. A deferred annuity can be considered as the difference of two annuities. Thus, in the above example the value at A is

$$300\,a_{\overline{8}|.05} - 300\,a_{\overline{2}|.05} = \$1381.10.$$

EXERCISE 93

1. A debt of $5000, with interest at 4% compounded annually, is amortized by five equal annual payments. Find the payment and construct an amortization schedule.

2. A loan of $2500, with interest at 6% compounded semiannually, is amortized by four equal semiannual payments. Find the payment and construct an amortization schedule.

3. A debt is amortized by $100 quarterly payments for five years. If money is worth 4% compounded quarterly, find (a) the present value of the debt and (b) the principal outstanding at the beginning of the third year. Hint for (b): Find the present value of the remaining payments.

4. A man borrows $5000 with interest at 6% payable annually. He will amortize the debt by equal annual payments for eight years. What part of his third payment is a repayment of principal?

5. A man deposits $300 at the end of each six months in a savings account paying 2% compounded semiannually. How much is in the account at the end of five years?

6. How much must be deposited at the end of each year in a fund paying 3% compounded annually, in order to be able to replace a $10,000 machine at the end of ten years?

7. What equal deposits at the end of each quarter will amount to $700 in six years, if money is worth 6% compounded quarterly?

8. A man deposits $500 at the end of each year in a fund paying 5% per annum. In how many years will the fund first exceed $20,000?

9. A $100, 5% bond, with semiannual dividends, is redeemable at par in ten years. Find the price to yield 4% compounded semiannually.

10. A $500, 6% bond, with annual dividends, is redeemable at 110% at the end of twenty years. Find the price to yield 6% per annum.

11. A $1000, 7% bond, with quarterly dividends, is redeemable at 105% at the end of ten years. Find the price to yield 8% compounded quarterly.

12. A $1000, 5% bond, with annual dividends, is redeemable at par at the end of thirty years. Find the price to yield per annum (a) 4%, (b) 5%, (c) 6%.

13. If money is worth 6% per annum, find the present value of a sequence of annual payments of $1000, the first due at the end of ten years and the last due at the end of twenty years.

14. On his 18th, 19th, 20th, and 21st birthdays a boy is to receive $1000. What is the value of this annuity on his 10th birthday, if money is worth 4% per annum?

15. A man agrees to discharge a debt of $5000 by paying a down payment and then paying $1000 at the end of each year for five years. If money is worth 5% per annum, what should the down payment be?

16. A man is to receive $1000 at the end of each of the first five years and $600 at the end of each of the next five years. If money is worth 5% per annum, what is the present value of his annuity? Hint: Consider as two annuities, one for $600 and one for $400.

17. If $200 is deposited at the end of each year for ten years in a fund which is invested at 4% per annum, what is the amount in the fund five years after the last deposit?

18. Find the present value and amount of an annuity in which $100 is paid at the *beginning* of each year for ten years at 4% per annum. NOTE. An annuity in which the payments are made at the beginning of the payment intervals is called an **annuity due.**

CHAPTER 19

Permutations and Combinations

143. Definition of Permutations and Combinations.
Each of the **arrangements** *in a definite order which can be made by taking some or all of a given number of things is called a* **permutation.**

Each of the **groups** *or* **selections,** *without regard to order, which can be made by taking some or all of a given number of things is called a* **combination.**

Illustration. The permutations of the letters a, b, and c, taken two at a time, are

$$ab, ba, ac, ca, bc, \text{ and } cb,$$

each representing a different *arrangement* of two letters.

The combinations of these same letters, taken two at a time, are

$$ab, ac, \text{ and } bc,$$

each representing a different *selection* of two letters.

From this illustration it is clear that in forming combinations we are concerned only with what things are in each selection, whereas in forming permutations we are also concerned with the arrangement in each selection. Thus, the single combination abc can be permuted in six different ways, namely,

$$abc, acb, bac, bca, cab, \text{ and } cba.$$

144. Fundamental Principle. The following principle is

the basis for the development of all subsequent work on permutations and combinations:

*If one thing can be done in **p** different ways, and when it has been done in any one of these ways a second thing can be done in **q** different ways, the number of different ways of doing the two things in the order stated is **p · q**.*

With *each* of the p different ways of doing the first thing, we can associate *any* of the q different ways of doing the second thing. Hence, for *all* the p different ways of doing the first thing there will be p · q different ways of doing the two things in the order stated.

Illustration. If there are four roads going from *A* to *B* and three roads going from *B* to *C*, we can travel 4 · 3 or 12 different routes in going from *A* to *C*.

Note 1. It is evident that the fundamental principle can be extended to include any number of events.

Example 1. How many integers, each of three different figures, can be formed from the digits 1, 2, 3, 4, 5, 6, and 7?

Solution: It is often helpful in applying the fundamental principle to regard the problem as one of filling places. Thus in this example, we choose *any one* of the seven digits to fill the first place. This number of choices is indicated by writing 7 over the first place. Then we choose any one

7 ·	6 ·	5

of the six remaining digits to fill the second place, and finally any one of the five remaining digits to fill the third place. Hence, we can form 7 · 6 · 5 or 210 different numbers. It is evident that the order in which the places are filled is immaterial.

Note 2. If repetition of digits were permissible in the above example, there would have been 7 · 7 · 7 = 343 numbers.

Example 2. Using the letters of the word *combine*, how many four-letter words can be formed? How many of these begin with a vowel and end with *m*?

Solution: We choose any one of the seven letters for the first place, any of the six remaining letters for the second place, and so on. In all, we have 7 · 6 · 5 · 4 = 840 words.

The second question demands special consideration for the first and last places; hence we consider these places first. We have only one choice for the last place, so we enter it and

7 ·	6 ·	5 ·	4

3 ·	5 ·	4 ·	1
vowel			*m*

put 1 over that place. Next we choose any one of the three vowels for the first place; and having selected one, we fill the second and third places with any of the remaining letters. Thus, we obtain $3 \cdot 5 \cdot 4 \cdot 1 = 60$ words of the type specified.

NOTE 3. We often use the expression " word " in a general sense to indicate any ordered arrangement of similar or dissimilar letters.

EXERCISE 94

1. How many permutations are there, taking the letters a, b, c, and d three at a time? Write out those beginning with b.

2. In how many ways can a selection be made, if a club of twelve members elects a president and a secretary?

3. How many five-letter words can be made with the letters in the word *equation*?

4. How many numbers of three figures each can be made from the digits 1, 2, 3, 4, and 7, (*a*) if repetitions are not allowed, (*b*) if repetitions are allowed?

5. At a dinner there is a choice of three salads, five entrees, and four desserts. If one of each is chosen, how many different dinners can be obtained?

6. A building has five entrances. In how many ways can one enter the building and leave by a different entrance?

7. A coat manufacturer makes five styles of coats out of seven different kinds of material, and has two kinds of buttons available. How many coats are needed to make a complete assortment?

8. How many signals of three flags each, in vertical order, can be given with seven flags of different colors?

9. Four persons enter a room in which there are six chairs. In how many ways can each select a chair?

10. From the digits 1, 2, 3, 4, 5, 7, and 9, how many odd numbers each of three different digits can be formed?

11. How many words of four letters each can be formed from the twenty-six letters of the alphabet, no letter being repeated in the same word?

12. How many fraternities can be named using three of the twenty-four letters in the Greek alphabet, (*a*) with no repetition of letters, (*b*) with repetition of letters?

13. If five men play on a basketball team and only two can play center, how many line-ups are possible?

14. Using the letters of the word *chosen*, how many four-letter words can be formed which end in a vowel?

15. In how many ways can five boys and four girls be seated in a row of nine seats with boys and girls in alternate seats?

16. How many numbers between 20,000 and 40,000 can be made using the five digits 1, 2, 3, 4, and 5?

17. In how many ways can a baseball coach assign nine players to play, if only two can pitch, and a third must catch?

18. From four different consonants and three different vowels, how many five-letter words can be made, each ending in a vowel and beginning with a consonant?

19. From the digits 0, 1, 2, 3, and 4, how many numbers, each of three different digits, can be formed? Hint: The hundreds' digit cannot be zero.

20. In how many ways can A, B, and C attend a play, if the play is given on five nights, A and B cannot attend the same night, and C cannot attend on two of the nights?

145. Permutations of Different Things. The symbol $_nP_r$ is defined to represent, and is read as, *the number of permutations of n different things taken r at a time.*

The number $_nP_r$ can be determined by the fundamental principle, since it is equivalent to the number of ways of filling r places by choosing from n different things. Thus, the first place can be filled in n ways, the second place in $(n-1)$ ways, and so on. The last or rth place can be filled with any one of the things remaining after $(r-1)$ places have been filled. Hence, there are $[n-(r-1)]$ choices for the rth place. By the fundamental principle, we obtain the formula

$$_nP_r = n(n-1)(n-2) \cdots (n-r+1). \qquad (1)$$

Setting $r = n$, we have the particular case of *the number of permutations of n different things taken all together*

$$_nP_n = n(n-1)(n-2) \cdots 3 \cdot 2 \cdot 1 = n! \qquad (2)$$

Illustration 1. $_6P_3 = 6 \cdot 5 \cdot 4 = 120$, $_4P_4 = 4! = 24$, $_nP_2 = n(n-1)$.

NOTE. While many problems involving permutations are readily solved by using the above formulas, it is often *simpler* to use the fundamental principle directly.

Example. How many permutations can be made taking all the letters in the word *equation*, if q must be followed by u?

Solution: Considering q and u to be fastened together in the order qu, we have seven things to permute. Hence, there are $_7P_7 = 5040$ different permutations.

Formulas (1) and (2) were derived on the assumption that the places to be filled were in a line; hence they are sometimes known as **linear permutations.** If the places to be filled were arranged in a ring, there would be fewer **different** arrangements; such distinct arrangements are called **cyclical permutations.**

Illustration 2. Corresponding to the six linear permutations *abc*, *acb*, *bac*, *bca*, *cab*, and *cba*, there are two cyclical permutations:

The number of cyclical arrangements in any problem may be determined by (*a*) placing one thing arbitrarily on the ring, and (*b*) using the fundamental principle to compute how the other places may be filled.

146. Permutation of Things Not All Different. A simple illustration shows that there are fewer permutations of *like* things than of *unlike* things. For instance, taken all at a time, there are six permutations of the letters *a*, *b*, and *c*, whereas there are only three distinct permutations of the letters *a*, *a*, and *b*, and only one permutation of the letters *a*, *a*, and *a*.

Example. Find the number of distinct permutations *P* which can be made by taking all the letters in the word *error*.

Solution: Consider the three *r*'s to be replaced by the three distinct letters r_1, r_2, and r_3. Then for *each* of the *P* permutations of the letters *e*, *r*, *r*, *o*, *r* we can arrange r_1, r_2, and r_3 in 3! ways, giving in all $P \cdot 3!$ permutations of the letters *e*, r_1, r_2, *o*, r_3. However, these five distinct letters taken all at a time can be permuted in 5! ways. Hence, we have

$$P \cdot 3! = 5! \quad \text{or} \quad P = 5!/3! = 20.$$

The above example illustrates the method of proof used in establishing the following theorem:

Theorem. *If* **P** *represents the number of distinct permutations of* **n** *things taken all at a time, when* **p** *are alike,* **q** *others are alike,* **r** *others are alike, and so on, then*

$$P = \frac{n!}{p!\, q!\, r! \cdots}.$$

EXERCISE 95

1. Find the value of (a) $_7P_4$, (b) $_{11}P_7$, (c) $_5P_5$.

2. Find the value of (a) $_7P_3$, (b) $_{50}P_2$, (c) $_6P_6$.

3. Given $_nP_2 = 56$, find n.

4. Given $_nP_3 = 9_nP_2$, find n.

5. Show that $_{20}P_2 = 19_5P_2$.

6. Show that $_{16}P_3 = 2_8P_4$.

7. Show that $_4P_1 + _4P_2 + _4P_3 + _4P_4 = 4^3$.

8. Six speakers are to be heard at a forum. (a) In how many ways can the order of their appearance be arranged? (b) If C must speak first? (c) If B must speak immediately after A?

9. If each of nine boys is to receive a book, in how many ways can four identical algebra books and five identical geometry books be distributed?

10. In how many ways can eight boys be arranged in a ring facing each other?

11. In how many ways can seven people take seats in a row of seven chairs if a certain three people are to be together?

12. How many permutations can be made of the letters in the word (a) *serene*, (b) *Mississippi*, when taken all at a time?

13. Show that $_nP_r = n!/(n - r)!$.

14. How many numbers, each of eight figures, can be made with the digits 2, 2, 3, 3, 3, 4, 5, and 5?

15. In how many different orders can seven people be seated at a round table?

16. (a) In how many orders can four boys and three girls be seated in a row? (b) In how many of these is a boy seated on each end?

17. How many distinct signals can be made with six flags displayed in vertical order all at one time, if three are yellow, two are blue, and one is red?

18. In how many ways can four French, three English, and three German books be arranged on a shelf so that all the books in each language are together?

19. If two cubical dice are thrown, in how many ways can they come up?

20. A contest offers one $25 first prize, five $10 second prizes, and ten $5 third prizes. If sixteen winners are chosen, in how many ways can the prizes be distributed among them?

21. In how many different orders can four men and four women be arranged in a circle with men and women alternating?

22. In flipping a coin ten consecutive times, in how many different orders can one obtain four heads and six tails?

23. Using the digits 1, 2, 3, 4, 5, 6, and 7 without repetitions, (*a*) how many numbers each of five figures can you form? (*b*) In how many does the digit 5 appear? (*c*) How many end in 25?

24. How many even numbers each of six figures can be made with the digits 2, 2, 3, 4, 5, and 5? Hint: Find the numbers (*a*) ending with 2 and (*b*) ending with 4; then add (*a*) and (*b*).

25. How many five-letter arrangements can be made from the letters of the word *algebra*, if the first three letters are to be vowels?

26. (*a*) How many permutations can be made with all the letters in the word *universal*? (*b*) How many of these begin with *u* and end with *s*? (*c*) In how many do the vowels and consonants alternate?

27. Using the digits 0, 2, 4, 5, 7, and 9, (*a*) how many numbers each of four different figures can you form? (*b*) How many of these are odd? (*c*) How many are numerically greater than 5000?

28. With the letters *A*, *B*, *C*, *D*, *E*, and *F*, (*a*) how many permutations each of five different letters can be formed? (*b*) In how many does the letter *C* occupy the middle position? (*c*) In how many are the letters *E* and *F* adjacent?

29. How many permutations can be made of the letters in the word *cyclical* taken all at a time? How many of these begin with *c* and end with *y*?

30. In how many ways can five people be seated at a round table, if *A* and *B* cannot be seated next to each other? Hint: Seat *A* first.

147. Combinations. The symbol $_nC_r$ is defined to represent, and is read as, *the number of combinations of **n** different things taken **r** at a time.*

Illustration 1. The different combinations of *a*, *b*, *c*, and *d* taken three at a time are (*a*, *b*, *c*), (*a*, *b*, *d*), (*a*, *c*, *d*), and (*b*, *c*, *d*); hence $_4C_3$ equals 4.

The basic difference between permutations and combinations is that of order, or arrangement. Thus, *each* of the $_nC_r$ combinations, consisting of *r* different things, gives rise to *r*! permutations by the mere rearranging of the order of the things in that particular combination. Hence, from all the $_nC_r$ combinations we can form $_nC_r \cdot r!$ different permutations, and these are the different permutations of *n* things taken *r* at a time. Therefore, we have $_nC_r \cdot r! = {_nP_r}$, or

$$_nC_r = \frac{_nP_r}{r!} = \frac{n(n-1)\cdots(n-r+1)}{r!}. \tag{1}$$

Illustration 2. From a group of five people a committee of three can be selected in $_5C_3$ ways, where $_5C_3 = \dfrac{5\cdot4\cdot3}{1\cdot2\cdot3} = 10$.

NOTE 1. Observe in $_nC_r$ that there are r factors in both the numerator and the denominator.

If the numerator and denominator of (1) are both multiplied by $(n-r)!$, the new numerator is

$$n(n-1)\cdots(n-r+1)\times(n-r)(n-r-1)\cdots2\cdot1$$

or $n!$ Thus (1) may be written compactly as

$$_nC_r = \frac{n!}{r!(n-r)!}. \tag{2}$$

Whenever r things are selected from a group of n things to form a combination, it is apparent that the remaining $(n-r)$ things also form a combination; hence the number of combinations in either case must be equal, that is

$$_nC_r = _nC_{n-r}.$$

NOTE 2. This relation is also obtained when $(n-r)$ is substituted for r in (2).

Example 1. From a group of six men and four women, how many committees can be selected, each consisting of four men and three women?

Solution: To find the number of committees specified, it is necessary

(a) to select a group of four men from six men,

(b) to select a group of three women from four women, and

(c) to apply the fundamental principle.

Since order is not involved, we have (a) $_6C_4 = 15$ groups, (b) $_4C_3 = 4$ groups, and (c) $15\cdot4$ or 60 different committees.

Example 2. From five different consonants and four different vowels, how many words can be made, each containing three consonants and two vowels?

Solution: We can choose three consonants in $_5C_3$, or 10 ways, and two vowels in $_4C_2$, or 6 ways. Hence the total number of combined groups is $10\cdot6$ or 60.

Since, in this case, *each* of these groups of five letters can be arranged among themselves in 5! ways, there will be $60\cdot5!$ or 7200 words of the type specified.

148. Combinations Taking Some or All of n Things.
In considering the numerical form of the symbol $_nC_r$, it is apparent that the binomial formula may be expressed as

$$(A + B)^n = A^n + {}_nC_1A^{n-1}B + {}_nC_2A^{n-2}B^2 + \cdots$$
$$+ {}_nC_rA^{n-r}B^r + \cdots + {}_nC_nB^n.$$

If in this relation we put $A = B = 1$, then

$$(1 + 1)^n = 1 + {}_nC_1 + {}_nC_2 + \cdots + {}_nC_r + \cdots + {}_nC_n,$$
or $\qquad {}_nC_1 + {}_nC_2 + \cdots + {}_nC_r + \cdots + {}_nC_n = 2^n - 1.$

That is, *the total number of combinations of n things taken successively $1, 2, 3, \cdots, n$ at a time is $(2^n - 1)$.*

Illustration. A man having six friends can invite one or more of them to dinner in $(2^6 - 1)$ or 63 different ways.

NOTE. The above relation can also be obtained by reasoning as follows: With *each* of n things we have two choices; we take it or we leave it. Hence, by the fundamental principle, we have 2^n ways of taking or leaving n things. Rejecting the possibility that all of the n things are left, we have the result stated above.

EXERCISE 96

1. Find the value of (a) $_8C_3$, (b) $_{15}C_9$, (c) $_{25}C_{21}$.
2. Find the value of (a) $_{10}C_4$, (b) $_{13}C_5$, (c) $_{100}C_{98}$.
3. Show that $_{12}C_5 + {}_{12}C_4 = {}_{13}C_5$.
4. Show that $_4C_1^2 + {}_4C_2^2 + {}_4C_3^2 + {}_4C_4^2 = {}_8C_4 - 1$.
5. How many different teams of five can be chosen from nine players?
6. In how many ways can a committee of four be chosen in a club having thirty-two members?
7. How many different hands of thirteen cards each can be made from a deck of fifty-two cards?
8. How many triangles will be formed by ten lines, if each line intersects all others and no three lines pass through the same point?
9. How many sums of money can be formed from a cent, a nickel, a dime, a quarter, and a half dollar?
10. From a group of ten different books, how many selections can be made by taking some or all of the books?
11. How many words of four different consonants and two different vowels can be made from the English alphabet of twenty-one consonants and five vowels?

12. How many numbers containing three different odd digits and two different even digits can be written? (The digit 0 is excluded.)

13. In how many ways can a committee of five be selected from twelve persons? If a certain person is to be included? If a certain person is to be excluded?

14. From a committee of eight people, how many subcommittees can be formed including some or all of the people?

15. How many committees of five women can be selected from nine women, if a certain two women refuse to be on the same committee?

16. In how many ways can twelve different books be divided equally among three people?

17. How many selections can a dealer make in buying one or more of nine paintings?

18. How many different hands of five cards each can be made from a deck of fifty-two cards? How many of these contain three aces and two kings?

19. In how many ways can a party of four or more be selected from eight persons?

20. If $_nC_{12} = {_nC_8}$, find $_nC_{18}$.

21. In how many ways can a committee of five be selected from seven Seniors and five Juniors, so that the committee contains (a) exactly three Seniors, (b) at least three Seniors, (c) at most three Seniors?

22. With three capitals, six consonants, and four vowels, how many different words can be formed, each beginning with a capital and containing three different consonants and two different vowels?

23. From five black balls and six white balls, in how many ways can we select five balls so that (a) exactly two are black, (b) at least two are black?

24. In how many ways can twelve boys be divided into three groups each containing four boys?

CHAPTER 20

Probability

149. Meaning of Probability. When an event *occurs* or *fails to occur* in a specified manner, we say that the **trial** of the event is a *success* or a *failure* respectively. The term **probability** is defined in mathematics as a quantity representing the likelihood of success in the occurrence of some particular event. For example, the probability that a toss of a coin will result in a head is one chance out of two possibilities.

The study of probability can follow two lines of development, depending on whether the term *probability* is defined (*a*) as a *mathematical* quantity depending on the theoretical nature of the event, or (*b*) as a *statistical* quantity depending on the past history of similar events.

150. Mathematical Probability. *If any trial of an event can succeed in* **s** *different ways and can fail in* **f** *different ways, and if each of the* (**s** + **f**) *ways is equally likely to occur, the probabilities of success* **p** *or of failure* **q** *are given respectively by*

$$p = \frac{s}{s+f}, \quad q = \frac{f}{s+f}.$$

In the definition it is evident that the sum $(p + q)$ is always **1.** Thus, if a probability of success is known to be $\frac{2}{5}$, the probability of failure *must* be $(1 - \frac{2}{5})$ or $\frac{3}{5}$. It is also apparent that any probability is a positive number not greater than 1. Furthermore, $p = 1$ means that *success is certain,* and $p = 0$ means that *failure is certain.*

NOTE 1. Instead of saying that the probability of success for an event is $s/(s + f)$, it is sometimes stated that *the* **odds** *are s to f in favor of the event, or f to s against the event.*

If p is the probability of success in one trial of an event, then the **probable number** of successes in N trials is defined as pN. Thus, if a die is cast 300 times, the probable number of times that an ace will come up is $\frac{1}{6} \cdot 300$ or 50.

If p is the probability that a person will receive a sum of money amounting to V dollars, his **expectation** is defined as pV dollars. Thus, if a person is to receive \$12 provided he throws an ace with one cast of a die, his expectation is $\frac{1}{6} \cdot$ \$12 or \$2.

In determining the probability of success for a single event, the following numbers are needed:

1. The total number of ways in which it is possible for the event to occur, and

2. The number of ways in which the event can occur as specified.

Example 1. A box contains six red balls and four blue balls. If four balls are drawn, find the probability that two are red and two are blue.

Solution: *1.* The total number of ways in which four balls can be chosen from a group of ten balls is $_{10}C_4$ or 210 ways.

2. Two red balls can be chosen from a group of six in $_6C_2$ or 15 ways, and two blue balls can be chosen from a group of four in $_4C_2$ or 6 ways. Hence, there are $15 \cdot 6$ or 90 groups, each of which contains two red and two blue balls.

Therefore, the probability of drawing two red and two blue balls is $\frac{90}{210}$ or $\frac{3}{7}$.

Example 2. In a race, the odds are 4 to 3 in favor of A's winning and 5 to 2 against B's winning. If a man gets \$10 if A wins and \$50 if B wins, what is the value of his expectation?

Solution: The probability of A's winning is $\frac{4}{7}$, and hence the expectation on A is $\frac{4}{7} \cdot$ \$10. The probability of B's winning is $\frac{2}{7}$, and hence the expectation on B is $\frac{2}{7} \cdot$ \$50. Therefore, the total expectation is $(\frac{40}{7} + \frac{100}{7})$ or \$20.

NOTE 2. Observe that the total expectation is the average return to be expected if the event is repeated many times. Thus, in 7000 races, we expect A to win 4000 times, making \$40,000; we expect B to win 2000 times, making \$100,000. Hence, on the average, we expect a return of \$140,000/7000 or \$20 per race.

151. Statistical Probability. *If an event has been known to occur S times out of N trials, the ratio S/N is called the* **relative frequency** *of success. If N is large, the statistical (or empirical) probability is defined as*

$$p = \frac{S}{N}.$$

Illustration. If it has been found that out of 1000 articles manufactured, 29 are defective, the relative frequency of defectiveness is $\frac{29}{1000}$, and the probability that any single article is defective is 0.029.

NOTE. The statistical probability p is of little or no value when N is small. Its reliability increases as N increases.

Statistically determined probabilities have many useful applications. For example, certain American life insurance companies have compiled their past experiences into a table called the **American Experience Table of Mortality** (Table IX). This table is a record of the time of death of 100,000 persons, all of whom were living at the age of 10 years.

Example. Find the probability that (*a*) a boy of 10 will live to be 20, (*b*) a man of 20 will live to be 60.

Solution: The mortality table (Table IX) shows that, out of 100,000 persons 10 years of age, 92,637 live to be 20 and 57,917 live to be 60. Hence (*a*) the probability of persons living from 10 to 20 is 92,637/100,000, or 0.926; (*b*) the probability of persons living from 20 to 60 is 57,917/92,637, or 0.625.

EXERCISE 97

1. If the probability of winning a contest is $\frac{3}{7}$, what is the probability of losing the contest?

2. The odds are 7 to 5 against a man winning \$60. What is his expectation?

3. What is the probability of throwing a double with one cast of two dice?

4. What is the probability of drawing a heart from a deck of fifty-two cards?

5. If the probability that a boy will get a job is $\frac{5}{8}$, what are the odds in favor of his getting a job?

6. From a deck of fifty-two cards, what is the probability (*a*) of drawing an ace, (*b*) of drawing a king or queen?

7. If two coins are tossed, what is the probability that they will both fall heads up?

8. A bag contains five white, six red, and nine black balls. If one ball is drawn, what is the probability that it is (*a*) white, (*b*) white or red?

9. A building has six elevators. Find the probability that two men, entering at random, will use the same elevator.

10. Find the expectation of a person who is to get a dollar if he draws a diamond from a deck of fifty-two cards.

11. If a letter is chosen at random from the word *succeeded*, what are the odds against its being an *e*?

12. A bag contains fifteen red balls and nine black balls. If three balls are drawn, what is the probability that (*a*) all are red, (*b*) two are red and one is black?

13. Four red books and three blue books are placed at random on a shelf. What is the probability that the blue books will be adjacent?

14. In a single throw of two dice, what is the probability of throwing (*a*) a five, (*b*) at most five?

15. A wallet contains nine $5 bills and six $10 bills. What is a person's expectation, if a bill is chosen at random?

16. The age groups in a certain college are divided as follows: seventeen, 23; eighteen, 49; nineteen, 67; twenty, 46; twenty-one, 38; and twenty-two or more, 21. Find the relative frequencies of the various age groups to the nearest percentage.

17. What is the probability that a man 25 years old will live at least ten years longer?

18. Find the probability that a man 60 years old will die within five years.

19. Find the probability that a man 30 years old will die during his fiftieth year.

20. What is the probability that a boy of fifteen (*a*) will not live to be 30 years of age, (*b*) will live to be more than 30 years of age?

21. At what age does a boy of 10 have the greatest chance of dying?

22. Ten people are to be seated by lot at a circular table. What is the probability that a particular couple will be seated in adjacent chairs?

23. Two digits are drawn from 1, 2, 3, 4, 5, 6, and 7. What are the odds against the digits being both even?

24. Five digits are chosen at random from 1, 2, 3, 4, 5, 6, 7, 8, and 9. What is the probability that three are odd and two are even?

25. If a die is cast and one receives an amount in dollars equal to the number thrown, what is his expectation?

26. If four dimes and three nickels are placed at random in a line, find the probability that the first and last coins are both nickels.

27. If the letters of the word *seated* are given a random arrangement, what is the probability that (a) the consonants and vowels will alternate, (b) the two e's will be adjacent?

28. In drawing a card from a deck of fifty-two cards, a spade pays 50 cents, a heart 30 cents, a diamond 10 cents, and a club nothing. Is it worth 25 cents to take a chance at this game?

29. A committee of four is chosen by lot from a group of five men and six women. What is the probability that the committee will consist of (a) two men and two women, (b) all men or all women?

30. A quartet is chosen by lot from six Seniors, five Juniors, and four Sophomores. What is the probability that it will consist of (a) all Seniors, (b) at least two Juniors?

152. Probabilities of Related Events. Thus far in the discussion of probability we have considered only the probability of success for a single event. Let us now consider the problem of determining probabilities when two or more events are involved.

Two events are said to be **dependent** or **independent** according as the occurrence of one *does* or *does not* affect the occurrence of the other. Thus in drawing two cards from a deck of fifty-two cards, the *first drawing* and the *second drawing* are two successive events. If the first card drawn is *not replaced*, then the second drawing is *dependent* on the outcome of the first; and if the first card is *replaced*, then the second drawing is *independent* of the first.

Illustration. If a king is drawn from a deck of fifty-two cards, the probability of drawing another king is $\frac{3}{51}$. If some card not a king is drawn first, the probability of drawing a king is $\frac{4}{51}$. If the first card is replaced, the probability of drawing a king is $\frac{4}{52}$, regardless of what happened in the first drawing.

Theorem 1. *If the probability of success of a first event is p_1 and if, after this event has succeeded, the probability of success of a* *second event is p_2, then the probability that both events succeed in the order stated is p_1p_2.*

Proof: Suppose that the first event can succeed in s_1 out of a total of n_1 different ways. Likewise suppose that the second event can succeed in s_2 out of a total of n_2 different ways. Then by the fundamental principle in Article 144, it follows that the two events in the order stated can succeed in s_1s_2 out of a total of n_1n_2 different ways. Hence

$$p = \frac{s_1s_2}{n_1n_2} = \frac{s_1}{n_1} \cdot \frac{s_2}{n_2} = p_1p_2.$$

NOTE 1. For n events, it is evident that $p = p_1p_2 \cdots p_n$.

Example 1. Two balls are drawn in succession from a bag containing five white and six black balls. Find the probability that the first ball is white and the second black, if the balls (*a*) are not replaced, (*b*) are replaced.

Solution: The probability of success on the first drawing is $\frac{5}{11}$.

(*a*) If the first drawing is successful, there remain in the bag 4 white and 6 black balls. Hence, the probability of success in the second drawing is $\frac{6}{10}$. Thus, $p = \frac{5}{11} \cdot \frac{6}{10} = \frac{3}{11}$.

(*b*) If the first ball is replaced, the probability of success in the second drawing is $\frac{6}{11}$. Thus, $p = \frac{5}{11} \cdot \frac{6}{11} = \frac{30}{121}$.

Two events are said to be **mutually exclusive** if *in any one trial* both events cannot succeed. Thus, the drawing of a king and the drawing of a queen from a deck of cards are two mutually exclusive events, whereas the drawing of a king and the drawing of a spade are *not* mutually exclusive events.

Theorem 2. *If the probabilities of two mutually exclusive events are p_1 and p_2, then the probability that in any single trial either one or the other of these two events succeeds is ($p_1 + p_2$).*

Proof: Out of the n ways in which the trial can occur, let s_1 and s_2 be the ways in which each of the two events can succeed. Because the two events are mutually exclusive, the s_1 ways are all different from the s_2 ways. Hence, the probability that either one or the other of the events will succeed is given by

$$p = \frac{s_1 + s_2}{n} = \frac{s_1}{n} + \frac{s_2}{n} = p_1 + p_2.$$

NOTE 2. For n mutually exclusive events, it is evident that

$$\bar{p} = p_1 + p_2 + \cdots + p_n.$$

In determining the probability of success for a certain event, the following procedure is often helpful:

1. Divide the event into mutually exclusive subevents in such a way that it is possible to

2. Find the probability of success for each subevent; then,

3. Add these probabilities in accordance with Theorem 2.

Example 2. A bag contains six red and four blue balls. If two balls are drawn at random, what is the probability that both balls are of the same color?

Solution: As given above, we have the following analysis:

1. Success is attained by drawing (*a*) 2 red balls or (*b*) 2 blue balls.

2. The respective probabilities are (*a*) $\frac{6}{10} \cdot \frac{5}{9}$ and (*b*) $\frac{4}{10} \cdot \frac{3}{9}$.

3. Hence the required probability is $\frac{5}{15} + \frac{2}{15} = \frac{7}{15}$.

NOTE 3. It is often advisable to verify a probability of success p by computing the probability of failure q, and testing $p + q = 1$. Thus, in the above example, failure is achieved by drawing (*a*) first a red and then a blue ball or (*b*) first a blue and then a red ball. The respective probabilities are (*a*) $\frac{6}{10} \cdot \frac{4}{9}$ and (*b*) $\frac{4}{10} \cdot \frac{6}{9}$. Hence, $q = \frac{4}{15} + \frac{4}{15} = \frac{8}{15}$.

EXERCISE 98

1. A bag contains twelve white, eight red, and four black balls. If one ball is drawn, what is the probability that it is either black or white?

2. One card is drawn from a deck of fifty-two cards. What is the probability of drawing (*a*) a king or queen, (*b*) a king or a spade?

3. The probabilities that *A* and *B* will pass a course are respectively $\frac{5}{6}$ and $\frac{3}{5}$. What is the probability that (*a*) both will pass, (*b*) only one will pass, (*c*) neither will pass?

4. If a coin is tossed and a die is cast, what is the probability of obtaining (*a*) a head and a four, (*b*) a head and more than a four?

5. The probability that *A* will live for ten years is $\frac{2}{3}$ and that *B* will live for ten years is $\frac{3}{4}$. What is the probability that (*a*) both will live for ten years, (*b*) only one will live for ten years?

6. One letter is selected at random from each of the words *success* and *resist*. What is the probability that (*a*) both are *s*'s, (*b*) one is *s*, (*c*) neither is *s*?

7. The odds against *A*'s winning a game are 4 to 3, and the odds favoring his winning another game are 3 to 2. What is the probability that he (*a*) wins both games, (*b*) loses both games?

8. *A* and *B* make one throw of two dice for $10. If seven is thrown *A* wins, if ten is thrown *B* wins, and if anything else is thrown they each win $5. What are the respective expectations for *A* and *B*?

9. Three cards are drawn from a deck of fifty-two cards. What is the probability that (*a*) all are spades, (*b*) all are of the same suit, (*c*) two are red and one is a spade?

10. From a group of seven men and five women, a committee of four is chosen by lot. Find the probability that the committee will consist of (*a*) all men, (*b*) two men and two women, (*c*) at least two men.

11. Two balls are drawn from a bag containing eight white, seven black, five red, and four blue balls. What is the probability that both balls are of the same color?

12. A man is 65 years of age and his wife is 60. Using the mortality table, compute the probability that both will live for five years.

13. One envelope contains five $1 bills and one $5 bill, and a second envelope contains four $1 bills and two $5 bills. If we select an envelope and then a bill at random, what is (*a*) the probability of getting a $1 bill, (*b*) the expectation?

14. A bag contains six red balls and four blue balls. If three balls are drawn, what is the probability that (*a*) all are red, (*b*) two are one color and the third is a different color?

15. If one digit is selected from each of the numbers 12,176 and 35,257, what is the probability that their sum is even?

16. From a box containing nine red and six blue balls, one ball is drawn and replaced, then a second ball is drawn. What is the probability that the two balls are (*a*) red, (*b*) of one color, (*c*) of different color?

17. Solve Problem 16, if the first ball is not replaced.

18. One bag contains six white and two black balls, and a second bag contains five white and three black balls. If one ball is drawn from each bag, find the probability that (*a*) both are white, (*b*) only one is white.

19. In Problem 18, if a bag is selected at random and one ball is drawn, what is the probability that it is white?

20. Three independent events have the probabilities $\frac{1}{2}$, $\frac{2}{3}$, and $\frac{3}{4}$, respectively. What is the probability that (*a*) none of the events succeed, (*b*) exactly one succeeds, (*c*) exactly two succeed, (*d*) all succeed?

21. *A* and *B* in that order cut a deck of fifty-two cards, replacing the cards after each cut. If the first who cuts a spade wins, what are their respective probabilities of winning?

22. If one digit is selected from each of the numbers 52,369, 44,521, and 36,721, what is the probability that their sum is even?

23. Two persons, whose probabilities of speaking the truth are $\frac{2}{3}$ and $\frac{3}{4}$ respectively, assert that a tossed coin fell heads up. What is the probability of the truth of this assertion? Hint: Find the probability that both are truthful, that both are untruthful, and compare.

24. One box contains nine white balls and one black ball, and a second box contains six white balls. If four balls at random are moved from the first box to the second, and if five balls are then moved back to the first box, find the probability that the black ball is in the second box.

153. Repeated Trials of an Event.

Theorem. *If the probability of success is p and the probability of failure is q, the probability that an event will succeed exactly r times in n trials is $_nC_r p^r q^{n-r}$.*

Proof: It is possible for r successes to occur out of n trials in $_nC_r$ different ways. Regardless of the order in which these r successes occur, the probability of each arrangement is $p^r q^{n-r}$. Hence, the probability for all arrangements of r successes out of n trials is given by the product $_nC_r \cdot p^r q^{n-r}$.

Example 1. A card is drawn from a deck of fifty-two cards and is then replaced. If this event is repeated six times, what is the probability that exactly two of the cards drawn are spades?

Solution: The probabilities of drawing a spade or not drawing a spade are respectively $\frac{1}{4}$ and $\frac{3}{4}$. Hence, the probability of drawing exactly two spades in six trials is

$$p = {}_6C_2(\tfrac{1}{4})^2(\tfrac{3}{4})^4 = 15 \cdot \tfrac{1}{16} \cdot \tfrac{81}{256} = \tfrac{1215}{4096}.$$

Since the expression $_nC_r p^r q^{n-r}$ is recognized as the $(n-r+1)$st term in the binomial expansion of $(p + q)^n$, it follows that the various probabilities of success in repeated trials are precisely the terms of the binomial expansion

$$(p + q)^n = p^n + np^{n-1}q + \frac{n(n - 1)}{1 \cdot 2} p^{n-2}q^2 + \cdots + q^n.$$

Thus, in n trials, the probability of n successes is p^n, $(n - 1)$ successes is $np^{n-1}q$, $(n - 2)$ successes is $\frac{1}{2} n(n - 1)p^{n-2}q^2$, and so on.

Example 2. Find the probability of throwing at least two aces in four throws of a die.

Solution: We obtain *at least* two aces when we obtain either two aces, three aces, or four aces. Hence, since $p = \frac{1}{6}$, $q = \frac{5}{6}$, $n = 4$, $r = 4$, 3, or 2, we have

$$p = (\tfrac{1}{6})^4 + 4(\tfrac{1}{6})^3(\tfrac{5}{6}) + 6(\tfrac{1}{6})^2(\tfrac{5}{6})^2$$
$$= \frac{1 + 20 + 150}{6^4} = \frac{171}{1296}.$$

EXERCISE 99

1. If a die is cast six times in succession, what is the probability that an ace comes up (a) just once, (b) at least once?

2. From a deck of fifty-two cards, a card is drawn and then replaced. In eight trials, what is the probability that (a) exactly two spades are drawn, (b) at least two spades are drawn?

3. If six coins are thrown on the floor, what is the probability that three heads and three tails appear?

4. The probability that a man wins at a certain game is $\frac{1}{3}$. What is the probability that, out of six games played, he wins (a) exactly two, (b) at least two?

5. A thinks of a positive integer and B guesses whether it is odd or even. In eight trials, what is the probability that B will make correct guesses in (a) six, (b) four, (c) at least four?

6. If eight calendar dates are chosen at random, what is the probability that exactly two of them will be Sundays? Hint: Use logarithms.

7. On the average, a certain boy can solve two out of three problems given to him. If five problems are given on a test and three are required for passing, what is the probability of his passing?

8. If on the average one automobile in every ten has faulty brakes, what is the probability that, out of five automobiles inspected, at least four have good brakes?

CHAPTER 21

Determinants

154. Introduction. In Articles 37 and 38 certain arrays of numbers were called determinants of the second and third order, and the values of these determinants were defined as follows:

$$\begin{vmatrix} a_1 & b_1 \\ a_2 & b_2 \end{vmatrix} = a_1b_2 - a_2b_1,$$

and

$$\begin{vmatrix} a_1 & b_1 & c_1 \\ a_2 & b_2 & c_2 \\ a_3 & b_3 & c_3 \end{vmatrix} = a_1b_2c_3 + a_2b_3c_1 + a_3b_1c_2 - a_1b_3c_2 - a_2b_1c_3 - a_3b_2c_1.$$

In this chapter we shall give a general definition of a determinant of any positive integral order n which will include the above definitions as special cases.

155. Inversions. The positive integers from 1 to n are said to be in **natural order** when they are arranged in order of increasing magnitude 1, 2, 3, $\cdots$, n. In any other arrangement of these integers, we say that there is an **inversion** of order when any integer precedes (is to the left of) a smaller integer.

Illustration 1. The arrangement 2, 1, 5, 3, 4 has three inversions because 5 precedes 4, 5 precedes 3, and 2 precedes 1.

Note. If a, b, c, d is the natural order for these four letters, then d, b, a, c has four inversions: d precedes c, d precedes b, d precedes a, and b precedes a.

Illustration 2. The product $a_2b_3c_1d_4$, with letters in natural order, has two inversions in the subscripts. The same product $c_1a_2b_3d_4$, with subscripts in natural order, has two inversions in the letters.

156. Definitions. Let us arrange a set of n^2 numbers, called **elements,** to form a square array consisting of n columns and n rows, and enclosed by two vertical bars. If the columns are denoted by letters and the rows by subscripts, we have

$$\Delta_n \equiv \begin{vmatrix} a_1 & b_1 & . & . & . & r_1 \\ a_2 & b_2 & . & . & . & r_2 \\ . & . & . & . & . & . \\ a_n & b_n & . & . & . & r_n \end{vmatrix}. \tag{1}$$

The array of numbers Δ_n, $n > 1$, is called a **determinant of the nth order,** *and it is a symbol representing the sum of all products formed by*

1. Taking as factors one, and only one, element from each row and each column, and

2. Prefixing each product with a **plus or minus** *sign according as the number of inversions of the subscripts is* **even or odd,** *after the letters of the product are arranged in the order that they appear in the first row of the determinant.*

Symbolically,

$$\Delta_n \equiv \sum \pm a_\alpha b_\beta \cdots r_\rho \tag{2}$$

where the indicated sum $\sum$ extends over all permutations $\alpha, \beta, \cdots, \rho$ of the integers $1, 2, \cdots, n$.

The algebraic sum (2) is called the **expansion** of the determinant, and the individual products with their proper sign are called **terms** of the determinant. The line of elements extending from the upper left corner to the lower right corner is called the **principal diagonal** of Δ_n.

NOTE 1. When $n = 2$ and $n = 3$, observe that the above definition is the same as those stated in Article 154.

NOTE 2. Since there are $n!$ ways of permuting n different numbers, it is apparent that there are $n!$ terms in the expansion (2). Thus, the expansion of a fourth-order determinant has 4! or 24 terms.

157. Properties of Determinants. In order to facilitate the discussion of the properties of determinants, some of the illustrations and proofs will be confined to third-order determinants. The extensions to the proofs for the general case will in most instances be evident.

Property I. *The value of Δ_n is not changed if corresponding rows and columns are interchanged. Thus, if*

$$\Delta_3 = \begin{vmatrix} a_1 & b_1 & c_1 \\ a_2 & b_2 & c_2 \\ a_3 & b_3 & c_3 \end{vmatrix} \text{ and } \Delta_3' = \begin{vmatrix} a_1 & a_2 & a_3 \\ b_1 & b_2 & b_3 \\ c_1 & c_2 & c_3 \end{vmatrix}, \text{ then } \Delta_3 = \Delta_3'.$$

Proof: By the definition of a determinant, Δ_3 and Δ_3' have exactly the same terms in their expansions except possibly for a difference in sign.

Consider any one of the six terms of Δ_3, say $a_2 b_3 c_1$. This term has no inversions in letters and two in subscripts; written as $a_2 c_1 b_3$, it has one inversion in letters and one in subscripts; and written as $c_1 a_2 b_3$, it has two inversions in letters and none in subscripts.

Thus, by interchanging adjacent factors, we see that each term of Δ_3 will have the same number of inversions in subscripts as the corresponding term of Δ_3' has in letters, and hence both will have the same sign.

NOTE. It follows directly from Property I that for every theorem concerning the *columns* of a determinant, there is a corresponding theorem concerning the *rows*.

Property II. *If each element of a column (or row) of Δ_n is zero, then $\Delta_n = 0$.*

Proof: Since each term of Δ_n must contain an element from the column of zeros, each term is zero, and hence $\Delta_n = 0$.

Property III. *If two columns (or rows) of Δ_n are interchanged to obtain the determinant Δ_n', then $\Delta_n' = -\Delta_n$.*

Proof: (*a*) If *adjacent* rows of a determinant are interchanged, this interchanges the corresponding adjacent subscripts in each term of the expansion. Hence the number of inversions in subscripts in each term is increased or decreased by 1. Thus the sign of each term, and consequently the sign of Δ_n, are changed.

(*b*) Now assume that two rows are separated by k other

rows. The two rows may be interchanged by $(2k+1)$ interchanges of adjacent rows: $(k+1)$ interchanges to bring the lower row to the position occupied by the upper row, and k interchanges to take the upper row down to the original position of the lower row. Since $(2k+1)$ is always an odd number, there is an odd number of changes in sign, and the sign of Δ_n is changed.

Illustration 1.
$$\begin{vmatrix} a_1 & b_1 & c_1 \\ a_2 & b_2 & c_2 \\ a_3 & b_3 & c_3 \end{vmatrix} = - \begin{vmatrix} c_1 & b_1 & a_1 \\ c_2 & b_2 & a_2 \\ c_3 & b_3 & a_3 \end{vmatrix}.$$

Property IV. *If two columns (or rows) of Δ_n are identical, then $\Delta_n = 0$.*

Proof: If we interchange the identical columns, the value of Δ_n changes to $-\Delta_n$ by Property III. Since, however, such an interchange leaves the determinant unaltered, we have $\Delta_n = -\Delta_n$. Thus, $2\Delta_n = 0$, or $\Delta_n = 0$.

Property V. *If each element of a column (or row) of Δ_n is multiplied by the same number k to obtain a new determinant Δ'_n, then $\Delta'_n = k\Delta_n$. Thus*

$$\begin{vmatrix} a_1 & kb_1 & c_1 \\ a_2 & kb_2 & c_2 \\ a_3 & kb_3 & c_3 \end{vmatrix} = k \begin{vmatrix} a_1 & b_1 & c_1 \\ a_2 & b_2 & c_2 \\ a_3 & b_3 & c_3 \end{vmatrix}.$$

Proof: Each term in the expansion of Δ'_n will contain one and only one element from the column which is multiplied by k. Thus each term of Δ'_n is k times the corresponding term of Δ_n, and hence $\Delta'_n = k\Delta_n$.

Illustration 2. Property V may be used to *simplify* determinants; thus,

$$\begin{vmatrix} 9 & 6 & -3 \\ 4 & 2 & 1 \\ 1 & -2 & 3 \end{vmatrix} = 2 \cdot \begin{vmatrix} 9 & 3 & -3 \\ 4 & 1 & 1 \\ 1 & -1 & 3 \end{vmatrix} = 6 \cdot \begin{vmatrix} 3 & 1 & -1 \\ 4 & 1 & 1 \\ 1 & -1 & 3 \end{vmatrix}.$$

Property VI. *If each element of a column (or row) of Δ_n is expressed as the sum of two or more terms, Δ_n can be expressed as the sum of two or more determinants. Thus,*

$$\begin{vmatrix} a_1 & b_1 + d_1 & c_1 \\ a_2 & b_2 + d_2 & c_2 \\ a_3 & b_3 + d_3 & c_3 \end{vmatrix} = \begin{vmatrix} a_1 & b_1 & c_1 \\ a_2 & b_2 & c_2 \\ a_3 & b_3 & c_3 \end{vmatrix} + \begin{vmatrix} a_1 & d_1 & c_1 \\ a_2 & d_2 & c_2 \\ a_3 & d_3 & c_3 \end{vmatrix}.$$

Proof: For $n = 3$, and in general, it is evident that each term in the expansion of the determinant on the left is equal to the sum of the corresponding terms in the expansion of the determinants on the right. For example,

$$a_2(b_3 + d_3)c_1 = a_2 b_3 c_1 + a_2 d_3 c_1.$$

Property VII. *If to each element of any column (or row) of Δ_n, we add k times the corresponding element of some other column (or row) to obtain a new determinant Δ_n', then $\Delta_n' = \Delta_n$. Thus,*

$$\begin{vmatrix} a_1 & b_1 + kc_1 & c_1 \\ a_2 & b_2 + kc_2 & c_2 \\ a_3 & b_3 + kc_3 & c_3 \end{vmatrix} = \begin{vmatrix} a_1 & b_1 & c_1 \\ a_2 & b_2 & c_2 \\ a_3 & b_3 & c_3 \end{vmatrix}.$$

Proof: Applying Property VI and Property V to Δ_3', we have

$$\Delta_3' = \begin{vmatrix} a_1 & b_1 & c_1 \\ a_2 & b_2 & c_2 \\ a_3 & b_3 & c_3 \end{vmatrix} + k \begin{vmatrix} a_1 & c_1 & c_1 \\ a_2 & c_2 & c_2 \\ a_3 & c_3 & c_3 \end{vmatrix}.$$

The second determinant on the right is zero by Property IV; hence $\Delta_3' = \Delta_3$.

EXERCISE 100

If $1, 2, 3, \cdots$ is the natural order, determine the number of inversions in each of the following:

1. 4132. **2.** 35214. **3.** 51342. **4.** 263541. **5.** 415362.

If $a, b, c, \cdots$ is the natural order, determine the number of inversions in each of the following:

6. dacb. **7.** eadbc. **8.** dceba. **9.** bdecfa. **10.** edacfb.

11. How many terms are there in Δ_4? in Δ_5? in Δ_6?

12. Show that the elements of the principal diagonal always form a positive term. Is this true for the elements of the other diagonal?

13. In the expansion of Δ_4, determine the signs of the terms (a) $a_1 b_3 c_2 d_4$, (b) $c_1 b_2 d_3 a_4$, (c) $b_4 d_1 c_3 a_2$.

14. In the expansion of Δ_5, determine the signs of the terms (a) $a_3 b_5 c_1 d_2 e_4$, (b) $c_1 e_2 b_3 a_4 d_5$, (c) $d_3 a_2 e_5 c_1 b_4$.

15. In the expansion of Δ_4, write the terms which (a) are positive, (b) contain b_2, (c) contain a_2c_4.

16. In the expansion of Δ_5, write the terms which contain (a) b_3e_1, (b) $a_2c_5e_4$.

State which properties of determinants are used in each of the following reductions:

17. $\begin{vmatrix} 2 & 3 & -1 \\ 1 & -2 & 0 \\ 0 & 0 & 0 \end{vmatrix} = 0.$ **18.** $\begin{vmatrix} 3 & -1 & 3 \\ 1 & 0 & -1 \\ 3 & -1 & 3 \end{vmatrix} = 0.$

19. $\begin{vmatrix} 3 & 3 & 1 \\ 2 & 1 & -2 \\ 4 & 2 & -2 \end{vmatrix} = 2\begin{vmatrix} 3 & 3 & 1 \\ 2 & 1 & -2 \\ 2 & 1 & -1 \end{vmatrix} = 2\begin{vmatrix} 3 & 3 & 1 \\ 2 & 1 & -2 \\ 0 & 0 & 1 \end{vmatrix}.$

20. $\begin{vmatrix} 4 & 1 & 3 & 2 \\ 2 & 2 & 6 & -4 \\ -1 & 0 & 1 & 6 \\ 2 & 3 & 0 & -2 \end{vmatrix} = 4\begin{vmatrix} 4 & 1 & 3 & 1 \\ 1 & 1 & 3 & -1 \\ -1 & 0 & 1 & 3 \\ 2 & 3 & 0 & -1 \end{vmatrix} = -4\begin{vmatrix} 4 & 1 & 3 & 1 \\ 2 & 3 & 0 & -1 \\ -1 & 0 & 1 & 3 \\ 1 & 1 & 3 & -1 \end{vmatrix}.$

21. $\begin{vmatrix} 1 & 3 & 1 \\ 2 & x+2 & 5 \\ 1 & 2 & 2 \end{vmatrix} = \begin{vmatrix} 1 & 2 & 1 \\ 2 & x & 5 \\ 1 & 1 & 2 \end{vmatrix} + \begin{vmatrix} 1 & 1 & 1 \\ 2 & 2 & 5 \\ 1 & 1 & 2 \end{vmatrix} = \begin{vmatrix} 1 & 2 & 1 \\ 2 & x & 5 \\ 1 & 1 & 2 \end{vmatrix}.$

22. $\begin{vmatrix} x & y & 1 \\ y & x & 1 \\ 1 & -1 & 0 \end{vmatrix} = \begin{vmatrix} x+y & y & 1 \\ x+y & x & 1 \\ 0 & -1 & 0 \end{vmatrix} = (x+y)\begin{vmatrix} 1 & y & 1 \\ 1 & x & 1 \\ 0 & -1 & 0 \end{vmatrix} = 0.$

23. $\begin{vmatrix} 1 & a & b+c \\ 1 & b & a+c \\ 1 & c & a+b \end{vmatrix} = \begin{vmatrix} 1 & a & b+c \\ 0 & b-a & a-b \\ 0 & c-a & a-c \end{vmatrix} = (b-a)(c-a)\begin{vmatrix} 1 & a & b+c \\ 0 & 1 & -1 \\ 0 & 1 & -1 \end{vmatrix} = 0.$

24. $\begin{vmatrix} 0 & 1 & 2 & 3 \\ -1 & 0 & 1 & 2 \\ -2 & -1 & 0 & 1 \\ -3 & -2 & -1 & 0 \end{vmatrix} = \begin{vmatrix} 0 & -1 & 2 & 1 \\ -1 & -1 & 1 & 1 \\ -2 & -1 & 0 & 1 \\ -3 & -1 & -1 & 1 \end{vmatrix} = 0.$

25. If the elements in one row (or column) of Δ_n are proportional to the corresponding elements of another row (or column), prove that $\Delta_n = 0$.

158. Expansion of a Determinant by Minors. *If in the determinant Δ_n of order n we omit (or cross out) the row and column containing a given element, say b_2, the remaining determinant of order $(n-1)$ is called the* **minor** *of b_2 and is denoted by B_2.*

Illustration 1. Three of the nine minors of Δ_3 are

$$A_3 = \begin{vmatrix} b_1 & c_1 \\ b_2 & c_2 \end{vmatrix}, \quad B_2 = \begin{vmatrix} a_1 & c_1 \\ a_3 & c_3 \end{vmatrix}, \quad C_2 = \begin{vmatrix} a_1 & b_1 \\ a_3 & b_3 \end{vmatrix}.$$

Fundamental Theorem. *A determinant Δ_n of order n may be expressed as the sum of the n products formed by multiplying the elements of any column (or row) by their respective minors and prefixing each product with a* **plus** *or* **minus** *sign according as the sum of the number of the column and the number of the row in which the element lies is* **even** *or* **odd**.

Illustration 2.

$$\begin{vmatrix} a_1 & b_1 & c_1 \\ a_2 & b_2 & c_2 \\ a_3 & b_3 & c_3 \end{vmatrix} = - b_1 \begin{vmatrix} a_2 & c_2 \\ a_3 & c_3 \end{vmatrix} + b_2 \begin{vmatrix} a_1 & c_1 \\ a_3 & c_3 \end{vmatrix} - b_3 \begin{vmatrix} a_1 & c_1 \\ a_2 & c_2 \end{vmatrix}$$
$$= - b_1 B_1 + b_2 B_2 - b_3 B_3.$$

Proof: (a) In the expansion of Δ_n we prove first that the sum of all terms containing the element a_1 is equal to $a_1 A_1$. This is true since A_1 is a sum of all products taking one, and only one, element from each of the rows except the first and from each of the columns except the first. Furthermore, when each term of A_1 is multiplied by the element a_1, there are no additional inversions of order in the subscripts, and hence the signs of the terms in $a_1 A_1$ are the same as the signs of the corresponding terms obtained from Δ_n.

(b) Second, we prove that the sum of all terms containing the element in the ith row and jth column is $(-1)^{i+j}$ times the product of the element and its minor. The element in the ith row and jth column can be transferred to the position occupied by a_1 in making $(i - 1)$ interchanges of adjacent rows and then $(j - 1)$ interchanges of adjacent columns. By Property III the new determinant has the value $\Delta_n' = (-1)^{i+j-2}\Delta_n$; and since these interchanges do not alter the relative position of the elements outside of the ith row and jth column, it follows from part (a) of the proof that the sum of all terms containing the given element is $(-1)^{i+j}$ times the product of the element and its minor.

(c) Lastly, since each term in the expansion of Δ_n contains one, and only one, element of a given column, the expansion may be expressed as the sum of terms containing (1) the first element of the column, (2) the second element of the column, and so on. These are the sums determined in part (*b*) of the proof, and hence the proof is completed.

Illustration 3. There are eight ways of expanding Δ_4 by minors:

$$\Delta_4 = a_1A_1 - a_2A_2 + a_3A_3 - a_4A_4$$
$$= - a_4A_4 + b_4B_4 - c_4C_4 + d_4D_4, \text{ and so on.}$$

Note. In expanding by minors, the accompanying diagram indicates the sign to be assigned to each term. Since these signs depend only on the position of the elements, they are often called *signs of position.*

$$\begin{vmatrix} + & - & + & . & . & . \\ - & + & - & . & . & . \\ + & - & + & . & . & . \\ . & . & . & . & . & . \\ . & . & . & . & . & . \end{vmatrix}$$

Corollary. *If, in the expansion of Δ_n by minors according to the elements of a given column (or row), the elements of this column (or row) are replaced by the corresponding elements of some other column (or row), the expression obtained is identically zero.*

Proof: By the fundamental theorem, the expansion of Δ_3 according to the first column is

$$\begin{vmatrix} a_1 & b_1 & c_1 \\ a_2 & b_2 & c_2 \\ a_3 & b_3 & c_3 \end{vmatrix} = a_1A_1 - a_2A_2 + a_3A_3.$$

If on both sides we replace the elements a_1, a_2, a_3 by c_1, c_2, c_3, we have

$$\begin{vmatrix} c_1 & b_1 & c_1 \\ c_2 & b_2 & c_2 \\ c_3 & b_3 & c_3 \end{vmatrix} = c_1A_1 - c_2A_2 + c_3A_3.$$

Since two columns are identical, the left side of this equation is zero, and we obtain $c_1A_1 - c_2A_2 + c_3A_3 = 0$. It is evident that a similar proof applies to a determinant of any order.

159. Evaluation of Determinants. Determinants of the second or third order may be evaluated with the definitions given in Article 154. To evaluate a determinant of order $n > 3$, the fundamental theorem is usually used. In order to minimize the computations the following procedure is suggested:

1. *Apply Property* VII (*if necessary*) *to obtain an element whose value is* $+ 1$ *or* $- 1$.

2. *Keep the column (or row) containing the unit element as a* **basic column** *and copy it into a blank determinant.*

3. Apply Property VII, *using the basic column, so that all other elements in the same* **row** *with the unit element are zero.*

4. Expand by minors according to the row containing the unit element and the zeros.

5. Repeat steps 1, 2, 3, and 4 until a determinant of order 2 or 3 is obtained.

Example 1. Evaluate the determinant

$$\begin{vmatrix} 2 & 4 & 2 & 5 \\ -6 & 2 & 2 & 4 \\ 3 & -3 & -3 & -2 \\ 8 & 5 & 3 & -7 \end{vmatrix}.$$

Solution: (1) Adding the third row to the second row gives:

$$\begin{vmatrix} 2 & 4 & 2 & 5 \\ -3 & -1 & -1 & 2 \\ 3 & -3 & -3 & -2 \\ 8 & 5 & 3 & -7 \end{vmatrix}.$$

(2) Keep the second column as the basic column, and (3) subtract three times the basic column from the first column; subtract the basic column from the third column, and add twice the basic column to the fourth column. The result is

$$\begin{vmatrix} -10 & 4 & -2 & 13 \\ 0 & -1 & 0 & 0 \\ 12 & -3 & 0 & -8 \\ -7 & 5 & -2 & 3 \end{vmatrix}.$$

(4) Expanding according to the second row gives

$$+ (-1)\begin{vmatrix} -10 & -2 & 13 \\ 12 & 0 & -8 \\ -7 & -2 & 3 \end{vmatrix} = 2\begin{vmatrix} -10 & 1 & 13 \\ 12 & 0 & -8 \\ -7 & 1 & 3 \end{vmatrix}.$$

Take the first row as a basic row in the new determinant:

$$2\begin{vmatrix} -10 & 1 & 13 \\ 12 & 0 & -8 \\ 3 & 0 & -10 \end{vmatrix} = -2\begin{vmatrix} 12 & -8 \\ 3 & -10 \end{vmatrix} = -2[(-120) - (-24)] = 192.$$

Example 2. Factor the determinant

$$\Delta = \begin{vmatrix} 1 & 1 & 1 \\ x & y & z \\ x^2 & y^2 & z^2 \end{vmatrix}. \qquad \Longleftarrow \text{N} \boxed{3}.$$

Solution: Subtracting the first column from both the second and third columns, we have

$$\Delta = \begin{vmatrix} 1 & 0 & 0 \\ x & y - x & z - x \\ x^2 & y^2 - x^2 & z^2 - x^2 \end{vmatrix} = \begin{vmatrix} y - x & z - x \\ y^2 - x^2 & z^2 - x^2 \end{vmatrix}.$$

Removing the factors $(y - x)$ and $(z - x)$ from the first and second columns respectively, we obtain

$$\Delta = (y - x)(z - x) \begin{vmatrix} 1 & 1 \\ y + x & z + x \end{vmatrix} = (y - x)(z - x)(z - y).$$

160. Applications of Determinants.

Many formulas in mathematics can often be represented compactly by use of determinants. A few such formulas are as follows:

(1) The equation of the straight line passing through the two distinct points (x_1, y_1) and (x_2, y_2) is given by

USE GEN EQNS

$Ax + By + C = 0$

$Ax^2 + Cy^2 + Cx + Dy + F = 0$

$$\begin{vmatrix} x & y & 1 \\ x_1 & y_1 & 1 \\ x_2 & y_2 & 1 \end{vmatrix} = 0.$$

(2) The equation of the circle passing through the three non-collinear points (x_1, y_1), (x_2, y_2), and (x_3, y_3) is given by

NOTE

$x^2 + y^2$

$$\begin{vmatrix} x^2 + y^2 & x & y & 1 \\ x_1^2 + y_1^2 & x_1 & y_1 & 1 \\ x_2^2 + y_2^2 & x_2 & y_2 & 1 \\ x_3^2 + y_3^2 & x_3 & y_3 & 1 \end{vmatrix} = 0.$$

(3) The equation of the conic,

$$Ax^2 + By^2 + Cx + Dy + F = 0,$$

passing through the four non-collinear points (x_1, y_1), (x_2, y_2), (x_3, y_3), and (x_4, y_4) is given by

$$\begin{vmatrix} x^2 & y^2 & x & y & 1 \\ x_1^2 & y_1^2 & x_1 & y_1 & 1 \\ x_2^2 & y_2^2 & x_2 & y_2 & 1 \\ x_3^2 & y_3^2 & x_3 & y_3 & 1 \\ x_4^2 & y_4^2 & x_4 & y_4 & 1 \end{vmatrix} = 0.$$

Example. Find the equation of the line passing through the points $(2, -1)$ and $(4, 5)$.

Solution: Here we have $x_1 = 2$, $y_1 = -1$, $x_2 = 4$, $y_2 = 5$. Hence, substituting in Formula (1), we obtain

$$\begin{vmatrix} x & y & 1 \\ 2 & -1 & 1 \\ 4 & 5 & 1 \end{vmatrix} = 0 \quad \text{or} \quad 3x - y - 7 = 0.$$

EXERCISE 101

Evaluate, using the fundamental theorem:

1. $\begin{vmatrix} 3 & -4 & 3 \\ 5 & 1 & 2 \\ 2 & 7 & -5 \end{vmatrix}.$
2. $\begin{vmatrix} 3 & 6 & -8 \\ -4 & 3 & 2 \\ 2 & -5 & 3 \end{vmatrix}.$
3. $\begin{vmatrix} 4 & 3 & -7 \\ 9 & 8 & 2 \\ -5 & 7 & 4 \end{vmatrix}.$

4. $\begin{vmatrix} -2 & 4 & 3 \\ 5 & 7 & 6 \\ 2 & -2 & 5 \end{vmatrix}.$
5. $\begin{vmatrix} 65 & 17 & 15 \\ 39 & 13 & 14 \\ 47 & 10 & 17 \end{vmatrix}.$
6. $\begin{vmatrix} 21 & 22 & 23 \\ 26 & 25 & 24 \\ 27 & 28 & 29 \end{vmatrix}.$

7. $\begin{vmatrix} 5 & 3 & -2 & 3 \\ 2 & -4 & 5 & 2 \\ 3 & 2 & 2 & -1 \\ 1 & 5 & 1 & 2 \end{vmatrix}.$
8. $\begin{vmatrix} 3 & 0 & 6 & 9 \\ 2 & -1 & 3 & 5 \\ 4 & 2 & 6 & -2 \\ 3 & 3 & 4 & 1 \end{vmatrix}.$

9. $\begin{vmatrix} -3 & 6 & 4 & 2 \\ 2 & 3 & -2 & -6 \\ 4 & 2 & 3 & 5 \\ -2 & 3 & 5 & 2 \end{vmatrix}.$
10. $\begin{vmatrix} 4 & 4 & -3 & 2 \\ -3 & -2 & 2 & 3 \\ 2 & 5 & 4 & -2 \\ 3 & -3 & -2 & 0 \end{vmatrix}.$

11. $\begin{vmatrix} 5 & 4 & 6 & -5 & 1 \\ 4 & 5 & 3 & 2 & 4 \\ -1 & 2 & -4 & 1 & 1 \\ 2 & 1 & 2 & 4 & -3 \\ -3 & -1 & 3 & 2 & 2 \end{vmatrix}.$
12. $\begin{vmatrix} 7 & 3 & 1 & 4 & 2 \\ 2 & 5 & 4 & 1 & 7 \\ 1 & 2 & 3 & 5 & 4 \\ 3 & 2 & 0 & 1 & 4 \\ 3 & 1 & 5 & 2 & 1 \end{vmatrix}.$

13. Solve $\begin{vmatrix} x & -3 & 3 \\ -1 & x & 2 \\ 1 & -1 & 1 \end{vmatrix} = 0.$
14. Solve $\begin{vmatrix} 3 & 2 & 1 \\ 2 & 1 & x \\ 1 & x & -1 \end{vmatrix} = 0.$

Find the equations of the lines determined by the points:

15. $(1, 0), (-2, 3).$ 16. $(3, -1), (2, 2).$ 17. $(4, 3), (-1, -2).$

Find the equations of the circles determined by the points:

18. $(1, 0), (0, 1), (2, 3).$ 19. $(-1, 1), (3, 0), (2, -1).$
20. $(5, 2), (3, 1), (-1, 2).$ 21. $(3, -2), (4, -1), (-1, 2).$

Find the equation of the conics, as given in (3), Article 160, determined by the points:

22. $(0, 0), (0, 1), (1, -1), (3, 3).$ 23. $(4, 4), (-4, 4), (4, -4), (0, 8).$

Express each of the following determinants in factored form:

24. $\begin{vmatrix} 1 & a & b \\ 1 & a^2 & b^2 \\ 1 & a^3 & b^3 \end{vmatrix}.$
25. $\begin{vmatrix} x & x^2 & yz \\ y & y^2 & xz \\ z & z^2 & xy \end{vmatrix}.$
26. $\begin{vmatrix} x & 1 & 1 \\ 1 & x & 1 \\ 1 & 1 & x \end{vmatrix}.$

27. $\begin{vmatrix} 1 & 1 & 1 & 1 \\ x & y & z & w \\ x^2 & y^2 & z^2 & w^2 \\ x^3 & y^3 & z^3 & w^3 \end{vmatrix}.$ 28. $\begin{vmatrix} 0 & 1 & 1 & 1 \\ 1 & b & a & a \\ 1 & b & a & b \\ 1 & 0 & 0 & a+b \end{vmatrix}.$

161. Solution of n Linear Equations in n Unknowns.
As an illustration, take $n = 3$, and consider the equations

$$\begin{cases} a_1x + b_1y + c_1z = k_1, & (1) \\ a_2x + b_2y + c_2z = k_2, & (2) \\ a_3x + b_3y + c_3z = k_3, & (3) \end{cases}$$

to be solved for the unknowns x, y, and z, if a solution exists.

For brevity in writing we assume the following notations:

$$\Delta = \begin{vmatrix} a_1 & b_1 & c_1 \\ a_2 & b_2 & c_2 \\ a_3 & b_3 & c_3 \end{vmatrix}, \tag{4}$$

and

$$\Delta_x = \begin{vmatrix} k_1 & b_1 & c_1 \\ k_2 & b_2 & c_2 \\ k_3 & b_3 & c_3 \end{vmatrix}, \Delta_y = \begin{vmatrix} a_1 & k_1 & c_1 \\ a_2 & k_2 & c_2 \\ a_3 & k_3 & c_3 \end{vmatrix}, \Delta_z = \begin{vmatrix} a_1 & b_1 & k_1 \\ a_2 & b_2 & k_2 \\ a_3 & b_3 & k_3 \end{vmatrix}. \tag{5}$$

To solve Equations (1), (2), and (3) for any unknown, say y, we proceed as follows: multiplying both sides of (1) by $-B_1$, (2) by $+B_2$, and (3) by $-B_3$, where B_1, B_2, and B_3 are the respective minors of b_1, b_2, and b_3 in Δ, we obtain

$$\begin{cases} -a_1B_1x - b_1B_1y - c_1B_1z = -k_1B_1, & (6) \\ +a_2B_2x + b_2B_2y + c_2B_2z = +k_2B_2, & (7) \\ -a_3B_3x - b_3B_3y - c_3B_3z = -k_3B_3. & (8) \end{cases}$$

Adding the left members of Equations (6), (7), and (8), we see, by the fundamental theorem and its corollary, that the coefficients of x, y, and z are 0, Δ, and 0 respectively. Adding the right members, we have

$$-k_1B_1 + k_2B_2 - k_3B_3 = \begin{vmatrix} a_1 & k_1 & c_1 \\ a_2 & k_2 & c_2 \\ a_3 & k_3 & c_3 \end{vmatrix} = \Delta_y.$$

Hence, $y \cdot \Delta = \Delta_y$; and following a similar procedure for the variables x and z, we find in general

$$x \cdot \Delta = \Delta_x, \quad y \cdot \Delta = \Delta_y, \quad z \cdot \Delta = \Delta_z. \tag{9}$$

Thus, if $\Delta \neq 0$, the only solution of the given system of equations is

$$x = \frac{\Delta_x}{\Delta}, \quad y = \frac{\Delta_y}{\Delta}, \quad z = \frac{\Delta_z}{\Delta}, \tag{10}$$

and the fact that these values give a solution to the original equations can be verified by substitution.

The above procedure is summarized in the following theorem which is known as

Cramer's Rule. *A system of n linear equations in n unknowns has a single solution provided that Δ, the determinant of the coefficients of the unknowns, is not zero. If the constant terms are written on the side of the equations opposite to that of the unknowns, the value of any unknown u is given by a fraction in which (a) the denominator is Δ, and (b) the numerator is the determinant Δ_u which is the same as Δ except that the constant terms have been substituted for the coefficients of the variable u.*

NOTE 1. If $\Delta = 0$ and any one or more of the determinants Δ_x, Δ_y, Δ_z, $\cdots$ are not zero, the system of equations has no solution and is said to be **inconsistent.**

NOTE 2. If $\Delta = 0$ and all of the determinants Δ_x, Δ_y, Δ_z, $\cdots$ are also zero, the system of equations may be **consistent** (have solutions) or **inconsistent** (have no solutions). If solutions do exist, there are infinitely many of them. To find these solutions, solve (if possible) $(n-1)$ of the equations for $(n-1)$ of the unknowns in terms of the nth unknown. A more detailed analysis of the possibilities in this category is beyond the scope of this book.

NOTE 3. If $k_1 = k_2 = k_3 = \cdots = 0$, the system of equations is called a system of **linear homogeneous equations.** This system always has the **trivial** solution $x = y = z = \cdots = 0$; and since $\Delta_x = \Delta_y = \Delta_z = \cdots = 0$, it is evident that Δ must be zero if a non-trivial solution is to exist.

Example 1. Solve $\begin{cases} 2x + 3y + z - w = 4, \\ x - y + 2z + 2w = -5, \\ 3x + 2y + z = -2, \\ y - 2z - 3w = 6. \end{cases}$

Solution: Applying Cramer's Rule, we have

$$\Delta = \begin{vmatrix} 2 & 3 & 1 & -1 \\ 1 & -1 & 2 & 2 \\ 3 & 2 & 1 & 0 \\ 0 & 1 & -2 & -3 \end{vmatrix} = -13; \quad \Delta_y = \begin{vmatrix} 2 & 4 & 1 & -1 \\ 1 & -5 & 2 & 2 \\ 3 & -2 & 1 & 0 \\ 0 & 6 & -2 & -3 \end{vmatrix} = -13;$$

$$y = \frac{-13}{-13} = 1.$$

find x, y

Similarly we find $x = -2$, $z = 2$, and $w = -3$.

THEN
SUBSTITUTE

Note 4. After finding y and z by determinants, it is simpler to sub-stitute in the last two of the given equations in order to find x and w.

Example 2. Solve $\begin{cases} x + y + 2z = 5, \\ 3x - 2y - z = 6, \\ 4x - y + z = 11. \end{cases}$

Solution: Applying Cramer's Rule, we find that $\Delta = \Delta_x = \Delta_y = \Delta_z = 0$. Hence, we solve the first two of the equations for x and y, obtaining

$$x = \frac{16 - 3z}{5}, \; y = \frac{9 - 7z}{5}.$$

These values of x and y satisfy the third given equation identically; hence

$$x = \frac{16 - 3c}{5}, \; y = \frac{9 - 7c}{5}, \; z = c$$

constitutes a solution of the given equations no matter what value is assigned to the arbitrary constant c.

OMIT **162. Solution of n Linear Equations in $(n - 1)$ Un-knowns.** A system of n linear equations in $(n - 1)$ unknowns will in general have no solution. However, such a system will have a single solution, if it is possible to solve $(n - 1)$ of the equations for the $(n - 1)$ unknowns, and if the values so obtained satisfy the remaining equation.

Note 1. A discussion of other circumstances in which infinitely many solutions may occur is beyond the scope of this book.

As an illustration, consider the equations

$$\begin{cases} a_1x + b_1y = k_1, & (1) \\ a_2x + b_2y = k_2, & (2) \\ a_3x + b_3y = k_3. & (3) \end{cases}$$

Suppose that Equations (1) and (2) are such that $\Delta \neq 0$. Then by Cramer's Rule, we have

$$x = \begin{vmatrix} k_1 & b_1 \\ k_2 & b_2 \end{vmatrix} \bigg/ \begin{vmatrix} a_1 & b_1 \\ a_2 & b_2 \end{vmatrix}, \; y = \begin{vmatrix} a_1 & k_1 \\ a_2 & k_2 \end{vmatrix} \bigg/ \begin{vmatrix} a_1 & b_1 \\ a_2 & b_2 \end{vmatrix}.$$

Substituting these values in (3), clearing of fractions, and transposing, we obtain

$$a_3 \begin{vmatrix} k_1 & b_1 \\ k_2 & b_2 \end{vmatrix} + b_3 \begin{vmatrix} a_1 & k_1 \\ a_2 & k_2 \end{vmatrix} - k_3 \begin{vmatrix} a_1 & b_1 \\ a_2 & b_2 \end{vmatrix} = 0;$$

hence, $$a_3 \begin{vmatrix} b_1 & k_1 \\ b_2 & k_2 \end{vmatrix} - b_3 \begin{vmatrix} a_1 & k_1 \\ a_2 & k_2 \end{vmatrix} + k_3 \begin{vmatrix} a_1 & b_1 \\ a_2 & b_2 \end{vmatrix} = 0.$$

By the fundamental theorem, this last expression can be written in the form

$$E \equiv \begin{vmatrix} a_1 & b_1 & k_1 \\ a_2 & b_2 & k_2 \\ a_3 & b_3 & k_3 \end{vmatrix} = 0,$$

which is a necessary condition to be satisfied by the coefficients of (1), (2), and (3) in order that the three equations will have the same solution. The determinant E is called the **eliminant** of the system of equations.

Extending the above procedure to n linear equations in $(n-1)$ unknowns, we have

Theorem. *If at least one of the determinants of order $(n-1)$ which can be formed from the coefficients of the unknowns is not equal to zero, then a system of n linear equations in $(n-1)$ unknowns will have a single solution when the eliminant of order n formed from the coefficients and the constant terms is zero.*

NOTE 2. If the eliminant is different from zero, it can be shown that the equations have no solution, *regardless* of other considerations.

Example. Find the equation of the line

$$Ax + By + C = 0, \tag{4}$$

which passes through the two distinct points (x_1, y_1) and (x_2, y_2).

Solution: Since the given points satisfy (4), we have

$$Ax_1 + By_1 + C = 0, \tag{5}$$
$$Ax_2 + By_2 + C = 0. \tag{6}$$

Considering A, B, and C as the unknowns, if the three equations (4), (5), and (6) are to have a solution other than the trivial solution $A = B = C = 0$, the eliminant must be zero; that is

$$\begin{vmatrix} x & y & 1 \\ x_1 & y_1 & 1 \\ x_2 & y_2 & 1 \end{vmatrix} = 0.$$

NOTE 3. Eliminants may be used to establish Formulas (2) and (3) of Article 160.

EXERCISE 102

Solve by determinants and check by substitution:

1. $\begin{cases} x - y + z = 4, \\ 3\,x + y - 2\,z = 2, \\ x - 2\,y - z = 1. \end{cases}$

2. $\begin{cases} 2\,x - y + z = 1, \\ x + 2\,y - z = 0, \\ -\,x + y + 2\,z = 5. \end{cases}$

3. $\begin{cases} 3\,x + 2\,y + z = 1, \\ x + 3\,y - 4\,z = 3, \\ y - z = 2. \end{cases}$

4. $\begin{cases} z - 2\,x + y = 9, \\ y - 3\,x - z = 2, \\ 2\,y + z - 5\,x = 5. \end{cases}$

5. $\begin{cases} x + y + z = 3, \\ y + 2\,z + w = 1, \\ z + 2\,w + x = 3, \\ w + 2\,x + y = 3. \end{cases}$

6. $\begin{cases} x + y + z - 2\,w = 1, \\ 3\,y - z - w = 6, \\ 4\,x - 3\,y - z + 3\,w = 6, \\ 7\,w - 2\,y = 3. \end{cases}$

7. $\begin{cases} x + 4\,y - z - 4\,w = 0, \\ 2\,x - z - w - 4 = 0, \\ 5\,w - 2\,y + z - 2 = 0, \\ 2\,x + 3\,y + z + w = 0. \end{cases}$

8. $\begin{cases} 2\,x + y = 5, \\ 3\,y - z = 1, \\ 4\,z + w = 9, \\ 5\,w - x = 3. \end{cases}$

9. $\begin{cases} x - 3\,y + z - u = 0, \\ 3\,v - x + 4\,z - 4\,u = 4, \\ x + y + z + u + v = 0, \\ 2\,y + 2\,u + x + v = 0, \\ 2\,z - y + u - 2 = 0. \end{cases}$

10. $\begin{cases} x + y - z = 0, \\ y + z - w = 1, \\ z + w - t = 2, \\ w + t - x = 8, \\ t + x - y = 4. \end{cases}$

Show that the following systems are consistent, and solve:

11. $\begin{cases} x + 2\,y + z = 4, \\ 2\,x - y + 3\,z = 3, \\ x - 8\,y + 3\,z = -\,6. \end{cases}$

12. $\begin{cases} 2\,x - y + z = 3, \\ 3\,x + 2\,y - z = 4, \\ 12\,x + y + z = 17. \end{cases}$

13. $\begin{cases} 2\,x - y = 5, \\ x - 4\,y = 6, \\ 3\,x + 2\,y = 4. \end{cases}$

14. $\begin{cases} x + 2\,y = 5, \\ y - 5\,x = 8, \\ 4\,x + 3\,y = 5. \end{cases}$

15. $\begin{cases} x + y + z = 5, \\ 2\,x - y + z = 12, \\ x + 2\,y - z = -\,5, \\ -\,x + y + 2\,z = 3. \end{cases}$

16. $\begin{cases} 2\,x + 3\,y = 1, \\ 2\,y - z = 0, \\ 3\,z - x = 7, \\ x + y + z = 2. \end{cases}$

Find the values of k for which the following systems have a single solution:

17. $\begin{cases} 2\,x + y = k, \\ kx - 3\,y = 4, \\ 3\,x + 2\,y = 1. \end{cases}$

18. $\begin{cases} 2\,x + 3\,y = k + 2, \\ y - kx = 4, \\ x + y = 1. \end{cases}$

19. Using eliminants, find the parabola in the form $y = Ax^2 + Bx + C$ which passes through the points $(1, 2)$, $(2, -1)$, and $(3, 0)$.

20. Using eliminants, find the hyperbola in the form $Axy + Bx + Cy + D = 0$ which passes through the points $(2, 0)$, $(-1, -1)$, and $(-3, 2)$.

CHAPTER 22

Partial Fractions

163. Definitions. The ratio of two polynomials is called a **rational fraction.** If the degree of the numerator is *less* than that of the denominator, the fraction is called a **proper fraction.** An improper fraction can always be reduced by division to a **mixed fraction** consisting of the sum of a polynomial and a proper fraction. We shall assume that all fractions considered are **irreducible;** that is, the numerator and the denominator have no common factor.

Illustration. (a) $\dfrac{x+1}{x^2+1}$ is a proper, irreducible fraction.

(b) The improper fraction $\dfrac{x^4 + 2x - 5}{x^2 + 2} = x^2 - 2 + \dfrac{2x - 1}{x^2 + 2}$.

In the study of fractions one learns the procedure by which two or more fractions can be combined into a single fraction. Thus, for example,

$$\frac{2}{x-3} + \frac{1}{x+1} = \frac{3x-1}{(x-3)(x+1)}.$$

In many branches of advanced mathematics, it is important to be able to reverse this procedure, that is, to represent a given fraction as the sum of simpler fractions. This inverse procedure is called the resolving of a given fraction into **partial fractions.**

The process of determining the partial fractions which correspond to a given proper fraction is based on the following theorem, whose proof is beyond the scope of this book:

Fundamental Theorem. *Any proper rational fraction may be resolved into a sum of partial fractions subject to the classifications listed below:*

Case I. *If a linear factor $(ax + b)$ occurs once as a factor of the denominator, there corresponds to this factor one partial fraction $\dfrac{A}{ax + b}$, where A is a constant and $A \neq 0$.*

Case II. *If a linear factor $(ax + b)$ occurs n times as a factor of the denominator, there corresponds to this factor n partial fractions*

$$\frac{A_1}{ax + b} + \frac{A_2}{(ax + b)^2} + \cdots + \frac{A_n}{(ax + b)^n},$$

where A_1, A_2, $\cdots$, A_n are constants and $A_n \neq 0$.

Case III. *If a quadratic factor $(ax^2 + bx + c)$ occurs once as a factor of the denominator, there corresponds to this factor one partial fraction $\dfrac{Ax + B}{ax^2 + bx + c}$, where A and B are constants and $Ax + B \neq 0$.*

Case IV. *If a quadratic factor $(ax^2 + bx + c)$ occurs n times as a factor of the denominator, there corresponds to this factor n partial fractions*

$$\frac{A_1x + B_1}{ax^2 + bx + c} + \frac{A_2x + B_2}{(ax^2 + bx + c)^2} + \cdots + \frac{A_nx + B_n}{(ax^2 + bx + c)^n},$$

where the A's and B's are constants, and $A_nx + B_n \neq 0$.

NOTE. Throughout this chapter it will be assumed that the quadratic factors mentioned above cannot be expressed as the product of two real linear factors.

164. Case I. Linear Factors, None Repeated.

Example. Resolve into partial fractions $\dfrac{x + 12}{(2x - 1)(x + 2)}$.

Solution: By the Fundamental Theorem, this fraction can be expressed in the form

$$\frac{x + 12}{(2x - 1)(x + 2)} = \frac{A}{2x - 1} + \frac{B}{x + 2}, \tag{1}$$

where A and B are constants to be determined. Clearing (1) of fractions, we obtain

$$x + 12 = A(x + 2) + B(2x - 1). \qquad (2)$$

There are two general methods of evaluating the constants A and B.

Method 1. Substitution. Both members of (2) are equal for all values of x except possibly $x = -2$ and $x = \frac{1}{2}$. However, it follows from Corollary 3, Article 110, that they are equal for all values of x including -2 and $\frac{1}{2}$. Hence, in order to make the coefficient of B equal to zero, set $x = \frac{1}{2}$. Then (2) reduces to

$$\tfrac{1}{2} + 12 = A(\tfrac{1}{2} + 2); \text{ hence } A = 5.$$

In order to make the coefficient of A equal to zero, set $x = -2$. Then (2) reduces to

$$-2 + 12 = B(-4 - 1); \text{ hence } B = -2.$$

Thus,

$$\frac{x + 12}{(2x - 1)(x + 2)} = \frac{5}{2x - 1} - \frac{2}{x + 2}, \qquad (3)$$

and the result may be checked by combining the partial fractions obtained.

Method 2. Equating Coefficients. On expanding (2) and collecting like powers of x, we have

$$x + 12 \equiv (A + 2B)x + (2A - B). \qquad (4)$$

Since (4) is an identity, the coefficients of like powers of x are equal (Corollary 3, Article 110). Hence we have

$$A + 2B = 1 \quad \text{and} \quad 2A - B = 12. \qquad (5)$$

Solving the equations in (5), we find that $A = 5$ and $B = -2$, these values being the same as those obtained by *Method 1.*

165. Case II. Linear Factors, Some Repeated.

Example. Resolve into partial fractions $\dfrac{7 - x^2}{(x + 1)(2 - x)^2}$.

Solution: By the Fundamental Theorem, this fraction can be expressed in the form

$$\frac{7 - x^2}{(x + 1)(2 - x)^2} = \frac{A}{x + 1} + \frac{B}{2 - x} + \frac{C}{(2 - x)^2}, \qquad (1)$$

where A, B, and C are constants to be determined. Clearing of fractions, we have

$$7 - x^2 = A(2 - x)^2 + B(x + 1)(2 - x) + C(x + 1). \qquad (2)$$

Setting $\quad x = -1, \qquad 6 = 9A, \qquad\qquad$ hence $A = \frac{2}{3}$.

Setting $\quad x = 2, \qquad 3 = 3C, \qquad\qquad$ hence $C = 1$.

Setting $\quad x = 0, \qquad 7 = 4A + 2B + C,$

Substituting, $\qquad 7 = \frac{8}{3} + 2B + 1, \qquad$ hence $B = \frac{5}{3}$.

Thus,

$$\frac{7 - x^2}{(x + 1)(2 - x)^2} = \frac{2}{3(x + 1)} + \frac{5}{3(2 - x)} + \frac{1}{(2 - x)^2}. \quad (3)$$

NOTE. Any convenient value of x may be taken as a third value in the above example. As a numerical check, choose any fourth value of x and substitute in (2), along with the determined values of the constants.

EXERCISE 103

Resolve into partial fractions:

1. $\dfrac{3x + 2}{x(x + 2)}$.

2. $\dfrac{2x + 19}{(x - 3)(x + 2)}$.

3. $\dfrac{11}{(2x - 1)(x + 5)}$.

4. $\dfrac{4}{x^2 - 4}$.

5. $\dfrac{5x - 1}{1 - x^2}$.

6. $\dfrac{7x}{3x^2 - 11x + 6}$.

7. $\dfrac{x^2 + 2}{x^2 + 2x}$.

8. $\dfrac{x^2 + 2x - 1}{x^2 + 3x + 2}$.

9. $\dfrac{x^2 + 2x + 2}{(x + 1)(x + 2)^2}$.

10. $\dfrac{x^2 + 1}{x^3 - x}$.

11. $\dfrac{5x^2 - 5x + 2}{2x^3 - x^2}$.

12. $\dfrac{2x^2 - x - 5}{(x + 1)(x^2 - 1)}$.

13. $\dfrac{x^2 + 2}{(x + 1)^3}$.

14. $\dfrac{x^2 + x - 3}{x^4 - x^3}$.

15. $\dfrac{x^3 + 2x - 1}{(x^2 - 1)(x^2 - x)}$.

16. $\dfrac{x^3}{(x - a)^3}$.

17. $\dfrac{a(7x - 2a)}{x^2(3x - a)}$.

18. $\dfrac{2x + a}{(x^2 + ax - 2a^2)^2}$.

19. $\dfrac{9x^2 - 6x - 49}{x^3 - x^2 - 8x + 12}$.

20. $\dfrac{6x^3 - 13x^2 - 8x - 1}{2x^3 - 5x^2 - 4x + 3}$.

166. Case III. Quadratic Factors, None Repeated.

Example. Resolve into partial fractions $\dfrac{4x^2 - 5x + 10}{(x - 2)(x^2 + x + 2)}$.

Solution: By the Fundamental Theorem, this fraction can be expressed in the form

$$\frac{4x^2 - 5x + 10}{(x - 2)(x^2 + x + 2)} = \frac{A}{x - 2} + \frac{Bx + C}{x^2 + x + 2}, \quad (1)$$

where A, B, and C are constants. Clearing (1) of fractions, we have

$$4x^2 - 5x + 10 = A(x^2 + x + 2) + (Bx + C)(x - 2). \quad (2)$$

Occasionally in the evaluation of the constants, some special procedure can be used to advantage. For example, setting $x = 2$ in (2) gives

$$16 - 10 + 10 = A(4 + 2 + 2), \text{ or } A = 2.$$

Thus (2) becomes

$$4x^2 - 5x + 10 = 2x^2 + 2x + 4 + (Bx + C)(x - 2).$$

Transposing, $\qquad 2x^2 - 7x + 6 = (Bx + C)(x - 2).$

Dividing by $(x - 2)$, $\qquad 2x - 3 = Bx + C.$

Hence,
$$\frac{4x^2 - 5x + 10}{(x-2)(x^2+x+2)} = \frac{2}{x-2} + \frac{2x-3}{x^2+x+2}.$$

167. Case IV. Quadratic Factors, Some Repeated.

Example. Resolve into partial fractions $\dfrac{x^3 + 2x + 8}{x(x^2+2)^2}$.

Solution: By the Fundamental Theorem, this fraction can be expressed in the form

$$\frac{x^3 + 2x + 8}{x(x^2+2)^2} = \frac{A}{x} + \frac{Bx+C}{x^2+2} + \frac{Dx+E}{(x^2+2)^2}, \quad (1)$$

where A, B, C, D, and E are constants. Clearing (1) of fractions, we have

$$x^3 + 2x + 8 = A(x^2+2)^2 + (Bx+C)x(x^2+2) + (Dx+E)x. \quad (2)$$

Two methods of determining the constants will be illustrated.

General Method. Since there are five constants to be determined, we let x assume any five convenient values and solve the linear equations obtained. Thus, when

$$
\left.
\begin{aligned}
x &= 0, & 8 &= 4A, \\
x &= 1, & 11 &= 9A + 3B + 3C + D + E, \\
x &= -1, & 5 &= 9A + 3B - 3C + D - E, \\
x &= 2, & 20 &= 36A + 24B + 12C + 4D + 2E, \\
x &= -2, & -4 &= 36A + 24B - 12C + 4D - 2E.
\end{aligned}
\right\} \quad (3)
$$

Solving the system of equations in (3), we obtain $A = 2$, $B = -2$, $C = 1$, $D = -4$, and $E = 0$. Hence we have

$$\frac{x^3 + 2x + 8}{x(x^2+2)^2} = \frac{2}{x} - \frac{2x-1}{x^2+2} - \frac{4x}{(x^2+2)^2}. \quad (4)$$

Optional Method. Setting $x = 0$ in (2), we find $A = 2$. Transpose the first term on the right side of (2), set $A = 2$, and divide through by x. Thus, we obtain

$$-2x^3 + x^2 - 8x + 2 = (Bx+C)(x^2+2) + (Dx+E). \quad (5)$$

It is evident that if the left side of (5) is divided by (x^2+2), the quotient obtained is $(Bx+C)$ and the remainder is $(Dx+E)$. Hence, making this division, we obtain

$$
\begin{array}{r}
-2x + 1 = Bx + C \\
x^2 + 2 \overline{\smash{\big)}\, -2x^3 + x^2 - 8x + 2} \\
\underline{-2x^3 - 4x} \\
x^2 - 4x \\
\underline{x^2 + 2} \\
-4x = Dx + E.
\end{array}
$$

This result leads to the same partial fractions as given in (4).

EXERCISE 104

Resolve into partial fractions:

1. $\dfrac{x + 6}{(x + 1)(x^2 + 4)}$.

2. $\dfrac{2\,x^2 - 9\,x - 5}{(2\,x^2 + 1)(4\,x - 3)}$.

3. $\dfrac{x - 1}{x^3 + x^2 + x}$.

4. $\dfrac{x - 1}{x^3 + x^2 + x + 1}$.

5. $\dfrac{2\,x^3 - x^2}{x^3 + 1}$.

6. $\dfrac{2\,x^3 - 5\,x^2 - x + 12}{(2\,x + 1)(x^2 - 3\,x + 1)}$.

7. $\dfrac{2\,x^2}{(x^2 + 2)^2}$.

8. $\dfrac{3\,x^2 + x + 2}{2\,x^4 + 3\,x^2 + 1}$.

9. $\dfrac{6(8 - 3\,x)}{(x + 2)(x^3 + 8)}$.

10. $\dfrac{28}{(x + 1)(x + 2)(x^2 + 3)}$.

11. $\dfrac{x + 1}{(x^2 + 1)(x^2 + 2)}$.

12. $\dfrac{x^3 + 2\,x^2 + 1}{x^4 + 2\,x^2 + 1}$.

13. $\dfrac{x - 4}{x(x^2 - x + 2)^2}$.

14. $\dfrac{x^4 + 2\,x^2 - x + 4}{(1 + x^2)(1 + x^3)}$.

15. $\dfrac{2\,x^5 + 4\,x}{x^6 - 1}$.

16. $\dfrac{3(16\,x^4 + 1)}{(4\,x^3 + x)^2}$.

17. $\dfrac{x^3}{x^6 + 3\,x^4 + 3\,x^2 + 1}$.

18. $\dfrac{x^4 - 7\,x^2 + 15\,x - 42}{x^4 - 3\,x^3 + 4\,x^2 - 8}$.

19. $\dfrac{(x - a)^2}{(x + a)(x^2 + a^2)^2}$.

20. $\dfrac{3\,ax(x + a)}{(x^2 + a^2)(x^2 + 4\,a^2)}$.

CHAPTER 23

Infinite Series

168. Sequences and Series. A succession of numbers formed according to some fixed rule is called a **sequence** of numbers. Thus,

$$1, \ 4, \ 9, \ 16, \ 25, \ \cdots$$

is a sequence having the rule that the nth term is given by n^2.

The indicated sum of a sequence of numbers is called a **series.** Thus, for the sequence $u_1, \ u_2, \ u_3, \ \cdots, \ u_n, \ \cdots$, the corresponding series is

$$u_1 + u_2 + u_3 + \cdots + u_n + \cdots.$$

A series is said to be **finite** if the number of terms is limited, and **infinite** if the number of terms is unlimited. In this chapter we shall use the word series to mean infinite series and the discussion will be restricted to series whose terms are real numbers.

A **general term** of a series is an expression involving n, such that by taking $n = 1, 2, 3$, etc., one obtains the first, second, third, etc., term of the series.

Example 1. If $u_n = n/(2\,n - 1)$, find $u_1, \ u_2, \ u_3, \ u_{n+1}$, and write the series.

Solution: Substituting the values 1, 2, 3, and $(n + 1)$ for n, we obtain

$$u_1 = \frac{1}{2(1) - 1}, \ u_2 = \frac{2}{2(2) - 1}, \ u_3 = \frac{3}{2(3) - 1}, \ u_{n+1} = \frac{(n + 1)}{2(n + 1) - 1}.$$

Hence, the series is

$$1 + \frac{2}{3} + \frac{3}{5} + \cdots + \frac{n}{2\,n-1} + \frac{n+1}{2\,n+1} + \cdots.$$

If the first few terms of a series are known, a form of the general term may be found by expressing the terms $u_1, u_2, u_3, \cdots$ as functions of the indices $1, 2, 3, \cdots$.

Example 2. Write an nth term of the series

$$\frac{2}{3^3} + \frac{4}{3^4} + \frac{6}{3^5} + \frac{8}{3^6} + \cdots.$$

Solution: Since

$$u_1 = \frac{2(1)}{3^{(1)+2}},\ u_2 = \frac{2(2)}{3^{(2)+2}},\ u_3 = \frac{2(3)}{3^{(3)+2}},\ u_4 = \frac{2(4)}{3^{(4)+2}},$$

it follows that

$$u_n = \frac{2\,n}{3^{n+2}}.$$

NOTE. A few terms of a series cannot determine the general term *uniquely.* Thus, in the above example, if $f(n)$ is an arbitrary function of n subject to the conditions that $f(1) = f(2) = f(3) = f(4) = 0$, the general term is

$$u_n = \frac{2\,n}{3^{n+2}} + f(n).$$

169. Limit of a Sequence. In any operations dealing with infinitely many elements the concept of a *limiting process* as given in the following definition is of fundamental importance:

Definition. *Let $S_1, S_2, \cdots, S_n, \cdots$ be the terms of an infinite sequence. The terms of this sequence are said to approach a constant S as a limit when the successive values of S_n are such that the absolute value of the difference $(S_n - S)$ ultimately becomes and remains less than any arbitrarily chosen small positive number. If the limit exists, we say that S is the limit of S_n, as n becomes infinite;* written symbolically,

$$\operatorname*{limit}_{n\to\infty} S_n = S, \quad \text{or} \quad \lim_{n\to\infty} S_n = S.$$

Illustration. (*a*) $1, \frac{1}{2}, \frac{1}{3}, \frac{1}{4}, \cdots$ approaches zero as a limit; (*b*) $1, \frac{1}{2}, 1, \frac{1}{3}, 1, \frac{1}{4}, \cdots$ has no limit; and (*c*) $1, \frac{1}{2}, 1, \frac{2}{3}, 1, \frac{3}{4}, \cdots$ approaches 1 as a limit.

NOTE. If S_n increases without bound as n becomes infinite, then $\lim_{n \to \infty} S_n$ does not exist. This situation is denoted by $\lim_{n \to \infty} S_n = \infty$.

170. Properties of Limits. The basic properties of limits are summarized in the following theorem, whose proof is omitted:

Theorem. *If A_n and B_n represent the general terms of two sequences, and if*

$$\lim_{n \to \infty} A_n = A, \quad and \quad \lim_{n \to \infty} B_n = B,$$

the following relations are true:

(1) $\lim_{n \to \infty} (A_n \pm B_n) = \lim_{n \to \infty} A_n \pm \lim_{n \to \infty} B_n = A \pm B,$

(2) $\lim_{n \to \infty} (A_n \cdot B_n) = \lim_{n \to \infty} A_n \cdot \lim_{n \to \infty} B_n = A \cdot B,$

(3) $\lim_{n \to \infty} (A_n/B_n) = \lim_{n \to \infty} A_n / \lim_{n \to \infty} B_n = A/B, \text{ if } B \neq 0.$

Illustration.

(a) $\lim_{n \to \infty} \dfrac{2n+1}{n} = \lim_{n \to \infty} \left(2 + \dfrac{1}{n}\right) = \lim_{n \to \infty} 2 + \lim_{n \to \infty} \dfrac{1}{n} = 2 + 0 = 2.$

(b) $\lim_{n \to \infty} \dfrac{n}{2n+1} = \lim_{n \to \infty} 1/\left(2 + \dfrac{1}{n}\right) = \lim_{n \to \infty} 1/\lim_{n \to \infty} \left(2 + \dfrac{1}{n}\right) = \dfrac{1}{2}.$

NOTE. To find the limit of a rational fraction of n as n becomes infinite, first divide the numerator and denominator by the highest power of n in the denominator, and then take the limit.

Example 1. Find the limit, as n becomes infinite, of the sequence whose nth term is $(n^2 - n)/(2n^2 + 1)$.

Solution: Dividing the numerator and denominator by n^2, we have

$$\lim_{n \to \infty} \frac{n^2 - n}{2n^2 + 1} = \lim_{n \to \infty} \frac{1 - \dfrac{1}{n}}{2 + \dfrac{1}{n^2}} = \frac{1}{2}.$$

Example 2. Evaluate $\lim_{n \to \infty} (3n^2 - 1)n!/(n + 1)!$.

Solution:

$$\lim_{n \to \infty} \frac{(3n^2 - 1)n!}{(n+1)!} = \lim_{n \to \infty} \frac{3n^2 - 1}{n + 1} \cdot \frac{n!}{n!} = \lim_{n \to \infty} \frac{3n - \dfrac{1}{n}}{1 + \dfrac{1}{n}} = \infty.$$

EXERCISE 105

Find the first three terms and the $(n + 1)$st term of the series whose nth term is as follows:

1. $\dfrac{1}{\sqrt{2\,n - 1}}.$ **2.** $\dfrac{n + 3}{n^2 + 1}.$ **3.** $\dfrac{2^n}{n(n + 1)}.$

4. $(-1)^{n-1}\,\dfrac{x^n}{(2\,n)!}.$ **5.** $(-1)^{n-1}\dfrac{2\,n - 1}{n^3}.$ **6.** $(-1)^{n-1}\,\dfrac{n + 1}{n(n+2)}.$

Find an nth term for each of the following series:

7. $\dfrac{1}{2^2} + \dfrac{1}{4^2} + \dfrac{1}{6^2} + \dfrac{1}{8^2} + \cdots.$ **8.** $\dfrac{3}{1!} + \dfrac{4}{2!} + \dfrac{5}{3!} + \dfrac{6}{4!} + \cdots.$

9. $1 + \tfrac{1}{4} + \tfrac{1}{9} + \tfrac{1}{16} + \cdots.$ **10.** $1 + \dfrac{x^2}{2!} + \dfrac{x^4}{4!} + \dfrac{x^6}{6!} + \cdots.$

11. $1 - \dfrac{1}{2^2} + \dfrac{1}{3^2} - \dfrac{1}{4^2} + \cdots.$

12. $\tfrac{1}{5}(\tfrac{2}{3}) - \tfrac{1}{7}(\tfrac{2}{3})^2 + \tfrac{1}{9}(\tfrac{2}{3})^3 - \tfrac{1}{11}(\tfrac{2}{3})^4 + \cdots.$

13. $\dfrac{3}{1 \cdot 2} + \dfrac{5}{2 \cdot 3} + \dfrac{7}{3 \cdot 4} + \dfrac{9}{4 \cdot 5} + \cdots.$

14. $\dfrac{x}{2} - \dfrac{2\,x^2}{2^3} + \dfrac{3\,x^3}{2^5} - \dfrac{4\,x^4}{2^7} + \cdots.$

If a sequence has the following general term, find the limit as n becomes infinite:

15. $\dfrac{2\,n}{3\,n - 1}.$ **16.** $\dfrac{n^2 + 1}{2\,n(2\,n + 1)}.$ **17.** $\dfrac{(n + 1)(n + 3)}{n(n + 2)(n + 4)}.$

18. $\dfrac{(2\,n - 1) \cdot n!}{(n + 1)!}.$ **19.** $\dfrac{(2\,n - 1)^2 \cdot 3^n}{(2\,n + 1)^2 \cdot 3^{n+1}}.$ **20.** $\dfrac{n \cdot 3^{n+1}}{(n + 1) \cdot 2^n}.$

Find (a) an nth term for the following sequences, and (b) the limit of each sequence as n becomes infinite:

21. $\tfrac{1}{2}, \tfrac{1}{4}, \tfrac{1}{6}, \tfrac{1}{8}, \cdots.$ **22.** $\tfrac{2}{1}, \tfrac{4}{3}, \tfrac{6}{5}, \tfrac{8}{7}, \cdots.$

23. $1, \tfrac{3}{4}, \tfrac{5}{9}, \tfrac{7}{16}, \cdots.$ **24.** $\dfrac{1!}{2^2}, \dfrac{2!}{3^2}, \dfrac{3!}{4^2}, \dfrac{4!}{5^2}, \cdots.$

25. $\tfrac{2}{3}, \tfrac{3}{7}, \tfrac{4}{11}, \tfrac{5}{15}, \cdots.$ **26.** $1, \tfrac{4}{3}, \tfrac{7}{5}, \tfrac{10}{7}, \cdots.$

27. $\dfrac{3}{1 \cdot 2}, \dfrac{5}{2 \cdot 3}, \dfrac{7}{3 \cdot 4}, \dfrac{9}{4 \cdot 5}, \cdots.$ **28.** $\dfrac{1 \cdot 3}{2}, \dfrac{3 \cdot 5}{4}, \dfrac{5 \cdot 7}{6}, \dfrac{7 \cdot 9}{8}, \cdots.$

29. $\dfrac{1 \cdot 3}{2 \cdot 4}, \dfrac{3 \cdot 5}{4 \cdot 6}, \dfrac{5 \cdot 7}{6 \cdot 8}, \dfrac{7 \cdot 9}{8 \cdot 10}, \cdots.$ **30.** $\dfrac{1^2}{2 \cdot 3}, \dfrac{2^2}{4 \cdot 5}, \dfrac{3^2}{6 \cdot 7}, \dfrac{4^2}{8 \cdot 9}, \cdots.$

171. Convergent and Divergent Series.

Let the sequence $S_1, S_2, \cdots, S_n, \cdots$ denote the respective partial sums of the series

$$u_1 + u_2 + u_3 + \cdots + u_n + \cdots;$$

that is,

$$S_1 = u_1, \quad S_2 = u_1 + u_2, \quad S_3 = u_1 + u_2 + u_3, \text{ and so on.}$$

Definition. *An infinite series is said to* **converge** *or* **be convergent** *if the partial sums* S_n *have a definite limit* S *as* n *becomes infinite; otherwise the series is said to* **diverge** *or* **be divergent.** *The limiting value* S *for a convergent series is called the* **sum** *of the series.*

NOTE. Observe that the *sum* of an infinite series, as defined above, is *not a sum* in the usual sense but is the result of a limiting process.

Illustration 1. In the series $\frac{1}{2} + \frac{1}{4} + \frac{1}{8} + \cdots + \frac{1}{2^n} + \cdots$, we have $S_1 = \frac{1}{2}, S_2 = \frac{1}{2} + \frac{1}{4} = \frac{3}{4}, S_3 = \frac{1}{2} + \frac{1}{4} + \frac{1}{8} = \frac{7}{8}$, and so on. In general, using the formula for a finite geometric series, we have

$$S_n = \frac{1}{2} + \frac{1}{4} + \cdots + \frac{1}{2^n} = 1 - \frac{1}{2^n}; \text{ and } \lim_{n \to \infty} S_n = 1 - 0 = 1.$$

Hence, the series converges and has a sum equal to 1.

Illustration 2. In the series $1 + 3 + 5 + \cdots + (2n - 1) + \cdots$, we have $S_1 = 1$, $S_2 = 4$, $S_3 = 9$, and so on. In general, $S_n = n^2$ and $\lim_{n \to \infty} n^2 = \infty$. Hence, the series diverges.

Illustration 3. Consider the series $1 - 1 + 1 - 1 + - \cdots$. If n is even, the sum is zero. If n is odd, the sum is 1. As n becomes infinite S_n does not approach a definite limit but oscillates between 0 and 1. Hence the series diverges. Such a series is called an **oscillating series.**

172. Fundamental Theorem on Convergence. In developing practicable methods for establishing the convergence or divergence of series, we shall use the following fundamental theorem, whose proof is beyond the scope of this book:

Theorem 1. *If a series of positive terms is such that* S_n *always remains less than some constant* **K,** *the series converges and its sum* S *is not greater than* **K.**

Illustration 1. Since each term of (a) $\frac{1}{1 \cdot 2} + \frac{1}{2 \cdot 2^2} + \frac{1}{3 \cdot 2^3} + \cdots + \frac{1}{n \cdot 2^n} + \cdots$ is less than or equal to the corresponding term of (b) $\frac{1}{2} + \frac{1}{2^2} + \frac{1}{2^3} + \cdots + \frac{1}{2^n} + \cdots$, it follows that $[S_n$ for $(a)] < [S_n$ for $(b)]$. However, in Article 171 it was shown that $[S_n$ for $(b)] < 1$ for all n. Hence, $[S_n$ for $(a)] < 1$; and, by Theorem 1, (a) converges.

Theorem 2. *If a series is convergent, the **n**th term must approach zero as **n** becomes infinite.*

Proof: Let the series

$$u_1 + u_2 + u_3 + \cdots + u_n + \cdots$$

have the sum S. Since $u_n = S_n - S_{n-1}$, it follows that

$$\lim_{n \to \infty} u_n = \lim_{n \to \infty} (S_n - S_{n-1}) = S - S = 0.$$

The above theorem states a *necessary* condition for convergence, but not a *sufficient* condition. That is, the fact that the nth term of a series approaches zero as n becomes infinite does **not** mean that the series is convergent.

Illustration 2. Consider the **harmonic series**

$$1 + \frac{1}{2} + \frac{1}{3} + \frac{1}{4} + \cdots + \frac{1}{n} + \cdots. \tag{1}$$

It is evident that

$$1 + \tfrac{1}{2} > \tfrac{1}{2} = \tfrac{1}{2},$$
$$\tfrac{1}{3} + \tfrac{1}{4} > \tfrac{2}{4} = \tfrac{1}{2},$$
$$\tfrac{1}{5} + \tfrac{1}{6} + \tfrac{1}{7} + \tfrac{1}{8} > \tfrac{4}{8} = \tfrac{1}{2},$$
$$\tfrac{1}{9} + \tfrac{1}{10} + \cdots + \tfrac{1}{15} + \tfrac{1}{16} > \tfrac{8}{16} = \tfrac{1}{2},$$
$$\cdot \quad \cdot \quad \cdot \quad \cdot \quad \cdot \quad \cdot \quad \cdot \quad \cdot$$

Adding the corresponding sides for k groups, we have

$$1 + \frac{1}{2} + \frac{1}{3} + \cdots + \frac{1}{2^k} > \frac{k}{2}.$$

Taking the limit as k becomes infinite, we see that (1) becomes infinite. Thus the harmonic series is divergent even though its nth term does approach zero as n becomes infinite.

Corollary. *If the **n**th term of a series does not approach zero as **n** becomes infinite, the series is divergent.*

Proof: Since $\lim_{u \to \infty} u_n = 0$ is a necessary condition for convergence, then $\lim_{n \to \infty} u_n = k \neq 0$ implies that the series is divergent.

Illustration 3. The series $1 + \dfrac{2}{3} + \dfrac{3}{5} + \cdots + \dfrac{n}{2n-1} + \cdots$ is divergent since $\lim_{n \to \infty} u_n = \lim_{n \to \infty} n/(2n-1) = \tfrac{1}{2}$.

173. Comparison Tests. One procedure for proving the convergence or divergence of a series is to compare the given series with a series whose convergence or divergence is known.

Consider the following two series whose terms are positive:

$$(A) \quad a_1 + a_2 + a_3 + \cdots + a_n + \cdots,$$
$$(U) \quad u_1 + u_2 + u_3 + \cdots + u_n + \cdots.$$

Theorem 1. *If* (A) *converges to a limit* A *and if each term of* (U) *is less than or equal to the corresponding term of* (A), *then* (U) *converges.*

Proof: Let

$A_n = a_1 + a_2 + \cdots + a_n$, and $U_n = u_1 + u_2 + \cdots + u_n$. Since $u_1 \leq a_1$, $u_2 \leq a_2$, and so on, we have $U_n \leq A_n$ for all values of n. Hence, taking the limit as n becomes infinite, we obtain

$$\lim_{n \to \infty} U_n \leq \lim_{n \to \infty} A_n = A.$$

Thus, by Theorem 1, Article 172, (U) converges.

Theorem 2. *If* (A) *diverges and if each term of* (U) *is greater than or equal to the corresponding term of* (A), *then* (U) *diverges.*

Proof: If (U) were a convergent series, then, since $u_n \geq a_n$, it would follow from Theorem 1 that (A) converges. This, however, contradicts the hypothesis that (A) diverges. Hence, (U) must diverge.

Note. The convergence or divergence of a series is unaffected by the omission or addition of a finite number of terms, since such an alteration merely changes the limiting value by a constant amount.

174. Series Used for Comparison. Any series whose convergence or divergence is known may be used as a comparison series for proving the convergence or divergence of an unknown series; the following are particularly useful:

Comparison series for convergence:

$$(C_1) \quad a + ar + ar^2 + \cdots + ar^{n-1} + \cdots \quad (a > 0, r < 1).$$
$$(C_2) \quad 1 + \frac{1}{2^p} + \frac{1}{3^p} + \cdots + \frac{1}{n^p} + \cdots \quad (p > 1).$$

Comparison series for divergence:

$$(D_1) \quad a + ar + ar^2 + \cdots + ar^{n-1} + \cdots \quad (a > 0, r \geq 1).$$
$$(D_2) \quad 1 + \frac{1}{2} + \frac{1}{3} + \cdots + \frac{1}{n} + \cdots.$$

The series (C_2)

$$1 + \frac{1}{2^p} + \frac{1}{3^p} + \cdots + \frac{1}{n^p} + \cdots$$

is known as the **p-series.** When $p = 1$, this series becomes the harmonic series (D_2) which was shown to be divergent in Illustration 2, Article 172. In order to establish the convergence of the p-series for $p > 1$, consider the inequalities

$$\frac{1}{2^p} + \frac{1}{3^p} < \frac{2}{2^p} = \frac{1}{2^{p-1}},$$

$$\frac{1}{4^p} + \frac{1}{5^p} + \frac{1}{6^p} + \frac{1}{7^p} < \frac{4}{4^p} = \frac{1}{4^{p-1}} = \left(\frac{1}{2^{p-1}}\right)^2,$$

$$\frac{1}{8^p} + \frac{1}{9^p} + \cdots + \frac{1}{14^p} + \frac{1}{15^p} < \frac{8}{8^p} = \frac{1}{8^{p-1}} = \left(\frac{1}{2^{p-1}}\right)^3,$$

· · · · · · · · · · · · · · · · · · ·

For $p > 1$, the geometric series

$$1 + \left(\frac{1}{2^{p-1}}\right) + \left(\frac{1}{2^{p-1}}\right)^2 + \left(\frac{1}{2^{p-1}}\right)^3 + \cdots$$

is convergent since the ratio $r = 1/2^{p-1}$ is less than 1. Hence, by comparison with

$$1 + \frac{1}{2^p} + \frac{1}{2^p} + \frac{1}{4^p} + \frac{1}{4^p} + \frac{1}{4^p} + \frac{1}{4^p} + \frac{1}{8^p} + \cdots$$

the series

$$1 + \frac{1}{2^p} + \frac{1}{3^p} + \frac{1}{4^p} + \frac{1}{5^p} + \cdots$$

is convergent.

NOTE. It is evident that for $p < 1$ the series is divergent, since each term is greater than the corresponding term of the divergent harmonic series.

Example 1. Determine the convergence or divergence of the following series by a comparison test:

$$\frac{1}{1 \cdot 3} + \frac{1}{2 \cdot 4} + \frac{1}{3 \cdot 5} + \cdots + \frac{1}{n(n + 2)} + \cdots.$$

Solution: Consider the p-series which, for $p = 2$, is known to converge

$$1 + \frac{1}{2^2} + \frac{1}{3^2} + \cdots + \frac{1}{n^2} + \cdots.$$

Comparing the respective nth terms of the series, we see that

$$\frac{1}{n^2 + 2n} < \frac{1}{n^2}$$

for all positive integral values of n; hence the given series converges.

Example 2. Determine the convergence or divergence of the following series by a comparison test:

$$\frac{2}{1 \cdot 3} + \frac{3}{2 \cdot 4} + \frac{4}{3 \cdot 5} + \cdots + \frac{n+1}{n(n+2)} + \cdots.$$

Solution: Considering the nth term of the given series, we see that for all positive integral values of n

$$\frac{n+1}{n(n+2)} = \frac{n+1}{n} \cdot \frac{1}{(n+2)} > \frac{1}{n+2}.$$

However, the series

$$\frac{1}{3} + \frac{1}{4} + \frac{1}{5} + \cdots + \frac{1}{n+2} + \cdots$$

is known to diverge (see Note, Article 173). Hence, the given series diverges.

175. Ratio Test. *In a series of positive terms*

$$u_1 + u_2 + u_3 + \cdots + u_n + u_{n+1} + \cdots \qquad (1)$$

suppose that

$$\lim_{n \to \infty} \frac{u_{n+1}}{u_n} = R.$$

Then,   *I. if $R < 1$, the series converges,*
II. if $R > 1$, the series diverges,
III. if $R = 1$, the test fails.

Proof: *I.* Since $R < 1$, there exists a number r between R and 1. Since $\lim_{n \to \infty} (u_{n+1}/u_n) = R$, by the definition of a limit, there is a term in the series, say the kth, such that for $n \geq k$ all ratios u_{n+1}/u_n are less than r. Thus we have

$$\frac{u_{k+1}}{u_k} < r, \text{ or } u_{k+1} < ru_k,$$

$$\frac{u_{k+2}}{u_{k+1}} < r, \text{ or } u_{k+2} < ru_{k+1} < r^2 u_k,$$

$$\frac{u_{k+3}}{u_{k+2}} < r, \text{ or } u_{k+3} < ru_{k+2} < r^3 u_k,$$

· · · · · · · · · · · ·

Hence each term of the series

$$u_{k+1} + u_{k+2} + u_{k+3} + \cdots + u_{k+m} + \cdots \qquad (2)$$

is less than the corresponding term of

$$u_k r + u_k r^2 + u_k r^3 + \cdots + u_k r^m + \cdots. \qquad (3)$$

However, (3) is convergent, since it is a geometric series with $r < 1$. Therefore, by comparison, (2) is also convergent as is (1) by the addition of the constant sum $(u_1 + u_2 + \cdots + u_k)$.

II. Since $R > 1$ and $\lim_{n \to \infty} (u_{n+1}/u_n) = R$, it follows from the definition of a limit that there is a term in the series, say the kth, such that for $n \geq k$ all ratios u_{n+1}/u_n are greater than 1; that is, the terms get larger. Hence $\lim_{n \to \infty} u_n$ is not zero and the series is divergent.

NOTE. Observe that the above proof is valid when R increases without bound as n becomes infinite. Hence a series is divergent if

$$\lim_{n \to \infty} u_{n+1}/u_n = \infty.$$

III. The failure of the test when $R = 1$ is illustrated by the harmonic series and the p-series for $p = 2$:

$$1 + \frac{1}{2} + \frac{1}{3} + \cdots + \frac{1}{n} + \frac{1}{n+1} + \cdots,$$

$$1 + \frac{1}{2^2} + \frac{1}{3^2} + \cdots + \frac{1}{n^2} + \frac{1}{(n+1)^2} + \cdots.$$

For each series $\lim_{n \to \infty} u_{n+1}/u_n$ is 1; however, the harmonic series is known to diverge and the p-series for $p = 2$ is known to converge.

Example 1. Using the ratio test, prove the convergence of the series

$$\frac{3}{2^1} + \frac{4}{2^2} + \frac{5}{2^3} + \cdots + \frac{n+2}{2^n} + \cdots.$$

Solution: Since $u_n = \dfrac{n+2}{2^n}$ and $u_{n+1} = \dfrac{n+3}{2^{n+1}}$, we have

$$\frac{u_{n+1}}{u_n} = \frac{n+3}{2^{n+1}} \div \frac{n+2}{2^n} = \frac{n+3}{n+2} \cdot \frac{1}{2}.$$

As n becomes infinite, we obtain

$$\lim_{n \to \infty} \frac{u_{n+1}}{u_n} = \lim_{n \to \infty} \frac{1}{2} \cdot \frac{n+3}{n+2} = \frac{1}{2} \lim_{n \to \infty} \left(1 + \frac{3}{n}\right) \Big/ \left(1 + \frac{2}{n}\right) = \frac{1}{2}.$$

Thus, since $R < 1$, the given series converges.

Example 2. Using the ratio test, prove the divergence of the series

$$\frac{1!}{10} + \frac{3!}{10^2} + \frac{5!}{10^3} + \cdots + \frac{(2n-1)!}{10^n} + \cdots.$$

Solution: Since $u_n = \dfrac{(2n-1)!}{10^n}$ and $u_{n+1} = \dfrac{(2n+1)!}{10^{n+1}}$, we have

$$\frac{u_{n+1}}{u_n} = \frac{(2n+1)!}{10^{n+1}} \div \frac{(2n-1)!}{10^n} = \frac{(2n+1)!}{(2n-1)!} \cdot \frac{1}{10}$$

$$= \frac{(2n+1)(2n)\cdot(2n-1)!}{(2n-1)!} \cdot \frac{1}{10} = \frac{2n^2+n}{5}.$$

As n becomes infinite, we obtain

$$\lim_{n \to \infty} \frac{u_{n+1}}{u_n} = \lim_{n \to \infty} \frac{2n^2+n}{5} = \infty.$$

Thus, since $R > 1$, the series is divergent.

Example 3. Apply the ratio test to the series

$$\frac{1}{1 \cdot 2 \cdot 3} + \frac{1}{2 \cdot 3 \cdot 4} + \frac{1}{3 \cdot 4 \cdot 5} + \cdots + \frac{1}{n(n+1)(n+2)} + \cdots.$$

Solution: Since

$$u_n = \frac{1}{n(n+1)(n+2)} \text{ and } u_{n+1} = \frac{1}{(n+1)(n+2)(n+3)},$$

we have

$$\frac{u_{n+1}}{u_n} = \frac{1}{(n+1)(n+2)(n+3)} \div \frac{1}{n(n+1)(n+2)} = \frac{n}{n+3}.$$

As n becomes infinite, we obtain

$$\lim_{n \to \infty} \frac{u_{n+1}}{u_n} = \lim_{n \to \infty} 1 \Big/ \left(1 + \frac{3}{n}\right) = 1.$$

Therefore, since $R = 1$, the test fails to determine whether the series is convergent or divergent, and other means must be used. For example, comparing with the p-series for $p = 3$, it can be shown that the given series is convergent.

EXERCISE 106

Show that each of the following series is divergent, using the corollary in Article 172:

1. $\frac{1}{2} + \frac{3}{4} + \frac{5}{6} + \frac{7}{8} + \cdots$.
2. $1 + \frac{4}{3} + \frac{9}{5} + \frac{16}{7} + \cdots$.
3. $\frac{4}{7} + \frac{7}{9} + \frac{10}{11} + \frac{13}{13} + \cdots$.
4. $1 + \frac{1}{4} + 1 + \frac{1}{9} + \cdots$.
5. $1 + \frac{4}{5} + \frac{6}{8} + \frac{8}{11} + \cdots$.
6. $\frac{1}{2} + \frac{4}{4} + \frac{7}{6} + \frac{10}{8} + \cdots$.

Determine the convergence or divergence of the following series, using a comparison test:

7. $\dfrac{1}{1 \cdot 2} + \dfrac{1}{2 \cdot 2^2} + \dfrac{1}{3 \cdot 2^3} + \cdots$.

8. $1 + \frac{1}{3} + \frac{1}{5} + \cdots$.

9. $\dfrac{1}{2!} + \dfrac{1}{4!} + \dfrac{1}{6!} + \cdots$.

10. $\dfrac{1}{1 \cdot 2} + \dfrac{1}{3 \cdot 4} + \dfrac{1}{5 \cdot 6} + \cdots$.

11. $\dfrac{1}{\sqrt{2}} + \dfrac{1}{\sqrt{4}} + \dfrac{1}{\sqrt{6}} + \cdots$.

12. $\dfrac{1}{1+1^2} + \dfrac{1}{1+2^2} + \dfrac{1}{1+3^2} + \cdots$.

Determine the convergence or divergence of the following series, using the ratio test. If the ratio test fails, use a comparison test.

13. $\dfrac{1}{3} + \dfrac{2}{3^2} + \dfrac{3}{3^3} + \cdots$.

14. $\dfrac{1!}{2} + \dfrac{2!}{2^2} + \dfrac{3!}{2^3} + \cdots$.

15. $\dfrac{1}{1 \cdot 3} + \dfrac{1}{3 \cdot 5} + \dfrac{1}{5 \cdot 7} + \cdots$.

16. $1 \cdot (\frac{1}{2}) + 2 \cdot (\frac{1}{2})^2 + 3 \cdot (\frac{1}{2})^3 + \cdots$.

17. $\dfrac{5}{1!} + \dfrac{5^2}{3!} + \dfrac{5^3}{5!} + \cdots$.

18. $\dfrac{2}{\pi} + \dfrac{4}{3\,\pi^2} + \dfrac{6}{5\,\pi^3} + \cdots$.

19. $\dfrac{4}{1 \cdot 2 \cdot 3} + \dfrac{5}{2 \cdot 3 \cdot 4} + \dfrac{6}{3 \cdot 4 \cdot 5} + \cdots$.

20. $\dfrac{1}{1} + \dfrac{1 \cdot 2}{1 \cdot 3} + \dfrac{1 \cdot 2 \cdot 3}{1 \cdot 3 \cdot 5} + \cdots$.

176. Alternating Series. A series whose terms are alternately positive and negative is called an **alternating series.**

Alternating Series Test. *If u_1, u_2, u_3, $\cdots$ are positive numbers, the alternating series*

$$u_1 - u_2 + u_3 - \cdots - u_{2k} + u_{2k+1} - \cdots$$

is convergent, provided that

$$(a)\ \ u_1 \geqq u_2 \geqq u_3 \geqq \cdots, \text{ and } (b)\ \lim_{n \to \infty} u_n = 0.$$

Proof: The sum of $2k$ terms of the series may be written in either of the following forms:

$$S_{2k} = (u_1 - u_2) + (u_3 - u_4) + \cdots + (u_{2k-1} - u_{2k}), \quad (1)$$
$$S_{2k} = u_1 - (u_2 - u_3) - \cdots - (u_{2k-2} - u_{2k-1}) - u_{2k}. \quad (2)$$

Since $u_n \geqq u_{n+1}$ for all n, each difference within the parentheses in (1) and (2) is either positive or zero. Hence (1) shows that S_{2k} is positive or zero, and (2) shows that $S_{2k} \leqq u_1$ for all positive integral values of k. Therefore, by Theorem 1, Article 172, S_{2k} approaches a definite limit, say S, as k becomes infinite.

Now consider an odd number of terms

$$S_{2k+1} = S_{2k} + u_{2k+1}.$$

By hypothesis, u_{2k+1} approaches zero as k becomes infinite; hence

$$\lim_{k \to \infty} S_{2k+1} = \lim_{k \to \infty} S_{2k} + \lim_{k \to \infty} u_{2k+1} = S + 0 = S.$$

Since S_n approaches the same limit S whether n is even or odd, it follows that the given series is convergent.

NOTE. It is necessary that the limit of the even sums be the same as the limit of the odd sums; otherwise the series would be oscillatory. Thus, in the series $1 - 1 + 1 - 1 + \cdots$, all even sums are 0 and all odd sums are 1. Hence, S_n oscillates as n becomes infinite. It can be shown in general that if $\lim_{n \to \infty} u_n \neq 0$, an alternating series is oscillatory.

Example. Test for convergence:

$$1 - \frac{1}{2} + \frac{1}{3} - \frac{1}{4} + \cdots + (-1)^{n-1} \frac{1}{n} + \cdots.$$

Solution: The given series is alternating with

$$u_n = \frac{1}{n} \quad \text{and} \quad u_{n+1} = \frac{1}{n+1}.$$

Since (a) $\dfrac{1}{n} > \dfrac{1}{n+1}$ for all n and (b) $\lim\limits_{n \to \infty} \dfrac{1}{n} = 0$, it follows from the alternating series test that the series is convergent.

As a direct consequence of the above theorem, we have

Corollary. *In a convergent alternating series, the error made in taking S_n as an approximation for the value S is less than the absolute value of u_{n+1}.*

Illustration. In the above example the sum of the first nine terms is 0.746 and the value of the series (see NOTE 2, page 283) differs from this by less than $u_{10} = 0.1$.

177. Absolute and Conditional Convergence. *A convergent series*

$$u_1 + u_2 + u_3 + \cdots + u_n + \cdots, \tag{1}$$

where the terms u_1, u_2, u_3, $\cdots$ may have different signs, is said to be **absolutely convergent** *if the series of absolute values,*

$$|u_1| + |u_2| + |u_3| + \cdots + |u_n| + \cdots \tag{2}$$

is convergent.

Illustration 1. The series $1 - \frac{1}{2} + \frac{1}{4} - \frac{1}{8} + \cdots$ is absolutely convergent, since $1 + \frac{1}{2} + \frac{1}{4} + \frac{1}{8} + \cdots$ is convergent.

If a series is convergent but not absolutely convergent, it is said to be **conditionally convergent.**

Illustration 2. The series $1 - \frac{1}{2} + \frac{1}{3} - \frac{1}{4} + \cdots$ is conditionally convergent, since $1 + \frac{1}{2} + \frac{1}{3} + \frac{1}{4} + \cdots$ is divergent.

Theorem 1. *A series is convergent if the series of its absolute values is convergent.*

Proof: Denote by S_n the sum of n terms of (1), by P_n the sum of the positive terms in S_n, and by N_n the sum of the absolute values of the negative terms in S_n; then $S_n = P_n - N_n$. Likewise, let S'_n denote the sum of n terms of (2); then $S'_n = P_n + N_n$.

By hypothesis, (2) converges; therefore S'_n approaches a limit, say S', as n becomes infinite. Since all terms in (2) are positive, we have $S'_n = P_n + N_n < S'$; hence, $P_n < S'$ and $N_n < S'$. Moreover, since P_n and N_n never decrease as n becomes infinite, it follows from Theorem 1, Article 172, that they approach limits, say P and N respectively. Hence, we have

$$\lim_{n \to \infty} S_n = \lim_{n \to \infty} (P_n - N_n) = P - N.$$

Therefore, the series (1) is convergent.

With Theorem 1 an evident extension to the ratio test can be made, as is summarized in the following theorem:

Theorem 2. *If in a series whose terms are not all positive the* **absolute value** *of the ratio of the $(n + 1)$st term to the nth term approaches a limit R as n becomes infinite, the series is convergent if $R < 1$ and divergent if $R > 1$. If $R = 1$, the test fails to determine the convergence or divergence of the series.*

In order to determine the convergence or divergence of a given series the following procedure of testing is suggested:

Tests for Convergence

1. If $\lim u_n \neq 0$ as $n \to \infty$, the series diverges.

2. If $\lim u_n = 0$ as $n \to \infty$, then try

(a) The alternating series test. If this test does not apply, try

(b) The ratio test. If this fails, try

(c) The comparison test on the series with all terms positive.

EXERCISE 107

Determine the convergence or divergence of the following series. State whether the convergence is conditional or absolute.

1. $\dfrac{1}{2} - \dfrac{3}{2^2} + \dfrac{5}{2^3} - \cdots.$

2. $1 - \dfrac{1}{2!} + \dfrac{1}{3!} - \cdots.$

3. $\frac{1}{4} - \frac{1}{6} + \frac{1}{8} - \cdots.$

4. $1 - \sqrt{2} + \sqrt{3} - \cdots.$

5. $\dfrac{1}{2 \cdot 3} - \dfrac{1}{4 \cdot 5} + \dfrac{1}{6 \cdot 7} - \cdots.$

6. $2^{-1} - 2^{-3} + 2^{-5} - \cdots.$

7. $\dfrac{3}{2!} - \dfrac{3^2}{4!} + \dfrac{3^3}{6!} - \cdots.$

8. $1 - \dfrac{1}{\sqrt{3}} + \dfrac{1}{\sqrt{5}} - \cdots.$

9. $\frac{2}{3} - \frac{4}{5} + \frac{6}{7} - \cdots.$

10. $\dfrac{1}{3^{\frac{3}{2}}} - \dfrac{1}{5^{\frac{3}{2}}} + \dfrac{1}{7^{\frac{3}{2}}} - \cdots.$

11. $2(\frac{1}{3}) - 4(\frac{1}{3})^2 + 6(\frac{1}{3})^3 - \cdots.$

12. $1 - \dfrac{1}{1.1} + \dfrac{1}{1.2} - \cdots.$

13. $\frac{1}{3} - \frac{2}{7} + \frac{3}{11} - \cdots.$

14. $\dfrac{1}{\log 2} - \dfrac{1}{\log 3} + \dfrac{1}{\log 4} - \cdots.$

15. $\dfrac{1}{3 \cdot 5^0} - \dfrac{1}{5 \cdot 5^1} + \dfrac{1}{7 \cdot 5^2} - \cdots.$

16. $\frac{2}{3} - \frac{3}{5} + \frac{4}{7} - \cdots.$

17. $\dfrac{1}{10} - \dfrac{2^2}{30} + \dfrac{3^3}{50} - \cdots.$

18. $10 - \dfrac{10^2}{3!} + \dfrac{10^3}{5!} - \cdots.$

19. $\dfrac{3}{1 \cdot 2} - \dfrac{4}{2 \cdot 3} + \dfrac{5}{3 \cdot 4} - \cdots.$

20. $\dfrac{1}{2\sqrt{3}} - \dfrac{1}{3\sqrt{5}} + \dfrac{1}{4\sqrt{7}} - \cdots.$

178. Power Series. If $a_0, a_1, a_2, \cdots$ are constants, a series of the form

$$a_0 + a_1x + a_2x^2 + \cdots + a_nx^n + \cdots$$

is called a **power series in x.** In general, a power series will converge for certain values of x and diverge for all other values. The set of values of x for which a power series is convergent is called the **interval of convergence** of the series. The extended ratio test, Theorem 2, Article 177, is used to determine the interval of convergence.

Example. Find the interval of convergence for the power series

$$x - \frac{x^2}{2} + \frac{x^3}{3} - \frac{x^4}{4} + \cdots.$$

Solution: Since

$$| u_n | = \left| \frac{x^n}{n} \right| \quad \text{and} \quad | u_{n+1} | = \left| \frac{x^{n+1}}{n + 1} \right|,$$

we have

$$\lim_{n\to\infty}\left|\frac{u_{n+1}}{u_n}\right| = \lim_{n\to\infty}\left|\frac{n}{n+1}\cdot x\right| = |x|.$$

By the ratio test, the series

converges if $|x| < 1$ *or* $-1 < x < 1,$

diverges if $|x| > 1$ *or* $x > 1, x < -1;$

the test fails if $|x| = 1$ *or* $x = 1, x = -1.$

When $x = 1$, the series becomes $1 - \frac{1}{2} + \frac{1}{3} - \frac{1}{4} + \cdots$, which has been shown to be convergent. When $x = -1$, the series

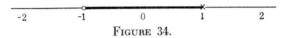

FIGURE 34.

becomes $-1 - \frac{1}{2} - \frac{1}{3} - \frac{1}{4} - \cdots$, which is the negative of the harmonic series and hence diverges. Thus, the interval of convergence for the given series is $-1 < x \leqq 1$.

NOTE. This interval of convergence is depicted graphically as shown in Figure 34.

179. Applications of Power Series. In the binomial series

I. $(1 + x)^n = 1 + nx + \dfrac{n(n-1)}{2!}x^2$

$$+ \frac{n(n-1)(n-2)}{3!}x^3 + \cdots, \quad |x| < 1,$$

we have a power series representation of the function $(1 + x)^n$ which is valid for all x in the interval of convergence. In more advanced mathematics, power series representations can be obtained for many functions, a few of which are listed:

II. $\sin x = x - \dfrac{x^3}{3!} + \dfrac{x^5}{5!} - \dfrac{x^7}{7!} + \cdots,$ $|x| < \infty.$

III. $\cos x = 1 - \dfrac{x^2}{2!} + \dfrac{x^4}{4!} - \dfrac{x^6}{6!} + \cdots,$ $|x| < \infty.$

IV. $e^x = 1 + x + \dfrac{x^2}{2!} + \dfrac{x^3}{3!} + \cdots,$ $|x| < \infty.$

V. $\ln(1 + x) = x - \dfrac{x^2}{2} + \dfrac{x^3}{3} - \dfrac{x^4}{4} + \cdots,$ $-1 < x \leqq 1.$

NOTE 1. In II and III the variable x must be expressed in radians ($180° = \pi$ radians). In IV the constant $e = 2.718 \cdots$ is the base of natural logarithms. In V $\ln x$ is the natural logarithm of x and when multiplied by 0.4343 gives $\log_{10} x$.

NOTE 2. Setting $x = 1$ in V, we have $1 - \frac{1}{2} + \frac{1}{3} - \frac{1}{4} + \cdots = \ln 2 = 0.69315$.

If the variable is sufficiently small, we may use the first few terms of the power series as an approximate formula for the function which it represents.

Illustration. *First approximation*   *Second approximation*

$$(1 + x)^n = 1 + nx = 1 + nx + \frac{1}{2} n(n - 1)x^2,$$
$$e^x = 1 + x = 1 + x + \frac{1}{2} x^2.$$

Example. Find the value of $\sin 10° = \sin \pi/18$ correct to three decimals.

Solution: Setting x equal to $\pi/18 = 0.1745$ in II, we have

$$\sin 10° = (0.1745) - \frac{(0.1745)^3}{3!} + \cdots$$
$$= 0.1745 - 0.0009 + \cdots = 0.174.$$

NOTE 3. Observe that, by the corollary in Article 176, the true value of $\sin 10°$ does not differ from $\pi/18$ by more than 0.0009.

EXERCISE 108

Find the interval of convergence, including the end points, of the following power series:

1. $x - \dfrac{x^3}{3} + \dfrac{x^5}{5} - \cdots$.   2. $1 - \dfrac{x^2}{2!} + \dfrac{x^4}{4!} - \cdots$.

3. $x + \dfrac{x^2}{2^2} + \dfrac{x^3}{2^4} + \cdots$.   4. $x + \dfrac{x^2}{2^2} + \dfrac{x^3}{3^2} + \cdots$.

5. $\dfrac{x}{1 \cdot 3} - \dfrac{x^2}{3 \cdot 3^2} + \dfrac{x^3}{5 \cdot 3^3} - \cdots$.   6. $\dfrac{x^2}{2 \cdot 4} + \dfrac{x^4}{4 \cdot 6} + \dfrac{x^6}{6 \cdot 8} + \cdots$.

7. $\dfrac{1}{2} \cdot \dfrac{x}{2} + \dfrac{3}{4} \cdot \dfrac{x^2}{4} + \dfrac{5}{6} \cdot \dfrac{x^3}{8} + \cdots$.   8. $1 - 2x + 3x^2 - \cdots$.

By a proper substitution in the series I, IV, and V, find the power series representations for the following functions:

9. $\sqrt{1 + x^2}$.   10. e^{-x}.   11. $\ln (1 - x)$.

12. e^{-x^2}.   13. $\ln (1 + x^2)$.   14. $1/\sqrt{1 - x}$.

Using the power series representation, evaluate the following, correct to three decimals:

15. $\cos 10°$.   16. $\ln 1.1$.   17. $e^{0.2}$.   18. $(1.25)^{\frac{3}{2}}$.   19. $\log_{10} 1.25$.

20. $e^{-\frac{1}{2}}$.   21. $\sin 18°$.   22. $(1.1)^{-10}$.   23. $\cos \frac{1}{2}$.   24. $\sqrt{1.5}$.

CHAPTER 24

Statistical Methods

180. The Arithmetic Mean. *The arithmetic mean, $\bar{x}$, of n numbers* x_1, x_2, $\cdots$, x_n, is the sum of the numbers divided by n; symbolically,*

$$\bar{x} = \frac{x_1 + x_2 + \cdots + x_n}{n}.$$

Illustration. The arithmetic mean of the numbers 2, 3, 5, and 8 is $\frac{1}{4}(2 + 3 + 5 + 8)$ or $4\frac{1}{2}$.

NOTE. The word **average** is often used instead of *mean;* however, the arithmetic mean is only one of several types of averages.

181. Notation for Sums. The symbol $\displaystyle\sum_{i=1}^{n}$, read as the sum on i from 1 to n, is used to denote the sum of n terms, each term being obtained from the expression which follows the symbol by substituting the numbers 1, 2, 3, $\cdots$, n successively for i. Σ is called the **sign of summation** and i the **index of summation.**

Illustration.
$$\sum_{i=1}^{4} u_i^2 = u_1^2 + u_2^2 + u_3^2 + u_4^2,$$
$$\sum_{r=1}^{n} r^2 = 1^2 + 2^2 + 3^2 + \cdots + n^2.$$

---

* In this chapter, all numbers are assumed to be real.

NOTE 1. When the index of summation is understood, it is often omitted. Thus, if $(x_1, x_2, \cdots, x_n)$ represents a set of values of x, then

$$\Sigma x = x_1 + x_2 + \cdots + x_n; \quad \Sigma x^2 = x_1^2 + x_2^2 + \cdots + x_n^2.$$

NOTE 2. Observe that the index itself has no effect on the sum. Thus, $\sum_{i=1}^{n} x_i$ has exactly the same meaning as $\sum_{k=1}^{n} x_k$.

182. Minimum Value of a Quadratic Function. *If a, b, and c are constants and $a > 0$, the function $f(x) \equiv ax^2 + bx + c$ has its least value when $x = - b/2 a$.*

Proof: Completing the square in the terms $(ax^2 + bx)$, we have

$$f(x) = a\left(x^2 + \frac{b}{a}x + \frac{b^2}{4\,a^2}\right) + c - \frac{b^2}{4\,a}$$
$$= a\left(x + \frac{b}{2\,a}\right)^2 + \frac{4\,ac - b^2}{4\,a}.$$

Since $a > 0$, the expression $a\left(x + \dfrac{b}{2\,a}\right)^2 \geqq 0$, and $f(x)$ has its least value when $\left(x + \dfrac{b}{2\,a}\right) = 0$, or $x = - b/2 a$.

Illustration. The function $f(x) \equiv 3\,x^2 - 4\,x + 1$ has its least value when $x = - (- 4)/2(3) = \frac{2}{3}$. That is, if a is any number other than $\frac{2}{3}$, then $f(a) > f(\frac{2}{3})$.

183. Deviations. *If x and u are any numbers, the expression $(x - u)$ is called the deviation of x from u.*

NOTE. If u is the *true value* of a measured quantity and x is an *observed value*, the deviation $(x - u)$ is called the **error** of the observation. Also, if u is the *most probable value* of a measured quantity and x is an *observed value*, the deviation $(x - u)$ is called the **residual** of the observation.

184. The Principle of Least Squares. *The most probable value of a measured quantity that can be derived from a series of direct observations $(x_1, x_2, \cdots, x_n)$ is that value u for which the sum of the squares of the residuals is a minimum.*

NOTE. The theory underlying the development of the above *principle of least squares* is beyond the scope of this book, and we present the principle as a **definition** of the **most probable value in the sense of least squares.**

Theorem. *If $(x_1, x_2, \cdots, x_n)$ is a set of observed values, their* **most probable value** *is the arithmetic mean $\bar{x} = \Sigma x/n$.*

Proof: Let u represent the most probable value; then, according to the principle of least squares, u is that value which minimizes the sum of the squares of the residuals

$$R(u) \equiv (x_1 - u)^2 + (x_2 - u)^2 + \cdots + (x_n - u)^2.$$

Writing $R(u)$ as a quadratic equation in u, we have

$$R(u) = (x_1^2 - 2\,x_1 u + u^2) + (x_2^2 - 2\,x_2 u + u^2) + \cdots + (x_n^2 - 2\,x_n u + u^2),$$
$$R(u) = nu^2 - 2(x_1 + x_2 + \cdots + x_n)u + (x_1^2 + x_2^2 + \cdots + x_n^2).$$

By Article 182, it follows that $R(u)$ has its least value when

$$u = -\frac{[-2(x_1 + x_2 + \cdots + x_n)]}{2 \cdot n} = \frac{x_1 + x_2 + \cdots + x_n}{n} = \frac{\Sigma x}{n}.$$

185. Standard Deviation. *If $(x_1, x_2, \cdots, x_n)$ represents a set of numbers and $\bar{x}$ their arithmetic mean, the positive number σ defined by the relation*

$$\sigma^2 = \frac{(x_1 - \bar{x})^2 + (x_2 - \bar{x})^2 + \cdots + (x_n - \bar{x})^2}{n} \qquad (1)$$

is called the **standard deviation,** *or* **root-mean-square deviation,** *of the x's.*

Expanding the numerator of (1) and using $\bar{x} = \Sigma x/n$, we may write (1) in the following form:

$$\sigma^2 = \frac{x_1^2 + x_2^2 + \cdots + x_n^2}{n} - \bar{x}^2 = \frac{1}{n}\Sigma x^2 - \bar{x}^2. \qquad (2)$$

In (1) it is evident that σ is small or large according as the x's are closely grouped around $\bar{x}$ or not. Thus, *the standard deviation of a set of numbers may be used as a measure of their dispersion.*

Illustration. For the numbers (2, 3, 4, 5, 6), we have $\bar{x} = 4$ and $\sigma = \sqrt{2} = 1.4$; whereas for the numbers (3, 3.5, 4, 4.5, 5) we have $\bar{x} = 4$ and $\sigma = \frac{1}{2}\sqrt{2} = 0.7$.

186. Computation of $\bar{x}$ and σ. The arithmetic mean and the standard deviation of a given set of numbers can often be determined more easily by considering the deviations of these numbers from an arbitrarily chosen constant a.

Theorem. *If* $(y_1, y_2, \cdots, y_n)$ *are the deviations of* $(x_1, x_2, \cdots, x_n)$ *from a constant* a, *that is, if*

$$y_1 = x_1 - a, \; y_2 = x_2 - a, \; \cdots, \; y_n = x_n - a,$$

then $\bar{x} = \bar{y} + a$ *and* $\sigma_x = \sigma_y$.

Proof: For $\bar{x}$, we have

$$\bar{x} = \frac{\Sigma x}{n} = \frac{(y_1 + a) + (y_2 + a) + \cdots + (y_n + a)}{n} = \frac{\Sigma y + na}{n}.$$

Since $\bar{y} = \Sigma y / n$, we obtain

$$\bar{x} = \bar{y} + a. \tag{1}$$

To prove the second part of the theorem, we observe that

$$\Sigma x^2 = (y_1 + a)^2 + (y_2 + a)^2 + \cdots + (y_n + a)^2$$
$$= (y_1^2 + y_2^2 + \cdots + y_n^2) + 2a(y_1 + y_2 + \cdots + y_n) + na^2.$$

Since $\Sigma y = n\bar{y}$, we can write the above equation in the form

$$\Sigma x^2 = \Sigma y^2 + 2na\bar{y} + na^2. \tag{2}$$

Substituting (1) and (2) in $\sigma_x^2 = \dfrac{1}{n}\Sigma x^2 - \bar{x}^2$, we obtain

$$\sigma_x^2 = \left(\frac{1}{n}\Sigma y^2 + 2a\bar{y} + a^2\right) - (\bar{y}^2 + 2a\bar{y} + a^2),$$

$$\sigma_x^2 = \frac{1}{n}\Sigma y^2 - \bar{y}^2 = \sigma_y^2. \tag{3}$$

Since the standard deviations are positive, it follows from (3) that $\sigma_x = \sigma_y$, and the theorem is proved.

Illustration. Given the values of x listed in the adjoining table. To compute $\bar{x}$ and σ, we choose for a any convenient value of the same order of magnitude as the x's; say $a = 145$. On completing the table, we have $\bar{y} = 1.5/6 = 0.25$. Hence, using (1), $\bar{x} = 145.25$.

From (3), we obtain

x	y	y^2
146.6	1.6	2.56
143.4	− 1.6	2.56
144.5	− 0.5	0.25
145.7	0.7	0.49
143.2	− 1.8	3.24
148.1	3.1	9.61
	$\Sigma y = 1.5$	$\Sigma y^2 = 18.71$

$$\sigma^2 = \tfrac{1}{6}(18.71) - (0.25)^2 = 3.056; \text{ hence } \sigma = 1.75.$$

NOTE. The constant a is sometimes called an **estimated mean,** or an **assumed mean.**

EXERCISE 109

Find the arithmetic mean of the following numbers:

1. 2, 6, $-$ 3, $-$ 1, 5.   **2.** 4, $-$ 3, 2, $-$ 5, 2.

3. $-$ 14, 16, 21, 18, 12.   **4.** 121, 314, 80, 104, 92.

Find the least value attained by the following functions for all real values of x:

5. $4 x^2 - 9 x + 3$.   **6.** $3 x^2 + 5 x - 1$.   **7.** $5 x^2 - 2 x - 7$.

Write the sums indicated in each of the following:

8. $\sum_{i=1}^{6} v_i$.   **9.** $\sum_{n=1}^{4} n^3$.   **10.** $\sum_{j=1}^{4} u_j^2$.   **11.** $\sum_{i=1}^{4} (k - x_i)$.

12. $\sum_{n=1}^{3} a_n b_n$.   **13.** $\sum_{k=3}^{7} 2 k^2$.   **14.** $\sum_{n=0}^{6} (-1)^n a_n$.   **15.** $\sum_{i=1}^{5} (2 i + 1)$.

Express each of the following in the summation notation:

16. $x_1^3 + x_2^3 + x_3^3 + x_4^3 + x_5^3 + x_6^3$.

17. $a_1 x_1 + a_2 x_2 + \cdots + a_m x_m$.

18. $3^2 + 4^2 + 5^2 + 6^2 + 7^2 + 8^2 + 9^2$.

19. $(x_1 - 2)^2 + (x_2 - 2)^2 + \cdots + (x_n - 2)^2$.

20. If $(v_1, v_2, \cdots, v_n)$ are given values of a variable v, what sum is meant by (a) $\Sigma 2 v$, (b) Σv^2, and (c) $\Sigma (v - 5)^2$?

If $(x_1, x_2, \cdots, x_n)$ are given values of a variable x, and k is a constant, prove each of the following:

21. $\Sigma k x = k \Sigma x$.   **22.** $\Sigma (x + k) = \Sigma x + nk$.

23. $\Sigma (x + k)^2 = \Sigma x^2 + 2 k \Sigma x + nk^2$.

Use the definitions to find the arithmetic mean and standard deviation for each of the following sets of numbers:

24. 5, 9, $-$ 7, 2, 4, 6, $-$ 1, 3, 8, $-$ 4.

25. 2.3, 2.7, 2.1, 2.2, 2.5, 3.0, 2.9, 2.0, 3.2, 3.1.

26. 17, 21, 42, 25, 19, 37, 30, 28, 32, 35.

Choose an assumed mean, and compute the arithmetic mean and the standard deviation for each of the following sets of numbers:

27. 498, 487, 505, 507, 499, 501, 492, 510, 504.

28. 1823, 1817, 1821, 1814, 1820, 1819, 1818, 1824.

29. $-$ 9.22, $-$ 9.35, $-$ 9.27, $-$ 9.31, $-$ 9.39, $-$ 9.25.

30. 4.07, 4.11, 4.17, 4.22, 4.19, 4.17, 4.12, 4.17.

31. For the years indicated, the following table gives the annual rainfall and snowfall in inches for New York City. Find the arithmetic mean and the standard deviation for each.

Year	1933	1934	1935	1936	1937	1938	1939	1940	1941	1942
Rain	49.7	45.0	32.6	46.3	48.1	46.4	35.7	45.0	36.2	49.6
Snow	52.5	29.6	32.8	11.9	13.9	31.9	22.2	35.0	8.7	22.4

32. The birth rate and death rate in the United States for each year from 1929 to 1940 are given in Problem 6, page 41. Find the arithmetic mean and standard deviation for each rate.

187. Curve Fitting by the Method of Least Squares. If a set of points representing experimental data is plotted, it is possible that these points may appear to lie somewhat closely upon a curve. This indicates that the data may approximately follow some simple mathematical law.

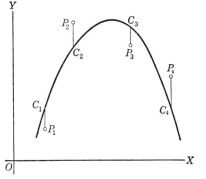

FIGURE 35.

Let P_1, P_2, P_3, ⋯ be the points determined by the data. The curve indicating their general trend is called an **empirical curve.** In general, the points P will not lie on the empirical curve but will be distributed above and below the curve as indicated in Figure 35.

The deviation of any point P from the corresponding point C on an empirical curve, where C is directly above or below P, is called the **y-residual** of P. Symbolically,

$$y\text{-residual} = (y \text{ of } P) - (y \text{ of } C).$$

For a given set of points, a curve of a selected type will be called the **best-fitting curve** *of that type when the sum of the squares of the y-residuals has the least value possible.*

NOTE. There is *usually* a single best-fitting curve of the type selected. However, it is possible that there may be more than one, or none at all.

188. Fitting a Line $y = ax + b$ to n Points. If one point (x_1, y_1) is given, the problem is trivial and any line of the form

$$y - y_1 = k(x - x_1),$$

where k is an arbitrary constant, gives a best fit.

If two distinct points (x_1, y_1) and (x_2, y_2) are given, where $x_1 \neq x_2$, the best-fitting line is the line that passes through the two given points.

Illustration. If the line $y = ax + b$ is to pass through the points $(1, -2)$ and $(3, 4)$, then

$$\left. \begin{array}{l} (-2) = a(1) + b, \\ (4) = a(3) + b, \end{array} \right\} \; ; \text{ hence } \begin{cases} a = 3, \\ b = -5. \end{cases}$$

Thus, the required line is $y = 3x - 5$.

If $P_0(x_0, y_0)$ is any point and $y = ax + b$ is any line, it follows from Article 187 that the y-residual R_0 of the point P_0 with respect to the given line is

$$R_0 = y_0 - (ax_0 + b).$$

Theorem. *If $n > 2$, the line $y = ax + b$ which best fits the non-collinear points $P_1(x_1, y_1)$, $P_2(x_2, y_2)$, $\cdots$, $P_n(x_n, y_n)$ is that line in which the values of a and b are determined by the* **normal equations**

FIGURE 36.

$$\begin{cases} \Sigma y = a\Sigma x + nb, \\ \Sigma xy = a\Sigma x_2 + b\Sigma x. \end{cases} \quad (1)$$

Proof: For simplicity we shall indicate the method of proof for the case when $n = 3$.

The y-residuals of the points P_1, P_2, and P_3 with respect to the line $y = ax + b$ are respectively

$$R_1 = y_1 - (ax_1 + b), \; R_2 = y_2 - (ax_2 + b), \; R_3 = y_3 - (ax_3 + b). \quad (2)$$

The problem is to determine a and b so that $\Sigma R^2 = R_1^2 + R_2^2 + R_3^2$ is a minimum.

From (2), we have

$$R_1^2 = y_1^2 + a^2 x_1^2 + b^2 - 2\,ax_1y_1 - 2\,by_1 + 2\,abx_1, \tag{3}$$
$$R_2^2 = y_2^2 + a^2 x_2^2 + b^2 - 2\,ax_2y_2 - 2\,by_2 + 2\,abx_2, \tag{4}$$
$$R_3^2 = y_3^2 + a^2 x_3^2 + b^2 - 2\,ax_3y_3 - 2\,by_3 + 2\,abx_3. \tag{5}$$

Adding (3), (4), and (5), we obtain

$$\Sigma R^2 = \Sigma y^2 + a^2\Sigma x^2 + 3\,b^2 - 2\,a\Sigma xy - 2\,b\Sigma y + 2\,ab\Sigma x. \tag{6}$$

Considering b as a constant, we may write ΣR^2 as a quadratic function of a; thus

$$\Sigma R^2 = (\Sigma x^2)a^2 + (2\,b\Sigma x - 2\Sigma xy)a + (\Sigma y^2 - 2\,b\Sigma y + 3\,b^2).$$

By Article 182, the value of a which gives ΣR^2 its least value is

$$a = -\frac{(2\,b\Sigma x - 2\Sigma xy)}{2(\Sigma x^2)}; \text{ hence } a\Sigma x^2 + b\Sigma x = \Sigma xy. \tag{7}$$

Similarly, by expressing ΣR^2 as a quadratic function of b, we find by Article 182 that a and b must satisfy the relation

$$a\Sigma x + 3\,b = \Sigma y. \tag{8}$$

NOTE 1. Since the proof is beyond the scope of this book, it will be assumed without proof that the solution (a, b) in (7) and (8) does in fact minimize the sum ΣR^2.

NOTE 2. It follows from the first equation in (1) that $\Sigma R = 0$.

Example. Find the line which best fits the points $(-1, -1)$, $(1, 1)$, $(2, 1)$, and $(4, 3)$.

Solution: For the given points, we have the following sums

$$\Sigma x = (-1) + (1) + (2) + (4) = 6,$$
$$\Sigma x^2 = (-1)^2 + (1)^2 + (2)^2 + (4)^2 = 22,$$
$$\Sigma y = (-1) + (1) + (1) + (3) = 4,$$
$$\Sigma xy = (-1)(-1) + (1)(1) + (2)(1) + (4)(3) = 16.$$

Substituting in (1), the normal equations are

$$4 = 6\,a + 4\,b \quad \text{and} \quad 16 = 22\,a + 6\,b.$$

Solving these equations for a and b, we find the equation of the best-fitting line to be $y = \frac{10}{13}\,x - \frac{2}{13}$.

189. Trend Lines. A set of statistical data arranged in accordance with its time of occurrence is called a **time series.**

Illustration. The following data collected by the Federal Power Commission gives the annual United States production of electric energy expressed in billions of kilowatt hours.

Time	1932	'33	'34	'35	'36	'37	'38	'39	'40	'41
Production	82	85	91	98	112	122	117	130	145	168

This set of data constitutes a time series, and the graph of the best-fitting linear function $y = at + b$ for a time series (t_1, y_1), (t_2, y_2), $\cdots$, (t_n, y_n) is called the **trend line** for the series.

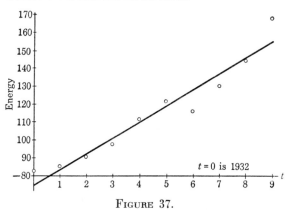

FIGURE 37.

Example. Find the trend line for the data in the above illustration.

Solution: Considering 1932 as time zero, we have the time series $(0, 82)$, $(1, 85)$, and so on. To find the best-fitting line $y = at + b$ we compute as follows:

t	y	t^2	ty
0	82	0	0
1	85	1	85
2	91	4	182
$\cdots$	$\cdots$	$\cdots$	$\cdots$
9	168	81	1512
$\Sigma t = 45$	$\Sigma y = 1150$	$\Sigma t^2 = 285$	$\Sigma ty = 5903$

Thus, the normal equations are

$$285\,a + 45\,b = 5903, \quad 45\,a + 10\,b = 1150.$$

Solving for a and b, we find the best-fitting line to be $y = 8.82\,t + 75.3$. This line, whose graph is shown in Figure 37, is the *trend line* for the given time series.

190. Fitting a Polynomial $y = f(x)$ to n Points.

If the coordinates of each of the n points (x_1, y_1), (x_2, y_2), $\cdots$, (x_n, y_n) are substituted in the equation,

$$y = a_0 x^m + a_1 x^{m-1} + \cdots + a_m, \tag{1}$$

we obtain n linear equations in the $(m + 1)$ coefficients a_0, a_1, $\cdots$, a_m. This system of equations will usually have *infinitely many solutions* if $n < (m + 1)$, *one solution* if $n = (m + 1)$, and *no solution* if $n > (m + 1)$.

Example 1. Find the parabola $y = ax^2 + bx + c$ which passes through the points $(1, 1)$, $(2, 3)$, and $(3, 9)$.

Solution: When the coordinates of each point are substituted in $y = ax^2 + bx + c$, we obtain the three equations

$$\begin{cases} 1 = a + b + c, \\ 3 = 4\,a + 2\,b + c, \\ 9 = 9\,a + 3\,b + c. \end{cases}$$

Solving, we find $a = 2$, $b = -4$, and $c = 3$. Hence, the equation of the required parabola is $y = 2\,x^2 - 4\,x + 3$.

When $n > (m + 1)$, a best-fitting curve of the form in (1) can usually be obtained by following a procedure similar to that used in determining a best-fitting line.

For example, consider the parabola $y = ax^2 + bx + c$ and the $n > 3$ points (x_1, y_1), (x_2, y_2), $\cdots$, (x_n, y_n). The y-residual corresponding to each of these points is $R_i = y_i - (ax_i^2 + bx_i + c)$.

Hence, for a best fit, the expression to be minimized is

$$\Sigma R^2 = \Sigma(y - ax^2 - bx - c)^2. \tag{2}$$

Writing (2) as a quadratic equation in a, b, and c, respectively, we have

$$\begin{cases} \Sigma R^2 = \Sigma(y - bx - c)^2 - 2\,a\Sigma x^2(y - bx - c) + a^2\Sigma x^4, & (3) \\ \Sigma R^2 = \Sigma(y - ax^2 - c)^2 - 2\,b\Sigma x(y - ax^2 - c) + b^2\Sigma x^2, & (4) \\ \Sigma R^2 = \Sigma(y - ax^2 - bx)^2 - 2\,c\Sigma(y - ax^2 - bx) + c^2 \cdot n. & (5) \end{cases}$$

By Article 182, (3), (4), and (5) will be a minimum when

$$\begin{cases} a = \Sigma x^2(y - bx - c)/\Sigma x^4, \\ b = \Sigma x(y - ax^2 - c)/\Sigma x^2, \\ c = \Sigma(y - ax^2 - bx)/n. \end{cases}$$

Simplifying, we obtain the three normal equations which determine the coefficients a, b, and c.

$$\begin{cases} \Sigma y = a\Sigma x^2 + b\Sigma x + cn, \\ \Sigma xy = a\Sigma x^3 + b\Sigma x^2 + c\Sigma x, \\ \Sigma x^2y = a\Sigma x^4 + b\Sigma x^3 + c\Sigma x^2. \end{cases}$$

Example 2. Find the parabola which best fits the points $(-2, -1)$, $(-1, 2)$, $(1, 3)$, and $(2, 3)$.

Solution: We have $\Sigma x = 0$, $\Sigma x^2 = 10$, $\Sigma x^3 = 0$, $\Sigma x^4 = 34$, $\Sigma y = 7$, $\Sigma xy = 9$, and $\Sigma x^2y = 13$; hence, the normal equations are

$$\begin{cases} 10\,a &+ 4\,c = 7, \\ & 10\,b &= 9, \\ 34\,a &+ 10\,c = 13. \end{cases}$$

Solving, we find $a = -\frac{1}{2}$, $b = \frac{9}{10}$, and $c = 3$. Hence the required parabola is $y = -\frac{1}{2}x^2 + \frac{9}{10}x + 3$.

EXERCISE 110

Find a line of the form $y = ax + b$ whose graph passes through the following points:

1. $(1, 3)$, $(4, 2)$.   **2.** $(-2, -5)$, $(4, 1)$.

Find a parabola of the form $y = ax^2 + bx + c$ whose graph passes through the following points:

3. $(-1, -2)$, $(0, 5)$, $(2, 7)$.   **4.** $(-2, 8)$, $(1, 2)$, $(1\frac{1}{3}, 4\frac{2}{3})$.

Find a cubic of the form $y = ax^3 + bx^2 + cx + d$ whose graph passes through the following points:

5. $(-1, 0)$, $(0, 1)$, $(1, 0)$, $(2, 3)$.
6. $(-3, -5)$, $(0, -2)$, $(1, 7)$, $(3, 1)$.

Find a line of the form $y = ax + b$ which best fits each of the following sets of points:

7.

x	1	3	6	7
y	-1	-1	2	4

8.

x	-2	1	3	7
y	-2	2	4	6

9.

x	-1	1	2	3	4
y	8	7	1	-1	-6

10.

x	0	1	3	5	8
y	0	2	4	5	8

Find a parabola of the form $y = ax^2 + bx + c$ which best fits each of the following sets of points:

11. Points in Problem 7.   **12.** Points in Problem 8.
13. Points in Problem 9.   **14.** Points in Problem 10.

15. The following table lists the annual United States production of lumber expressed in billions of board feet. Find the trend line for the data.

Year	1932	'33	'34	'35	'36	'37	'38	'39	'40	'41
Lumber production	10	14	15	20	24	26	22	25	29	33

16. The annual wholesale price index in the United States is given in the following table. The index number 100 is chosen to represent the average prices in 1926. Determine the trend line and estimate the index for 1943.

Year	1933	'34	'35	'36	'37	'38	'39	'40	'41	'42
Index no.	66	75	80	81	86	79	77	79	87	99

17. The number of radio sets in use in the United States is given in the following table for the years indicated. Determine the trend line and estimate the number in use for 1950.

Year	1934	'35	'36	'37	'38	'39	'40	'41	'42	'43
Millions of radios	28	30	33	38	41	45	51	56	59	57

18. The total resources of the Federal Reserve Banks is given in the following table for the years indicated. Determine the trend line.

Year	1933	'34	'35	'36	'37	'38	'39	'40	'41	'42
Billions of dollars	7.0	8.4	11.0	12.5	12.9	15.6	19.0	23.3	24.4	29.0

19. Using the first five entries in the table on page 40, find the linear trend of the United States population in the various age groups listed. Compare this linear trend with the estimates given.

20. To determine a best-fitting function of the form $y = ax^3 + b$, find the normal equations which a and b must satisfy.

191. Standard Error of Estimate. In order to measure the closeness with which a best line $y = ax + b$ will fit a set of n points, we use the **standard error of estimate**, which is defined as the **root-mean-square of the y-residuals**; symbolically,

$$S_y = \sqrt{\frac{1}{n} \Sigma (y - ax - b)^2}.$$

In this definition it is apparent that the value of S_y will be large or small according as the points are widely scattered or close to the best line.

Illustration. The standard error for the best line determined in the example in Article 188 is

$$S_y = \sqrt{\frac{1}{4}\left[\left(\frac{-1}{13}\right)^2 + \left(\frac{5}{13}\right)^2 + \left(\frac{-5}{13}\right)^2 + \left(\frac{1}{13}\right)^2\right]} = \frac{1}{13}\sqrt{13} = 0.277.$$

NOTE. The statistical study of sets of points is similar in many respects to that of sets of values. Thus, for a set of values, (1) *the sum of the deviations from the arithmetic mean is zero*, (2) *the sum of the squares of the deviations from the arithmetic mean is a minimum*, and (3) *the standard deviation is used to measure the scatter of the values about the arithmetic mean.* Similarly, for a set of points, (1) *the sum of the y-residuals from the best line is zero*, (2) *the sum of the squares of the y-residuals from the best line is a minimum*, and (3) *the standard error of estimate is used to measure the scatter of the points about the best line.*

192. Coefficient of Correlation. In Article 191 the value of S_y was determined by first obtaining the best line and then computing the respective residuals. In more advanced texts it is shown that S_y can be expressed in the following form:

$$S_y = \sigma_y\sqrt{1 - r^2} \tag{1}$$

where

$$r = \frac{\sum_{i=1}^{n}(x_i - \bar{x})(y_i - \bar{y})}{\sqrt{\left[\sum_{i=1}^{n}(x_i - \bar{x})^2\right]\left[\sum_{i=1}^{n}(y_i - \bar{y})^2\right]}}. \tag{2}$$

The constant r is called the **coefficient of correlation between x and y**; and its value, rather than S_y, is usually used as a measure of the degree to which a best line fits a set of points.

Illustration. In the illustration in Article 191, we find $\sigma_y = \sqrt{2}$; hence $r = 5/\sqrt{26} = 0.981$.

The coefficient of correlation has the following properties:

(a) Since S_y and σ_y are real numbers, we see from (1) that $r^2 \leqq 1$; that is, r is a number between -1 and $+1$.

(b) If all the given points lie on the best line, then $S_y = 0$ and r is $+1$ or -1. In this case there is said to be **perfect correlation** between x and y. As the numerical value of r decreases, the poorer becomes the fit.

(c) Using Equation (2) to compute r, we can show that r is positive or negative according as the coefficient a, in the best line $y = ax + b$, is positive or negative. Thus, if y increases as x increases, there is said to be *positive correlation* between the variables; and if y decreases as x increases, the correlation is *negative*.

(d) Since a change in the unit of measuring x (or y) introduces the same constant factor in the numerator and the denominator of (2), it follows that the value of r is independent of the units used to measure x (or y).

Note. In Equation (2) r is expressed in terms of the deviations of the x's and y's from their respective arithmetic means. These deviations are unaltered if a constant is added to all the x's or to all the y's. This fact may be used to reduce the size of the numbers when computing r.

EXERCISE 111

Find the standard error of estimate and the coefficient of correlation of x and y in each of the following:

1.

x	1	3	4	7
y	1	2	5	6

2.

x	-2	1	3	5
y	6	3	4	-2

3.

x	0	1	2	3	4	5	6	7	8	9
y	-5	-4	-3	-1	0	3	4	5	7	8

4.

x	-4	-4	-2	-1	0	2	3	4	6	6
y	3	2	1	1	1	0	-1	-1	-2	-3

5. The height in inches and weight in pounds of ten students are given in the following table. Find the coefficient of correlation between the heights and weights.

Student	A	B	C	D	E	F	G	H	I	J
Height	59	60	62	66	68	68	69	70	70	73
Weight	135	146	141	150	147	155	165	162	185	170

6. In two examinations given in a course, ten students made the scores listed in the following table. Find the coefficient of correlation between the two examinations.

Student	A	B	C	D	E	F	G	H	I	J
Exam. 1	62	65	69	70	73	75	79	80	87	93
Exam. 2	71	62	65	71	81	69	78	86	85	78

7. The wholesale price index for foods in the United States and this country's steel output in millions of tons are given in the following table for the years indicated. Find the coefficient of correlation between the two entries.

Year	1935	'36	'37	'38	'39	'40	'41	'42
Food index	84	82	86	74	70	71	83	99
Steel output	38	53	57	32	53	67	83	86

8. The national income in billions of dollars and the federal automotive taxes in millions of dollars are given in the following table for the years indicated. Find the coefficient of correlation between the two entries.

Year	1935	'36	'37	'38	'39	'40	'41	'42
Income	56	65	72	64	71	78	96	120
Taxes	257	297	324	267	320	411	562	625

Tables

TABLE I POWERS AND ROOTS

N	N^2	$\sqrt{N}$	N^3	$\sqrt[3]{N}$	N	N^2	$\sqrt{N}$	N^3	$\sqrt[3]{N}$
1	1	1.000	1	1.000	51	2 601	7.141	132 651	3.708
2	4	1.414	8	1.260	52	2 704	7.211	140 608	3.733
3	9	1.732	27	1.442	53	2 809	7.280	148 877	3.756
4	16	2.000	64	1.587	54	2 916	7.348	157 464	3.780
5	25	2.236	125	1.710	55	3 025	7.416	166 375	3.803
6	36	2.449	216	1.817	56	3 136	7.483	175 616	3.826
7	49	2.646	343	1.913	57	3 249	7.550	185 193	3.849
8	64	2.828	512	2.000	58	3 364	7.616	195 112	3.871
9	81	3.000	729	2.080	59	3 481	7.681	205 379	3.893
10	100	3.162	1 000	2.154	60	3 600	7.746	216 000	3.915
11	121	3.317	1 331	2.224	61	3 721	7.810	226 981	3.936
12	144	3.464	1 728	2.289	62	3 844	7.874	238 328	3.958
13	169	3.606	2 197	2.351	63	3 969	7.937	250 047	3.979
14	196	3.742	2 744	2.410	64	4 096	8.000	262 144	4.000
15	225	3.873	3 375	2.466	65	4 225	8.062	274 625	4.021
16	256	4.000	4 096	2.520	66	4 356	8.124	287 496	4.041
17	289	4.123	4 913	2.571	67	4 489	8.185	300 763	4.062
18	324	4.243	5 832	2.621	68	4 624	8.246	314 432	4.082
19	361	4.359	6 859	2.668	69	4 761	8.307	328 509	4.102
20	400	4.472	8 000	2.714	70	4 900	8.367	343 000	4.121
21	441	4.583	9 261	2.759	71	5 041	8.426	357 911	4.141
22	484	4.690	10 648	2.802	72	5 184	8.485	373 248	4.160
23	529	4.796	12 167	2.844	73	5 329	8.544	389 017	4.179
24	576	4.899	13 824	2.884	74	5 476	8.602	405 224	4.198
25	625	5.000	15 625	2.924	75	5 625	8.660	421 875	4.217
26	676	5.099	17 576	2.962	76	5 776	8.718	438 976	4.236
27	729	5.196	19 683	3.000	77	5 929	8.775	456 533	4.254
28	784	5.292	21 952	3.037	78	6 084	8.832	474 552	4.273
29	841	5.385	24 389	3.072	79	6 241	8.888	493 039	4.291
30	900	5.477	27 000	3.107	80	6 400	8.944	512 000	4.309
31	961	5.568	29 791	3.141	81	6 561	9.000	531 441	4.327
32	1 024	5.657	32 768	3.175	82	6 724	9.055	551 368	4.344
33	1 089	5.745	35 937	3.208	83	6 889	9.110	571 787	4.362
34	1 156	5.831	39 304	3.240	84	7 056	9.165	592 704	4.380
35	1 225	5.916	42 875	3.271	85	7 225	9.220	614 125	4.397
36	1 296	6.000	46 656	3.302	86	7 396	9.274	636 056	4.414
37	1 369	6.083	50 653	3.332	87	7 569	9.327	658 503	4.431
38	1 444	6.164	54 872	3.362	88	7 744	9.381	681 472	4.448
39	1 521	6.245	59 319	3.391	89	7 921	9.434	704 969	4.465
40	1 600	6.325	64 000	3.420	90	8 100	9.487	729 000	4.481
41	1 681	6.403	68 921	3.448	91	8 281	9.539	753 571	4.498
42	1 764	6.481	74 088	3.476	92	8 464	9.592	778 688	4.514
43	1 849	6.557	79 507	3.503	93	8 649	9.644	804 357	4.531
44	1 936	6.633	85 184	3.530	94	8 836	9.695	830 584	4.547
45	2 025	6.708	91 125	3.557	95	9 025	9.747	857 375	4.563
46	2 116	6.782	97 336	3.583	96	9.216	9.798	884 736	4.579
47	2 209	6.856	103 823	3.609	97	9 409	9.849	912 673	4.595
48	2 304	6.928	110 592	3.634	98	9 604	9.899	941 192	4.610
49	2 401	7.000	117 649	3.659	99	9 801	9.950	970 299	4.626
50	2 500	7.071	125 000	3.684	100	10 000	10.000	1000 000	4.642
N	N^2	$\sqrt{N}$	N^3	$\sqrt[3]{N}$	N	N^2	$\sqrt{N}$	N^3	$\sqrt[3]{N}$

TABLE II　　　TRIGONOMETRIC FUNCTIONS

θ	Sin θ	Cos θ	Tan θ	θ	Sin θ	Cos θ	Tan θ
0°	.00 00	1.00 00	.00 00	45°	.70 71	.70 71	1.00 00
1°	.01 75	.99 98	.01 75	46°	.71 93	.69 47	1.03 55
2°	.03 49	.99 94	.03 49	47°	.73 14	.68 20	1.07 24
3°	.05 23	.99 86	.05 24	48°	.74 31	.66 91	1.11 06
4°	.06 98	.99 76	.06 99	49°	.75 47	.65 61	1.15 04
5°	.08 72	.99 62	.08 75	50°	.76 60	.64 28	1.19 18
6°	.10 45	.99 45	.10 51	51°	.77 71	.62 93	1.23 49
7°	.12 19	.99 25	.12 28	52°	.78 80	.61 57	1.27 99
8°	.13 92	.99 03	.14 05	53°	.79 86	.60 18	1.32 70
9°	.15 64	.98 77	.15 84	54°	.80 90	.58 78	1.37 64
10°	.17 36	.98 48	.17 63	55°	.81 92	.57 36	1.42 81
11°	.19 08	.98 16	.19 44	56°	.82 90	.55 92	1.48 26
12°	.20 79	.97 81	.21 26	57°	.83 87	.54 46	1.53 99
13°	.22 50	.97 44	.23 09	58°	.84 80	.52 99	1.60 03
14°	.24 19	.97 03	.24 93	59°	.85 72	.51 50	1.66 43
15°	.25 88	.96 59	.26 79	60°	.86 60	.50 00	1.73 21
16°	.27 56	.96 13	.28 67	61°	.87 46	.48 48	1.80 40
17°	.29 24	.95 63	.30 57	62°	.88 29	.46 95	1.88 07
18°	.30 90	.95 11	.32 49	63°	.89 10	.45 40	1.96 26
19°	.32 56	.94 55	.34 43	64°	.89 88	.43 84	2.05 03
20°	.34 20	.93 97	.36 40	65°	.90 63	.42 26	2.14 45
21°	.35 84	.93 36	.38 39	66°	.91 35	.40 67	2.24 60
22°	.37 46	.92 72	.40 40	67°	.92 05	.39 07	2.35 59
23°	.39 07	.92 05	.42 45	68°	.92 72	.37 46	2.47 51
24°	.40 67	.91 35	.44 52	69°	.93 36	.35 84	2.60 51
25°	.42 26	.90 63	.46 63	70°	.93 97	.34 20	2.74 75
26°	.43 84	.89 88	.48 77	71°	.94 55	.32 56	2.90 42
27°	.45 40	.89 10	.50 95	72°	.95 11	.30 90	3.07 77
28°	.46 95	.88 29	.53 17	73°	.95 63	.29 24	3.27 09
29°	.48 48	.87 46	.55 43	74	.96 13	.27 56	3.48 74
30°	.50 00	.86 60	.57 74	75°	.96 59	.25 88	3.73 21
31°	.51 50	.85 72	.60 09	76°	.97 03	.24 19	4.01 08
32°	.52 99	.84 80	.62 49	77°	.97 44	.22 50	4.33 15
33°	.54 46	.83 87	.64 94	78°	.97 81	.20 79	4.70 46
34°	.55 92	.82 90	.67 45	79°	.98 16	.19 08	5.14 46
35°	.57 36	.81 92	.70 02	80°	.98 48	.17 36	5.67 13
36°	.58 78	.80 90	.72 65	81°	.98 77	.15 64	6.31 38
37°	.60 18	.79 86	.75 36	82°	.99 03	.13 92	7.11 54
38°	.61 57	.78 80	.78 13	83°	.99 25	.12 19	8.14 43
39°	.62 93	.77 71	.80 98	84°	.99 45	.10 45	9.51 44
40°	.64 28	.76 60	.83 91	85°	.99 62	.08 72	11.43 01
41°	.65 61	.75 47	.86 93	86°	.99 76	.06 98	14.30 07
42°	.66 91	.74 31	.90 04	87°	.99 86	.05 23	19.08 11
43°	.68 20	.73 14	.93 25	88°	.99 94	.03 49	28.63 63
44°	.69 47	.71 93	.96 57	89°	.99 98	.01 75	57.29 00
45°	.70 71	.70 71	1.00 00	90°	1.00 00	.00 00	———
θ	Sin θ	Cos θ	Tan θ	θ	Sin θ	Cos θ	Tan θ

TABLE III   LOGARITHMS OF NUMBERS

N	0	1	2	3	4	5	6	7	8	9
10	0 000	043	086	128	170	212	253	294	334	374
11	414	453	492	531	569	607	645	682	719	755
12	0 792	828	864	899	934	969	*004	*038	*072	*106
13	1 139	173	206	239	271	303	335	367	399	430
14	461	492	523	553	584	614	644	673	703	732
15	1 761	790	818	847	875	903	931	959	987	*014
16	2 041	068	095	122	148	175	201	227	253	279
17	304	330	355	380	405	430	455	480	504	529
18	553	577	601	625	648	672	695	718	742	765
19	2 788	810	833	856	878	900	923	945	967	989
20	3 010	032	054	075	096	118	139	160	181	201
21	222	243	263	284	304	324	345	365	385	404
22	424	444	464	483	502	522	541	560	579	598
23	617	636	655	674	692	711	729	747	766	784
24	802	820	838	856	874	892	909	927	945	962
25	3 979	997	*014	*031	*048	*065	*082	*099	*116	*133
26	4 150	166	183	200	216	232	249	265	281	298
27	314	330	346	362	378	393	409	425	440	456
28	472	487	502	518	533	548	564	579	594	609
29	624	639	654	669	683	698	713	728	742	757
30	4 771	786	800	814	829	843	857	871	886	900
31	4 914	928	942	955	969	983	997	*011	*024	*038
32	5 051	065	079	092	105	119	132	145	159	172
33	185	198	211	224	237	250	263	276	289	302
34	315	328	340	353	366	378	391	403	416	428
35	441	453	465	478	490	502	514	527	539	551
36	563	575	587	599	611	623	635	647	658	670
37	682	694	705	717	729	740	752	763	775	786
38	798	809	821	832	843	855	866	877	888	899
39	5 911	922	933	944	955	966	977	988	999	*010
40	6 021	031	042	053	064	075	085	096	107	117
41	128	138	149	160	170	180	191	201	212	222
42	232	243	253	263	274	284	294	304	314	325
43	335	345	355	365	375	385	395	405	415	425
44	435	444	454	464	474	484	493	503	513	522
45	532	542	551	561	571	580	590	599	609	618
46	628	637	646	656	665	675	684	693	702	712
47	721	730	739	749	758	767	776	785	794	803
48	812	821	830	839	848	857	866	875	884	893
49	902	911	920	928	937	946	955	964	972	981
50	6 990	998	*007	*016	*024	*033	*042	*050	*059	*067
51	7 076	084	093	101	110	118	126	135	143	152
52	160	168	177	185	193	202	210	218	226	235
53	243	251	259	267	275	284	292	300	308	316
54	7 324	332	340	348	356	364	372	380	388	396
N	0	1	2	3	4	5	6	7	8	9

Prop. Parts

	43	42	41	40
1	4.3	4.2	4.1	4
2	8.6	8.4	8.2	8
3	12.9	12.6	12.3	12
4	17.2	16.8	16.4	16
5	21.5	21.0	20.5	20
6	25.8	25.2	24.6	24
7	30.1	29.4	28.7	28
8	34.4	33.6	32.8	32
9	38.7	37.8	36.9	36

	39	38	37	36
1	3.9	3.8	3.7	3.6
2	7.8	7.6	7.4	7.2
3	11.7	11.4	11.1	10.8
4	15.6	15.2	14.8	14.4
5	19.5	19.0	18.5	18.0
6	23.4	22.8	22.2	21.6
7	27.3	26.6	25.9	25.2
8	31.2	30.4	29.6	28.8
9	35.1	34.2	33.3	32.4

$\log e = 0.4343$

	35	34	33	32
1	3.5	3.4	3.3	3.2
2	7.0	6.8	6.6	6.4
3	10.5	10.2	9.9	9.6
4	14.0	13.6	13.2	12.8
5	17.5	17.0	16.5	16.0
6	21.0	20.4	19.8	19.2
7	24.5	23.8	23.1	22.4
8	28.0	27.2	26.4	25.6
9	31.5	30.6	29.7	28.8

$\log \pi = 0.4971$

	31	30	29	28
1	3.1	3	2.9	2.8
2	6.2	6	5.8	5.6
3	9.3	9	8.7	8.4
4	12.4	12	11.6	11.2
5	15.5	15	14.5	14.0
6	18.6	18	17.4	16.8
7	21.7	21	20.3	19.6
8	24.8	24	23.2	22.4
9	27.9	27	26.1	25.2

	27	26	25	24
1	2.7	2.6	2.5	2.4
2	5.4	5.2	5.0	4.8
3	8.1	7.8	7.5	7.2
4	10.8	10.4	10.0	9.6
5	13.5	13.0	12.5	12.0
6	16.2	15.6	15.0	14.4
7	18.9	18.2	17.5	16.8
8	21.6	20.8	20.0	19.2
9	24.3	23.4	22.5	21.6

Prop. Parts

N	0	1	2	3	4	5	6	7	8	9
55	7 404	412	419	427	435	443	451	459	466	474
56	482	490	497	505	513	520	528	536	543	551
57	559	566	574	582	589	597	604	612	619	627
58	634	642	649	657	664	672	679	686	694	701
59	709	716	723	731	738	745	752	760	767	774
60	7 782	789	796	803	810	818	825	832	839	846
61	853	860	868	875	882	889	896	903	910	917
62	924	931	938	945	952	959	966	973	980	987
63	7 993	*000	*007	*014	*021	*028	*035	*041	*048	*055
64	8 062	069	075	082	089	096	102	109	116	122
65	129	136	142	149	156	162	169	176	182	189
66	195	202	209	215	222	228	235	241	248	254
67	261	267	274	280	287	293	299	306	312	319
68	325	331	338	344	351	357	363	370	376	382
69	388	395	401	407	414	420	426	432	439	445
70	8 451	457	463	470	476	482	488	494	500	506
71	513	519	525	531	537	543	549	555	561	567
72	573	579	585	591	597	603	609	615	621	627
73	633	639	645	651	657	663	669	675	681	686
74	692	698	704	710	716	722	727	733	739	745
75	751	756	762	768	774	779	785	791	797	802
76	808	814	820	825	831	837	842	848	854	859
77	865	871	876	882	887	893	899	904	910	915
78	921	927	932	938	943	949	954	960	965	971
79	8 976	982	987	993	998	*004	*009	*015	*020	*025
80	9 031	036	042	047	053	058	063	069	074	079
81	085	090	096	101	106	112	117	122	128	133
82	138	143	149	154	159	165	170	175	180	186
83	191	196	201	206	212	217	222	227	232	238
84	243	248	253	258	263	269	274	279	284	289
85	294	299	304	309	315	320	325	330	335	340
86	345	350	355	360	365	370	375	380	385	390
87	395	400	405	410	415	420	425	430	435	440
88	445	450	455	460	465	469	474	479	484	489
89	494	499	504	509	513	518	523	528	533	538
90	9 542	547	552	557	562	566	571	576	581	586
91	590	595	600	605	609	614	619	624	628	633
92	638	643	647	652	657	661	666	671	675	680
93	685	689	694	699	703	708	713	717	722	727
94	731	736	741	745	750	754	759	763	768	773
95	777	782	786	791	795	800	805	809	814	818
96	823	827	832	836	841	845	850	854	859	863
97	868	872	877	881	886	890	894	899	903	908
98	912	917	921	926	930	934	939	943	948	952
99	9 956	961	965	969	974	978	983	987	991	996

Prop. Parts

	23	22	21	20
1	2.3	2.2	2.1	2
2	4.6	4.4	4.2	4
3	6.9	6.6	6.3	6
4	9.2	8.8	8.4	8
5	11.5	11.0	10.5	10
6	13.8	13.2	12.6	12
7	16.1	15.4	14.7	14
8	18.4	17.6	16.8	16
9	20.7	19.8	18.9	18

	19	18	17	16
1	1.9	1.8	1.7	1.6
2	3.8	3.6	3.4	3.2
3	5.7	5.4	5.1	4.8
4	7.6	7.2	6.8	6.4
5	9.5	9.0	8.5	8.0
6	11.4	10.8	10.2	9.6
7	13.3	12.6	11.9	11.2
8	15.2	14.4	13.6	12.8
9	17.1	16.2	15.3	14.4

	15	14	13	12
1	1.5	1.4	1.3	1.2
2	3.0	2.8	2.6	2.4
3	4.5	4.2	3.9	3.6
4	6.0	5.6	5.2	4.8
5	7.5	7.0	6.5	6.0
6	9.0	8.4	7.8	7.2
7	10.5	9.8	9.1	8.4
8	12.0	11.2	10.4	9.6
9	13.5	12.6	11.7	10.8

	11	10	9	8
1	1.1	1	0.9	0.8
2	2.2	2	1.8	1.6
3	3.3	3	2.7	2.4
4	4.4	4	3.6	3.2
5	5.5	5	4.5	4.0
6	6.6	6	5.4	4.8
7	7.7	7	6.3	5.6
8	8.8	8	7.2	6.4
9	9.9	9	8.1	7.2

	7	6	5	4
1	0.7	0.6	0.5	0.4
2	1.4	1.2	1.0	0.8
3	2.1	1.8	1.5	1.2
4	2.8	2.4	2.0	1.6
5	3.5	3.0	2.5	2.0
6	4.2	3.6	3.0	2.4
7	4.9	4.2	3.5	2.8
8	5.6	4.8	4.0	3.2
9	6.3	5.4	4.5	3.6

Prop. Parts	N	0	1	2	3	4	5	6	7	8	9

TABLE IV   COMPOUND AMOUNT: $(1 + i)^n$

n	1%	1½%	2%	2½%	3%	4%	5%	6%
1	1.01 00	1.01 50	1.02 00	1.02 50	1.03 00	1.04 00	1.05 00	1.06 00
2	1.02 01	1.03 02	1.04 04	1.05 06	1.06 09	1.08 16	1.10 25	1.12 36
3	1.03 03	1.04 57	1.06 12	1.07 69	1.09 27	1.12 49	1.15 76	1.19 10
4	1.04 06	1.06 14	1.08 24	1.10 38	1.12 55	1.16 99	1.21 55	1.26 25
5	1.05 10	1.07 73	1.10 41	1.13 14	1.15 93	1.21 67	1.27 63	1.33 82
6	1.06 15	1.09 34	1.12 62	1.15 97	1.19 41	1.26 53	1.34 01	1.41 85
7	1.07 21	1.10 98	1.14 87	1.18 87	1.22 99	1.31 59	1.40 71	1.50 36
8	1.08 29	1.12 65	1.17 17	1.21 84	1.26 68	1.36 86	1.47 75	1.59 38
9	1.09 37	1.14 34	1.19 51	1.24 89	1.30 48	1.42 33	1.55 13	1.68 95
10	1.10 46	1.16 05	1.21 90	1.28 01	1.34 39	1.48 02	1.62 89	1.79 08
11	1.11 57	1.17 79	1.24 34	1.31 21	1.38 42	1.53 95	1.71 03	1.89 83
12	1.12 68	1.19 56	1.26 82	1.34 49	1.42 58	1.60 10	1.79 59	2.01 22
13	1.13 81	1.21 36	1.29 36	1.37 85	1.46 85	1.66 51	1.88 56	2.13 29
14	1.14 95	1.23 18	1.31 95	1.41 30	1.51 26	1.73 17	1.97 99	2.26 09
15	1.16 10	1.25 02	1.34 59	1.44 83	1.55 80	1.80 09	2.07 89	2.39 66
16	1.17 26	1.26 90	1.37 28	1.48 45	1.60 47	1.87 30	2.18 29	2.54 04
17	1.18 43	1.28 80	1.40 02	1.52 16	1.65 28	1.94 79	2.29 20	2.69 28
18	1.19 61	1.30 73	1.42 82	1.55 97	1.70 24	2.02 58	2.40 66	2.85 43
19	1.20 81	1.32 70	1.45 68	1.59 87	1.75 35	2.10 68	2.52 70	3.02 56
20	1.22 02	1.34 69	1.48 59	1.63 86	1.80 61	2.19 11	2.65 33	3.20 71
21	1.23 24	1.36 71	1.51 57	1.67 96	1.86 03	2.27 88	2.78 60	3.39 96
22	1.24 47	1.38 76	1.54 60	1.72 16	1.91 61	2.36 99	2.92 53	3.60 35
23	1.25 72	1.40 84	1.57 69	1.76 46	1.97 36	2.46 47	3.07 15	3.81 97
24	1.26 97	1.42 95	1.60 84	1.80 87	2.03 28	2.56 33	3.22 51	4.04 89
25	1.28 24	1.45 09	1.64 06	1.85 39	2.09 38	2.66 58	3.38 64	4.29 19
26	1.29 53	1.47 27	1.67 34	1.90 03	2.15 66	2.77 25	3.55 57	4.54 94
27	1.30 82	1.49 48	1.70 69	1.94 78	2.22 13	2.88 34	3.73 35	4.82 23
28	1.32 13	1.51 72	1.74 10	1.99 65	2.28 79	2.99 87	3.92 01	5.11 17
29	1.33 45	1.54 00	1.77 58	2.04 64	2.35 66	3.11 87	4.11 61	5.41 84
30	1.34 78	1.56 31	1.81 14	2.09 76	2.42 73	3.24 34	4.32 19	5.74 35
31	1.36 13	1.58 65	1.84 76	2.15 00	2.50 01	3.37 31	4.53 80	6.08 81
32	1.37 49	1.61 03	1.88 45	2.20 38	2.57 51	3.50 81	4.76 49	6.45 34
33	1.38 87	1.63 45	1.92 22	2.25 89	2.65 23	3.64 84	5.00 32	6.84 06
34	1.40 26	1.65 90	1.96 07	2.31 53	2.73 19	3.79 43	5.25 33	7.25 10
35	1.41 66	1.68 39	1.99 99	2.37 32	2.81 39	3.94 61	5.51 60	7.68 61
36	1.43 08	1.70 91	2.03 99	2.43 25	2.89 83	4.10 39	5.79 18	8.14 73
37	1.44 51	1.73 48	2.08 07	2.49 33	2.98 52	4.26 81	6.08 14	8.63 61
38	1.45 95	1.76 08	2.12 23	2.55 57	3.07 48	4.43 88	6.38 55	9.15 43
39	1.47 41	1.78 72	2.16 47	2.61 96	3.16 70	4.61 64	6.70 48	9.70 35
40	1.48 89	1.81 40	2.20 80	2.68 51	3.26 20	4.80 10	7.04 00	10.28 57
41	1.50 38	1.84 12	2.25 22	2.75 22	3.35 99	4.99 31	7.39 20	10.90 29
42	1.51 88	1.86 88	2.29 72	2.82 10	3.46 07	5.19 28	7.76 16	11.55 70
43	1.53 40	1.89 69	2.34 32	2.89 15	3.56 45	5.40 05	8.14 97	12.25 05
44	1.54 93	1.92 53	2.39 01	2.96 38	3.67 15	5.61 65	8.55 72	12.98 55
45	1.56 48	1.95 42	2.43 79	3.03 79	3.78 16	5.84 12	8.98 50	13.76 46
46	1.58 05	1.98 35	2.48 66	3.11 39	3.89 50	6.07 48	9.43 43	14.59 05
47	1.59 63	2.01 33	2.53 63	3.19 17	4.01 19	6.31 78	9.90 60	15.46 59
48	1.61 22	2.04 35	2.58 71	3.27 15	4.13 23	6.57 05	10.40 13	16.39 39
49	1.62 83	2.07 41	2.63 88	3.35 33	4.25 62	6.83 33	10.92 13	17.37 75
50	1.64 46	2.10 52	2.69 16	3.43 71	4.38 39	7.10 67	11.46 74	18.42 02

TABLE V   PRESENT VALUE: $(1 + i)^{-n}$

n	1%	$1\frac{1}{2}\%$	2%	$2\frac{1}{2}\%$	3%	4%	5%	6%
1	.990 10	.985 22	.980 39	.975 61	.970 87	.9&1 54	.952 38	.943 40
2	.980 30	.970 66	.961 17	.951 81	.942 60	.924 56	.907 03	.890 00
3	.970 59	.956 32	.942 32	.928 60	.915 14	.889 00	.863 84	.839 62
4	.960 98	.942 18	.923 85	.905 95	.888 49	.854 80	.822 70	.792 09
5	.951 47	.928 26	.905 73	.883 85	.862 61	.821 93	.783 53	.747 26
6	.942 05	.914 54	.887 97	.862 30	.837 48	.790 31	.746 22	.704 96
7	.932 72	.901 03	.870 56	.841⨍27	.813 09	.759 92	.710 68	.665 06
8	.923 48	.887 71	.853 49	.820 75	.789 41	.730 69	.676 84	.627 41
9	.914 34	.874 59	.836 76	.800 73	.766 42	.702 59	.644 61	.591 90
10	.905 29	.861 67	.820 35	.781 20	.744 09	.675 56	.613 91	.558 39
11	.896 32	.848 93	.804 26	.762 14	.722 42	.649 58	.584 68	.526 79
12	.887 45	.836 39	.788 49	.743 56	.701 38	.624 60	.556 84	.496 97
13	.878 66	.824 03	.773 03	.725 42	.680 95	.600 57	.530 32	.468 84
14	.869 96	.811 85	.757 88	.707 73	.661 12	.577 48	.505 07	.442 30
15	.861 35	.799 85	.743 01	.690 47	.641 86	.555 26	.481 02	.417 27
16	.852 82	.788 03	.728 45	.673 62	.623 17	.533 91	.458 11	.393 65
17	.844 38	.776 39	.714 16	.657 20	.605 02	.513 37	.436 30	.371 36
18	.836 02	.764 91	.700 16	.641 17	.587 39	.493 63	.415 52	.350 34
19	.827 74	.753 61	.686 43	.625 53	.570 29	.474 64	.395 73	.330 51
20	.819 54	.742 47	.672 97	.610 27	.553 68	.456 39	.376 89	.311 80
21	.811 43	.731 50	.659 78	.595 39	.537 55	.438 83	.358 94	.294 16
22	.803 40	.720 69	.646 84	.580 86	.521 89	.421 96	.341 85	.277 51
23	.795 44	.710 04	.634 16	.566 70	.506 69	.405 73	.325 57	.261 80
24	.787 57	.699 54	.621 72	.552 88	.491 93	.390 12	.310 07	.246 98
25	.779 77	.689 21	.609 53	.539 39	.477 61	.375 12	.295 30	.233 00
26	.772 05	.679 02	.597 58	.526 23	.463 69	.360 65	.281 24	.219 81
27	.764 40	.668 99	.585 86	.513 40	.450 19	.346 82	.267 85	.207 37
28	.756 84	.659 10	.574 37	.500 88	.437 08	.333 48	.255 09	.195 63
29	.749 34	.649 36	.563 11	.488 66	.424 35	.320 69	.242 95	.184 56
30	.741 92	.639 76	.552 07	.476 74	.411 99	.308 32	.231 38	.174 11
31	.734 58	.630 31	.541 25	.465 11	.399 99	.296 46	.220 36	.164 25
32	.727 30	.620 99	.530 63	.453 77	.388 34	.285 06	.209 87	.154 96
33	.720 10	.611 82	.520 23	.442 70	.377 03	.274 09	.199 87	.146 19
34	.712 97	.602 77	.510 03	.431 91	.366 04	.263 55	.190 35	.137 91
35	.705 91	.593 87	.500 03	.421 37	.355 38	.253 42	.181 29	.130 11
36	.698 92	.585 09	.490 22	.411 09	.345 03	.243 67	.172 66	.122 74
37	.692 00	.576 44	.480 61	.401 07	.334 98	.234 30	.164 44	.115 79
38	.685 15	.567 92	.471 19	.391 28	.325 23	.225 29	.156 61	.109 24
39	.678 37	.559 53	.461 95	.381 74	.315 75	.216 62	.149 15	.103 06
40	.671 65	.551 26	.452 89	.372 43	.306 56	.208 29	.142 05	.097 22
41	.665 00	.543 12	.444 01	.363 35	.297 63	.200 28	.135 28	.091 72
42	.658 42	.535 09	.435 30	.354 48	.288 96	.192 57	.128 84	.086 53
43	.651 90	.527 18	.426 77	.345 84	.280 54	.185 17	.122 70	.081 63
44	.645 45	.519 39	.418 40	.337 40	.272 37	.178 05	.116 86	.077 01
45	.639 05	.511 71	.410 20	.329 17	.264 44	.171 20	.111 30	.072 65
46	.632 73	.504 15	.402 15	.321 15	.256 74	.164 61	.106 09	.068 54
47	.626 46	.496 70	.394 27	.313 31	.249 26	.158 28	.100 95	.064 66
48	.620 26	.489 36	.386 54	.305 67	.242 00	.152 19	.096 14	.061 00
49	.614 12	.482 13	.378 96	.298 22	.234 95	.146 34	.091 56	.057 55
50	.608 04	.475 00	.371 53	.290 94	.228 11	.140 71	.087 20	.054 29

TABLE VI PRESENT VALUE OF AN ANNUITY: $a_{\overline{n}|i}$

n	1%	$1\frac{1}{2}\%$	2%	$2\frac{1}{2}\%$	3%	4%	5%	6%
1	.99 01	.98 52	.98 04	.97 56	.97 09	.96 15	.95 24	.94 34
2	1.97 04	1.95 59	1.94 16	1.92 74	1.91 35	1.88 61	1.85 94	1.83 34
3	2.94 10	2.91 22	2.88 39	2.85 60	2.82 86	2.77 51	2.72 32	2.67 30
4	3.90 20	3.85 44	3.80 77	3.76 20	3.71 71	3.62 99	3.54 60	3.46 51
5	4.85 34	4.78 26	4.71 35	4.64 58	4.57 97	4.45 18	4.32 95	4.21 24
6	5.79 55	5.69 72	5.60 14	5.50 81	5.41 72	5.24 21	5.07 57	4.91 73
7	6.72 82	6.59 82	6.47 20	6.34 94	6.23 03	6.00 21	5.78 64	5.58 24
8	7.65 17	7.48 59	7.32 55	7.17 01	7.01 97	6.73 27	6.46 32	6.20 98
9	8.56 60	8.36 05	8.16 22	7.97 09	7.78 61	7.43 53	7.10 78	6.80 17
10	9.47 13	9.22 22	8.98 26	8.75 21	8.53 02	8.11 09	7.72 17	7.36 01
11	10.36 76	10.07 11	9.78 68	9.51 42	9.25 26	8.76 05	8.30 64	7.88 69
12	11.25 51	10.90 75	10.57 53	10.25 78	9.95 40	9.38 51	8.86 33	8.38 38
13	12.13 37	11.73 15	11.34 84	10.98 32	10.63 50	9.98 56	9.39 36	8.85 27
14	13.00 37	12.54 34	12.10 62	11.69 09	11.29 61	10.56 31	9.89 86	9.29 50
15	13.86 51	13.34 32	12.84 93	12.38 14	11.93 79	11.11 84	10.37 97	9.71 22
16	14.71 79	14.13 13	13.57 77	13.05 50	12.56 11	11.65 23	10.83 78	10.10 59
17	15.56 23	14.90 76	14.29 19	13.71 22	13.16 61	12.16 57	11.27 41	10.47 73
18	16.39 83	15.67 26	14.99 20	14.35 34	13.75 35	12.65 93	11.68 96	10.82 76
19	17.22 60	16.42 62	15.67 85	14.97 89	14.32 38	13.13 39	12.08 53	11.15 81
20	18.04 56	17.16 86	16.35 14	15.58 92	14.87 75	13.59 03	12.46 22	11.46 99
21	18.85 70	17.90 01	17.01 12	16.18 45	15.41 50	14.02 92	12.82 12	11.76 41
22	19.66 04	18.62 08	17.65 80	16.76 54	15.93 69	14.45 11	13.16 30	12.04 16
23	20.45 58	19.33 09	18.29 22	17.33 21	16.44 36	14.85 68	13.48 86	12.30 34
24	21.24 34	20.03 04	18.91 39	17.88 50	16.93 55	15.24 70	13.79 86	12.55 04
25	22.02 32	20.71 96	19.52 35	18.42 44	17.41 31	15.62 21	14.09 39	12.78 34
26	22.79 52	21.39 86	20.12 10	18.95 06	17.87 68	15.98 28	14.37 52	13.00 32
27	23.55 96	22.06 76	20.70 69	19.46 40	18.32 70	16.32 96	14.64 30	13.21 05
28	24.31 64	22.72 67	21.28 13	19.96 49	18.76 41	16.66 31	14.89 81	13.40 62
29	25.06 58	23.37 61	21.84 44	20.45 35	19.18 85	16.98 37	15.14 11	13.59 07
30	25.80 77	24.01 58	22.39 65	20.93 03	19.60 04	17.29 20	15.37 25	13.76 48
31	26.54 23	24.64 61	22.93 77	21.39 54	20.00 04	17.58 85	15.59 28	13.92 91
32	27.26 96	25.26 71	23.46 83	21.84 92	20.38 88	17.87 36	15.80 27	14.08 40
33	27.98 97	25.87 90	23.98 86	22.29 19	20.76 58	18.14 76	16.00 25	14.23 02
34	28.70 27	26.48 17	24.49 86	22.72 38	21.13 18	18.41 12	16.19 29	14.36 81
35	29.40 86	27.07 56	24.99 86	23.14 52	21.48 72	18.66 46	16.37 42	14.49 82
36	30.10 75	27.66 07	25.48 88	23.55 63	21.83 23	18.90 83	16.54 69	14.62 10
37	30.79 95	28.23 71	25.96 95	23.95 73	22.16 72	19.14 26	16.71 13	14.73 68
38	31.48 47	28.80 51	26.44 06	24.34 86	22.49 25	19.36 79	16.86 79	14.84 60
39	32.16 30	29.36 46	26.90 26	24.73 03	22.80 82	19.58 45	17.01 70	14.94 91
40	32.83 47	29.91 58	27.35 55	25.10 28	23.11 48	19.79 28	17.15 91	15.04 63
41	33.49 97	30.45 90	27.79 95	25.46 61	23.41 24	19.99 31	17.29 44	15.13 80
42	34.15 81	30.99 41	28.23 48	25.82 06	23.70 14	20.18 56	17.42 32	15.22 45
43	34.81 00	31.52 12	28.66 16	26.16 64	23.98 19	20.37 08	17.54 59	15.30 62
44	35.45 55	32.04 06	29.08 00	26.50 38	24.25 43	20.54 88	17.66 28	15.38 32
45	36.09 45	32.55 23	29.49 02	26.83 30	24.51 87	20.72 00	17.77 41	15.45 58
46	36.72 72	33.05 65	29.89 23	27.15 42	24.77 54	20.88 47	17.88 01	15.52 44
47	37.35 37	33.55 32	30.28 66	27.46 75	25.02 47	21.04 29	17.98 10	15.58 90
48	37.97 40	34.04 26	30.67 31	27.77 32	25.26 67	21.19 51	18.07 72	15.65 00
49	38.58 81	34.52 47	31.05 21	28.07 14	25.50 17	21.34 15	18.16 87	15.70 76
50	39.19 61	34.99 97	31.42 36	28.36 23	25.72 98	21.48 22	18.25 59	15.76 19

TABLE VII   AMOUNT OF AN ANNUITY: $s_{\overline{n}|i}$

n	1%	1½%	2%	2½%	3%	4%	5%	6%
1	1.00 00	1.00 00	1.00 00	1.00 00	1.00 00	1.00 00	1.00 00	1.00 00
2	2.01 00	2.01 50	2.02 00	2.02 50	2.03 00	2.04 00	2.05 00	2.06 00
3	3.03 01	3.04 52	3.06 04	3.07 56	3.09 09	3.12 16	3.15 25	3.18 36
4	4.06 04	4.09 09	4.12 16	4.15 25	4.18 36	4.24 65	4.31 01	4.37 46
5	5.10 10	5.15 23	5.20 40	5.25 63	5.30 91	5.41 63	5.52 56	5.63 71
6	6.15 20	6.22 96	6.30 81	6.38 77	6.46 84	6.63 30	6.80 19	6.97 53
7	7.21 35	7.32 30	7.43 43	7.54 74	7.66 25	7.89 83	8.14 20	8.39 38
8	8.28 57	8.43 28	8.58 30	8.73 61	8.89 23	9.21 42	9.54 91	9.89 75
9	9.36 85	9.55 93	9.75 46	9.95 45	10.15 91	10.58 28	11.02 66	11.49 13
10	10.46 22	10.70 27	10.94 97	11.20 34	11.46 39	12.00 61	12.57 79	13.18 08
11	11.56 68	11.86 33	12.16 87	12.48 35	12.80 78	13.48 64	14.20 68	14.97 16
12	12.68 25	13.04 12	13.41 21	13.79 56	14.19 20	15.02 58	15.91 71	16.86 99
13	13.80 93	14.23 68	14.68 03	15.14 04	15.61 78	16.62 68	17.71 30	18.88 21
14	14.94 74	15.45 04	15.97 39	16.51 90	17.08 63	18.29 19	19.59 86	21.01 51
15	16.09 69	16.68 21	17.29 34	17.93 19	18.59 89	20.02 36	21.57 86	23.27 60
16	17.25 79	17.93 24	18.63 93	19.38 02	20.15 69	21.82 45	23.65 75	25.67 25
17	18.43 04	19.20 14	20.01 21	20.86 47	21.76 16	23.69 75	25.84 04	28.21 29
18	19.61 47	20.48 94	21.41 23	22.38 63	23.41 44	25.64 54	28.13 24	30.90 57
19	20.81 09	21.79 67	22.84 06	23.94 60	25.11 69	27.67 12	30.53 90	33.76 00
20	22.01 90	23.12 37	24.29 74	25.54 47	26.87 04	29.77 81	33.06 60	36.78 56
21	23.23 92	24.47 05	25.78 33	27.18 33	28.67 65	31.96 92	35.71 93	39.99 27
22	24.47 16	25.83 76	27.29 90	28.86 29	30.53 68	34.24 80	38.50 52	43.39 23
23	25.71 63	27.22 51	28.84 50	30.58 44	32.45 29	36.61 79	41.43 05	46.99 58
24	26.97 35	28.63 35	30.42 19	32.34 90	34.42 65	39.08 26	44.50 20	50.81 56
25	28.24 32	30.06 30	32.03 03	34.15 78	36.45 93	41.64 59	47.72 71	54.86 45
26	29.52 56	31.51 40	33.67 09	36.01 17	38.55 30	44.31 17	51.11 35	59.15 64
27	30.82 09	32.98 67	35.34 43	37.91 20	40.70 96	47.08 42	54.66 91	63.70 58
28	32.12 91	34.48 15	37.05 12	39.85 98	42.93 09	49.96 76	58.40 26	68.52 81
29	33.45 04	35.99 87	38.79 22	41.85 63	45.21 89	52.96 63	62.32 27	73.63 98
30	34.78 49	37.53 87	40.56 81	43.90 27	47.57 54	56.08 49	66.43 88	79.05 82
31	36.13 27	39.10 18	42.37 94	46.00 03	50.00 27	59.32 83	70.76 08	84.80 17
32	37.49 41	40.68 83	44.22 70	48.15 03	52.50 28	62.70 15	75.29 88	90.88 98
33	38.86 90	42.29 86	46.11 16	50.35 40	55.07 78	66.20 95	80.06 38	97.34 32
34	40.25 77	43.93 31	48.03 38	52.61 29	57.73 02	69.85 79	85.06 70	104.18 38
35	41.66 03	45.59 21	49.99 45	54.92 82	60.46 21	73.65 22	90.32 03	111.43 48
36	43.07 69	47.27 60	51.99 44	57.30 14	63.27 59	77.59 83	95.83 63	119.12 09
37	44.50 76	48.98 51	54.03 43	59.73 39	66.17 42	81.70 22	101.62 81	127.26 81
38	45.95 27	50.71 99	56.11 49	62.22 73	69.15 94	85.97 03	107.70 95	135.90 42
39	47.41 23	52.48 07	58.23 72	64.78 30	72.23 42	90.40 91	114.09 50	145.05 85
40	48.88 64	54.26 79	60.40 20	67.40 26	75.40 13	95.02 55	120.79 98	154.76 20
41	50.37 52	56.08 19	62.61 00	70.08 76	78.66 33	99.82 65	127.83 98	165.04 77
42	51.87 90	57.92 31	64.86 22	72.83 98	82.02 32	104.81 96	135.23 18	175.95 05
43	53.39 78	59.79 20	67.15 95	75.66 08	85.48 39	110.01 24	142.99 33	187.50 76
44	54.93 18	61.68 89	69.50 27	78.55 23	89.04 84	115.41 29	151.14 30	199.75 80
45	56.48 11	63.61 42	71.89 27	81.51 61	92.71 99	121.02 94	159.70 02	212.74 35
46	58.04 59	65.56 84	74.33 06	84.55 40	96.50 15	126.87 06	168.68 52	226.50 81
47	59 62 63	67.55 19	76.81 72	87.66 79	100.39 65	132.94 54	178.11 94	241.09 86
48	61.22 26	69.56 52	79.35 35	90.85 96	104.40 84	139.26 32	188.02 54	256.56 45
49	62.83 48	71.60 87	81.94 06	94.13 11	108.54 06	145.83 37	198.42 67	272.95 84
50	64.46 32	73.68 28	84.57 94	97.48 43	112.79 69	152.66 71	209.34 80	290.33 59

TABLE VIII PERIODIC PAYMENT OF AN ANNUITY: $a_{\overline{n}|i}^{-1} = s_{\overline{n}|i}^{-1} + i$

n	1%	1½%	2%	2½%	3%	4%	5%	6%
1	1.010 00	1.015 00	1.020 00	1.025 00	1.030 00	1.040 00	1.050 00	1.060 00
2	.507 51	.511 28	.515 05	.518 83	.522 61	.530 20	.537 80	.545 44
3	.340 02	.343 38	.346 75	.350 14	.353 53	.360 35	.367 21	.374 11
4	.256 28	.259 44	.262 62	.265 82	.269 03	.275 49	.282 01	.288 59
5	.206 04	.209 09	.212 16	.215 25	.218 35	.224 63	.230 97	.237 40
6	.172 55	.175 53	.178 53	.181 55	.184 60	.190 76	.197 02	.203 36
7	.148 63	.151 56	.154 51	.157 50	.160 51	.166 61	.172 82	.179 14
8	.130 69	.133 58	.136 51	.139 47	.142 46	.148 53	.154 72	.161 04
9	.116 74	.119 61	.122 52	.125 46	.128 43	.134 49	.140 69	.147 02
10	.105 58	.108 43	.111 33	.114 26	.117 23	.123 29	.129 50	.135 87
11	.096 45	.099 29	.102 18	.105 11	.108 08	.114 15	.120 39	.126 79
12	.088 85	.091 68	.094 56	.097 49	.100 46	.106 55	.112 83	.119 28
13	.082 41	.085 24	.088 12	.091 05	.094 03	.100 14	.106 46	.112 96
14	.076 90	.079 72	.082 60	.085 54	.088 53	.094 67	.101 02	.107 58
15	.072 12	.074 94	.077 83	.080 77	.083 77	.089 94	.096 34	.102 96
16	.067 94	.070 77	.073 65	.076 60	.079 61	.085 82	.092 27	.098 95
17	.064 26	.067 08	.069 97	.072 93	.075 95	.082 20	.088 70	.095 44
18	.060 98	.063 81	.066 70	.069 67	.072 71	.078 99	.085 55	.092 36
19	.058 05	.060 88	.063 78	.066 76	.069 81	.076 14	.082 75	.089 62
20	.055 42	.058 25	.061 16	.064 15	.067 22	.073 58	.080 24	.087 18
21	.053 03	.055 87	.058 78	.061 79	.064 87	.071 28	.078 00	.085 00
22	.050 86	.053 70	.056 63	.059 65	.062 75	.069 20	.075 97	.083 05
23	.048 89	.051 73	.054 67	.057 70	.060 81	.067 31	.074 14	.081 28
24	.047 07	.049 92	.052 87	.055 91	.059 05	.065 59	.072 47	.079 68
25	.045 41	.048 26	.051 22	.054 28	.057 43	.064 01	.070 95	.078 23
26	.043 87	.046 73	.049 70	.052 77	.055 94	.062 57	.069 56	.076 90
27	.042 45	.045 32	.048 29	.051 38	.054 56	.061 24	.068 29	.075 70
28	.041 12	.044 00	.046 99	.050 09	.053 29	.060 01	.067 12	.074 59
29	.039 90	.042 78	.045 78	.048 89	.052 11	.058 88	.066 05	.073 58
30	.038 75	.041 64	.044 65	.047 78	.051 02	.057 83	.065 05	.072 65
31	.037 68	.040 57	.043 60	.046 74	.050 00	.056 86	.064 13	.071 79
32	.036 89	.039 58	.042 61	.045 77	.049 05	.055 95	.063 28	.071 00
33	.035 73	.038 64	.041 69	.044 86	.048 16	.055 10	.062 49	.070 27
34	.034 84	.037 76	.040 82	.044 01	.047 32	.054 31	.061 76	.069 60
35	.034 00	.036 93	.040 00	.043 21	.046 54	.053 58	.061 07	.068 97
36	.033 21	.036 15	.039 23	.042 45	.045 80	.052 89	.060 43	.068 39
37	.032 47	.035 41	.038 51	.041 74	.045 11	.052 24	.059 84	.067 86
38	.031 76	.034 72	.037 82	.041 07	.044 46	.051 63	.059 28	.067 36
39	.031 09	.034 05	.037 17	.040 44	.043 84	.051 06	.058 76	.066 89
40	.030 46	.033 43	.036 56	.039 84	.043 26	.050 52	.058 28	.066 46
41	.029 85	.032 83	.035 97	.039 27	.042 71	.050 02	.057 82	.066 06
42	.029 28	.032 26	.035 42	.038 73	.042 19	.049 54	.057 39	.065 68
43	.028 73	.031 72	.034 89	.038 22	.041 70	.049 09	.056 99	.065 33
44	.028 20	.031 21	.034 39	.037 73	.041 23	.048 66	.056 62	.065 01
45	.027 71	.030 72	.033 91	.037 27	.040 79	.048 26	.056 26	.064 70
46	.027 23	.030 25	.033 45	.036 83	.040 36	.047 88	.055 93	.064 41
47	.026 77	.029 80	.033 02	.036 41	.039 96	.047 52	.055 61	.064 15
48	.026 33	.029 37	.032 60	.036 01	.039 58	.047 18	.055 32	.063 90
49	.025 91	.028 96	.032 20	.035 62	.039 21	.046 86	.055 04	.063 66
50	.025 51	.028 57	.031 82	.035 26	.038 87	.046 55	.054 78	.063 44

TABLE IX   AMERICAN EXPERIENCE TABLE OF MORTALITY

Age	Number Living	Number of Deaths	Age	Number Living	Number of Deaths	Age	Number Living	Number of Deaths
10	100 000	749	40	78 106	765	70	38 569	2 391
11	99 251	746	41	77 341	774	71	36 178	2 448
12	98 505	743	42	76 567	785	72	33 730	2 487
13	97 762	740	43	75 782	797	73	31 243	2 505
14	97 022	737	44	74 985	812	74	28 738	2 501
15	96 285	735	45	74 173	828	75	26 237	2 476
16	95 550	732	46	73 345	848	76	23 761	2 431
17	94 818	729	47	72 497	870	77	21 330	2 369
18	94 089	727	48	71 627	896	78	18 961	2 291
19	93 362	725	49	70 731	927	79	16 670	2 196
20	92 637	723	50	69 804	962	80	14 474	2 091
21	91 914	722	51	68 842	1 001	81	12 383	1 964
22	91 192	721	52	67 841	1 044	82	10 419	1 816
23	90 471	720	53	66 797	1 091	83	8 603	1 648
24	89 751	719	54	65 706	1 143	84	6 955	1 470
25	89 032	718	55	64 563	1 199	85	5 485	1 292
26	88 314	718	56	63 364	1 260	86	4 193	1 114
27	87 596	718	57	62 104	1 325	87	3 079	933
28	86 878	718	58	60 779	1 394	88	2 146	744
29	86 160	719	59	59 385	1 468	89	1 402	555
30	85 441	720	60	57 917	1 546	90	847	385
31	84 721	721	61	56 371	1 628	91	462	246
32	84 000	723	62	54 743	1 713	92	216	137
33	83 277	726	63	53 030	1 800	93	79	58
34	82 551	729	64	51 230	1 889	94	21	18
35	81 822	732	65	49 341	1 980	95	3	3
36	81 090	737	66	47 361	2 070			
37	80 353	742	67	45 291	2 158			
38	79 611	749	68	43 133	2 243			
39	78 862	756	69	40 890	2 321			

Answers

The answers to most of the odd-numbered problems are given below. A pamphlet containing the answers to the even-numbered problems can be obtained on request of the instructor.

Exercise 1, Page 3

1. $3 < 7$. **3.** $-4 < 1$. **5.** $\frac{1}{2} > -\frac{1}{2}$. **7.** $1.42 > \sqrt{2}$.
9. $-\sqrt{7}, -2\frac{1}{2}, 0, \frac{19}{21}, \frac{1}{2}\pi, 2$. **11.** -5. **13.** 0. **15.** 8. **17.** -6.
19. -25. **21.** -4. **23.** -120. **25.** -4. **27.** -2. **29.** 0.

Exercise 2, Page 6

1. $3; 3, 2, 1, 0$. **3.** $3; 1, 3, 2, 0$. **5.** $(a)\ \frac{1}{3}\pi$, $(b)\ \frac{1}{3}\pi r^2$. **7.** y^{23}.
9. x^7. **11.** $a^8 x^9$. **13.** $8\,x^3/27\,y^6$. **15.** y^5/x^{10}. **17.** $b^5 c^{13}$.
19. $-a - 2\,b$. **21.** $3\,x - 6$. **23.** $m + n - 3$. **25.** $-3\,x - y$.
27. $4\,a + 4\,b$. **29.** $2\,x^2 - (xy - y^2); 2\,x^2 + (-xy + y^2)$

Exercise 3, Page 7

1. $18\,x^2 - 9\,x - 9$. **3.** $\frac{1}{4}x^2 + \frac{4}{5}xy - \frac{1}{3}y^2$. **5.** $-1.1\,x + 0.3\,y + 1.9$.
7. $3\,a - 3\,c$. **9.** $\frac{5}{6}x^2 + \frac{3}{2}y^2 - \frac{23}{15}$. **11.** $x + 5\,y$. **13.** $7\,a^2 + a$.
15. $x^4 - 2\,x^3 + x^2 - 2\,x + 1$. **17.** $\frac{1}{6}a + \frac{5}{6}b + \frac{1}{2}$.
19. $-0.9\,a - 8.9\,b - 1.6\,c$. **21.** $-x^3 + 9\,x^2 - 5\,x - 10$.
23. $-x - 2\,y$. **25.** $5\,bc - 2\,ac$. **27.** $2\,a - 6\,b + 3\,c$.
29. $3\,x^2 + x + 1$.

Exercise 4, Page 9

1. $6\,x^2 - 10\,x$. **3.** $6\,ax - 15\,ay$. **5.** $2\,x^2 - 7\,x - 15$.
7. $9\,x^2 - 24\,x + 16$. **9.** $4\,a^2 + b^2 + c^2 - 4\,ab - 4\,ac + 2\,bc$.
11. $x^3 - y^3$. **13.** $18\,a^3 + 9\,a^2 b - 8\,ab^2 + 7\,b^3$.
15. $x^5 + 2\,x^4 - 2\,x^3 - 4\,x^2 - 3\,x + 2$. **17.** $6\,a^3 - 17\,a^2 - 31\,a + 12$.
19. $x^{k+1} - a^2 x^{k-1} + a^k x + a^{k+1}$.

Exercise 5, Page 10

1. $-y + 2x.$ **3.** $2a^2b - 4ab^2 - 3.$ **5.** $2x + 3.$

7. $y + 3 - \dfrac{1}{3y - 2}.$ **9.** $5x - 1 - \dfrac{3}{x - 1}.$ **11.** $a^2 - 6a + 2.$

13. $-x^3 - x^2 - 2x + 3 + \dfrac{1}{x - 2}.$ **15.** $2x - 1.$ **17.** $a^2 + 2a - 2.$

19. $x^{2n} + 3x^n + 1.$

Exercise 6, Page 12

1. $6ax - 8a^2.$ **3.** $4mx - 4my + 8mz.$ **5.** $x^2 - 16.$

7. $a^2b^2 - 4c^2.$ **9.** $25 - 20xy + 4x^2y^2.$ **11.** $9a^2x^2 - 30axy + 25y^2.$

13. $-x^2 + 16x - 64.$ **15.** $x^4 - 2x^2 - 120.$ **17.** $6y^2 + y - 1.$

19. $-9p^2 + 30p - 25.$ **21.** $x^3 - 8.$ **23.** $27y^3 + 1.$

25. $x^2 + y^2 + z^2 + 2xy - 2xz - 2yz.$ **27.** $4p^2 + q^2 + 9r^2 - 4pq - 12pr + 6qr.$ **29.** $a^2 + 2ab + b^2 - 9.$ **31.** $x^2 - 2xy + y^2 - 7x + 7y + 10.$ **33.** $x^2 - 4xy + 4y^2 + 4x - 8y + 4.$

35. $4a^2 + 4ab + b^2 - 4.$ **37.** $p^2 + 4pq + 4q^2 - r^2.$

39. $a^2 + 2ab + b^2 - c^2.$

Exercise 7, Page 13

1. $5ab(b + 5a).$ **3.** $a^4b^3(b^2 + a^2 - ab).$ **5.** $(a - x)(a + x).$

7. $(10 + 9x)(10 - 9x).$ **9.** $(\tfrac{2}{3}a + \tfrac{1}{2})(\tfrac{2}{3}a - \tfrac{1}{2}).$ **11.** $(x - 7)(x + 6).$

13. $(10 - x)(2 + x).$ **15.** $(2a + 1)(2a + 3).$ **17.** $(5x - 8)(10x + 13).$

19. $(ax + 1)(a^2x^2 - ax + 1).$ **21.** $(\tfrac{1}{2}p - 5)(\tfrac{1}{4}p^2 + \tfrac{5}{2}p + 25).$

23. $4a^2(a + 1)(a - 1).$ **25.** $a^2x(x - a)(x^2 + ax + a^2).$

27. $(x + y)^2(x - y)^2.$ **29.** $(5x + 2y)(x + 4y).$ **31.** $(a + b)(a + b + 1).$

33. $a(x^2 + y^2)(x + y)(x - y).$ **35.** $(x^2 - 3y^2)(x + 2y)(x - 2y).$

37. $(3x - 2)(x + 1)(2 + 3x)(1 - x).$ **39.** $(x + y)(2x - y).$

Exercise 8, Page 14

1. $(a + b)(m - n).$ **3.** $(p + 3)(3p^2 + 1).$ **5.** $(a - 1)(c - d).$

7. $(a - 3b)(3a^2 - 2b^2).$ **9.** $(x + y + 1)(x + y - 1).$ **11.** $(a + c)(a - b).$

13. $(a + b)(a + b + 1).$ **15.** $(3a + 2x - y)(3a - 2x + y).$

17. $(x + y)(x^2 - xy + y^2 - 1).$ **19.** $(ax + b)(bx + a).$

Exercise 9, Page 15

1. $(x + 1)(x^2 + x - 1).$ **3.** $(x + 1)(x^2 + x - 8).$

5. $(x + 1)(x + 2)(x + 3).$ **7.** $(x - 1)(x - 2)(x^2 - 2).$

9. $(x - 2)(x^2 - x + 2).$ **11.** $(x - 3)(x^2 + x + 3).$

13. $(x - 2)(x + 1)(x^2 - x + 2).$ **15.** $(x - 1)^2(x - 2)(x + 4).$

17. $(x - y)^2(x - 5y).$ **19.** $(x - 1)^2(x + 2)(x^2 + x + 3).$

21. $(x^2 + 2x + 3)(x^2 - 2x + 3).$ **23.** $(x^2 + 3xy + y^2)(x^2 - 3xy + y^2).$

25. $(3y^2 + 5y + 4)(3y^2 - 5y + 4).$ **27.** $(x + y)(x^4 - x^3y + x^2y^2 - xy^3 + y^4).$

29. $(a^2 + x^2)(a + x)(a - x).$ **31.** $(x^4 + 9a^2)(x^2 + 3a)(x^2 - 3a).$

33. $(a + b)(a^6 - a^5b + a^4b^2 - a^3b^3 + a^2b^4 - ab^5 + b^6).$

Exercise 10, Page 16

1. $3; 3^2 \cdot 5^2$.   **3.** $2 \cdot 13; 2^2 \cdot 3 \cdot 13^2$.   **5.** $2^2 ac; 2^2 \cdot 3 \cdot 13\, a^3b^2c^2$.
7. $3; 2^2 \cdot 3\, ax^2y^2$.   **9.** $7\, ab; 2^3 \cdot 3 \cdot 7\, a^2b^2$.   **11.** $(x + 2)$;
$(x + 2)^2(x - 4)(x^2 - 2\, x + 4)$.   **13.** $1; (x + 1)(x + 2)(x - 3)$.
15. $(a - b); (a^4 + b^4)(a^2 + b^2)(a + b)(a - b)$.

Exercise 11, Page 19

1. $\frac{1}{7}$.   **3.** 1.6.   **5.** $1/(a - b)$.   **7.** $x = \pm\, a$.   **9.** 16.   **11.** $6\, a^2x$.
13. $65\, ab^3$.   **15.** $a^2 - 5\, a + 6$.   **17.** 1.   **19.** $- 2\, ax - a$.   **21.** $4\, x/7\, z$.
23. $2\, bx^2/5\, ay^3$.   **25.** $1/(ax - 1)$.   **27.** $- 3/2\, y$.
29. $(x - 1)/(x + 1)$.   **31.** $ax/(ax + 1)$.   **33.** $3(x + y)/(x - y)$.
35. $(x + 1)/(x - 1)$.   **37.** $(a + b - c)/(a - b + c)$.
39. $(x + 3)/(x + 4)$.

Exercise 12, Page 21

1. $(6\, x + 55)/60$.   **3.** 0.   **5.** $(a + 2\, b)/ab$.
7. $13\, y/(2\, y + 3)(3\, y - 2)$.   **9.** $(7\, x^2 - 4\, x + 1)/2(x + 1)(x - 1)$.
11. $2/(x + 1)(x + 2)(x + 3)$.   **13.** $1/(x + 2)(x + 1)$.   **15.** $2/(a + b)$.
17. $(a - b)/(x + a)(x + b)$.   **19.** $35/6(x - 2)$.
21. $1/(1+2\, a)(1-a)(2-3\, a)$.   **23.** $(5\, x+8)/(2\, x-1)(x + 1)(x + 2)$.
25. $2\, xy/(xy + 1)(xy - 1)$.   **27.** $1/(x + 3)$.   **29.** 0.

Exercise 13, Page 23

1. $4\, ax/3\, b^2y$.   **3.** $28\, mp^2/5\, nq^2$.   **5.** $a(a - 1)/(a + 1)$.
7. $3\, x^2/5\, a$.   **9.** $m + n$.   **11.** ad/bc.   **13.** $(2 + a)/(1 - a)$.
15. $y/(x - 1)$.   **17.** $2\, a^2/(a + 2\, x)(2\, a + 3\, x)$.   **19.** $- a$.
21. $3/2\, x$.   **23.** $4\, x - 7$.   **25.** $x + y$.   **27.** $\frac{1}{2}$.   **29.** 1.

Exercise 14, Page 24

1. $(4\, x + 5)/(x + 2)$.   **3.** $- (11\, x + 37)/(x + 4)$.
5. $(x + 1)/(x - 1)$.   **7.** $x - y$.   **9.** $(a + 1)(a - 1)/a$.   **11.** $- x/y$.
13. $1/x$.   **15.** $(4\, m^2 + 2\, m + 1)/(2\, m + 1)$.   **17.** $(1 + x)/2$.
19. $- x - y$.   **21.** 1.   **23.** a.   **25.** $x^2/(x - y)$.
27. $a(a + b + c)/c(a - b + c)$.   **29.** $(x - 3)/(x - 4)$.

Exercise 15, Page 28

1. $x = - 4$.   **3.** $x = 8$.   **5.** $x = 5$.   **7.** $x = 0.7$.   **9.** $x = \frac{1}{2}$.
11. $x = 4$.   **13.** $x = - 2$.   **15.** $x = 1$.   **17.** $x = 7$.   **19.** $x = 2$.
21. $x = 3$.   **23.** $x = - 5$.   **25.** $x = 2$.   **27.** $x = 4$.   **29.** $x = - \frac{1}{8}$.
31. $x = a$.   **33.** $x = - 3$.   **35.** $x = ab/(c - a - b)$.
37. $x = 3\, a + 5\, b$.   **39.** $x = p/q$.   **41.** $h = 4\, V/\pi d^2$.
43. $n = (l - a + d)/d$.   **45.** $p = (K - PV + Pv)/(v - V)$.
47. $r = eR/(E - e)$.   **49.** $n = Ir/(E - IR)$.

Exercise 16, Page 30

1. $2n + 2$.   **3.** $\frac{6}{5}x$.   **5.** $\frac{1}{2}(P - 8)$.   **7.** $25q + 10d$.
9. $y + x - 4$.   **11.** $x + 10$.   **13.** $2g$.   **15.** $mx/60h$.   **17.** $12x + 1$.
19. $a(x + 100y)/100x$.

Exercise 17, Page 33

1. 26, 28, and 30.   **3.** 300 bars.   **5.** 150 lb.   **7.** 10 ft. by 14 ft.
9. 36 minutes.   **11.** 8 years old.   **13.** 64.   **15.** 4.8%.
17. 320 horses.   **19.** 15 days.   **21.** $\frac{5}{7}$.   **23.** 11 : 48 A.M.   **25.** 144.
27. 70.   **29.** $(am + bn)/(a + b)$.   **33.** A, 36; B, 24.

Exercise 18, Page 38

1. $3; -1; -3; \frac{1}{2}; -2$.   **3.** $\frac{2}{3}; \frac{5}{4}; 0; \frac{3}{5}; -2$.   **5.** -1;
$(2 - 3a)/(a - 1); (1 - 4x)/2x$.   **7.** $-3; \frac{4}{5}; a/5$.   **9.** $18; -6\frac{1}{2}$;
$2x - 1$.   **11.** $2hx + h^2 - 3h$.   **13.** 0.   **17.** 0.
19. $y = (3x + 2)/(4 - x)$.

Exercise 20, Page 43

3. 4 and 7.   **5.** $(-2, 2)$.   **7.** 13.   **9.** (a) isosceles; (b) 5, $6\frac{1}{2}$, $6\frac{1}{2}$.
11. $49\frac{1}{2}$.

Exercise 22, Page 48

1. $(-2, -1)$.   **3.** $(-1, 2)$.   **5.** Inconsistent.   **7.** $(3, 1)$.
9. $(4, -6)$.   **11.** $(-1.8, -0.7)$.   **13.** $(-0.2, 1.2)$.   **15.** $(0.6, 0.5)$.

Exercise 23, Page 49

1. $x = 2, y = 4$.   **3.** $x = 1, y = -2$.   **5.** $x = \frac{3}{4}, y = -\frac{1}{2}$.
7. $x = 2, y = 1$.   **9.** $x = 3, y = -2$.   **11.** $x = \frac{1}{2}, y = \frac{3}{2}$.
13. $x = 4, y = -3$.   **15.** $x = -1, y = 3$.   **17.** $x = 2, y = 1$.
19. $x = \frac{1}{5}, y = \frac{1}{7}$.   **21.** $x = 5, y = 3$.   **23.** $x = 4, y = 5$.
25. $x = -2, y = -1$.   **27.** $x = 2, y = 3$.   **29.** $x = 1, y = -3$.
31. $x = c - 2d, y = 3c + d$.   **33.** $x = 5c/a, y = -c/b$.
35. $x = 2a - b, y = a - 2b$.

Exercise 24, Page 52

1. $x = 3, y = -1, z = -2$.   **3.** $x = 1, y = 2, z = 1$.
5. $x = 4, y = 2, z = 3$.   **7.** $x = 2, y = -1, z = -\frac{1}{3}$.
9. $x = 2, y = 3, z = 4$.   **11.** $x = 3, y = 2, z = -6$.
13. $x = 2, y = -3, z = 5$.   **15.** $x = a, y = a + 1, z = a + 2$.
17. $x = 3, y = -2, z = -3, w = 1$.

Exercise 26, Page 55

1. 13.   **3.** 14.   **5.** -163.   **7.** $a^2 + b^2 + c^2 + 1$.   **9.** $x = 2$.

Exercise 28, Page 58

1. 5 and 3.　**3.** 2 m.p.h.　**5.** 5 m.p.h.　**7.** A, 21; B, 19.
9. A, 30¢; B, 21¢.　**11.** 36.　**13.** 400 mi.　**15.** Man 29, sons 5 and 8.
17. Tea 50¢, coffee 40¢.　**19.** \$3000.　**21.** 13 ft. by 17 ft.　**23.** 60 mi.
25. 6 hrs.　**27.** 84 mi.　**29.** \$4 per yd.

Exercise 29, Page 64

1. x^7.　**3.** y^{16}.　**5.** 3^8.　**7.** $1/z^3$.　**9.** $1/x^2y$.　**11.** a^{25}.　**13.** $-b^{16}$.
15. $9\,a^4$.　**17.** $a^4b^6c^2$.　**19.** $8\,a^3b^6$.　**21.** a^4/x^8.　**23.** $\frac{1}{4}\,x^2$.
25. $a^5b^{15}/32\,x^{10}$.　**27.** 2^6.　**29.** x^4.　**31.** a^{n^2-n}.　**33.** $a^{2x}b^{x^2-x}$.
35. $2^m a^m/x^{2m}$.　**37.** x^2y^{2n-2}/z^4.　**39.** $16\,m^{10}n^8$.　**41.** $3\,p^4/4\,q$.
43. $\frac{1}{2}\,a^2x^5$.　**45.** 1.　**47.** a^m.　**49.** b^{n^2}.　**51.** x^{2a}.

Exercise 30, Page 65

1. ± 5.　**3.** ± 8.　**5.** $\pm a$.　**7.** $\pm x^2y$.　**9.** $\pm 4\,a^2$.　**11.** 2.
13. -4.　**15.** a.　**17.** $4\,xy^2$.　**19.** $-a^9$.　**21.** 12.　**23.** 3.　**25.** -6.
27. 2.　**29.** $4\,mn$.　**31.** a^2b^3.　**33.** 20.　**35.** $3\,a$.　**37.** 13.　**39.** $3\,a^2$.
41. $\frac{1}{6}$.

Exercise 31, Page 68

1. 5.　**3.** 2.　**5.** $\frac{1}{4}$.　**7.** -1.　**9.** $\frac{9}{4}$.　**11.** $\frac{1}{4}$.　**13.** $\frac{1}{4}$.　**15.** 81.
17. $-\frac{1}{4}$.　**19.** -1.　**21.** 4.　**23.** 4.　**25.** 2.　**27.** $\frac{1}{2}$.　**29.** 1.
31. $\frac{4}{3}$.　**33.** 1.　**35.** $\frac{3}{2}$.　**37.** $a^{\frac{2}{3}}$.　**39.** $b^{\frac{1}{2}}$.　**41.** $c^{\frac{1}{2}}$.　**43.** x^3.　**45.** a^4.
47. z^6.　**49.** x^2.　**51.** $35\,a^{\frac{4}{3}}x^{\frac{1}{6}}$.　**53.** $a^{\frac{5}{2}}b^4$.　**55.** $x^5y^{\frac{11}{2}}$.　**57.** $\frac{1}{4}\,x^{-\frac{2}{3}}$.
59. $4\,x$.　**61.** $(a^2+b^2)/ab$.　**63.** $(4\,b-a)/2\,ab$.　**65.** $2\,x/y$.
67. $1/(x+y)$.　**69.** $x/(x-1)$.　**71.** $a^{\frac{1}{6}}$.　**73.** z/y.　**75.** $(a-1)/a^3$.
77. x.　**79.** $x^{2a}y^{2a-2}$.　**81.** x^{n-1}.　**83.** a^k.　**85.** $x-y$.
87. $2\,a^{\frac{1}{2}}-a^{\frac{3}{2}}b^{\frac{1}{2}}+6\,a^{-1}b^{-\frac{1}{2}}-3$.　**89.** $a^2-3\,a+2$.　**91.** 27.
93. $2(x+1)^{-\frac{1}{3}}$.　**95.** $(x-1)/x^2$.

Exercise 32, Page 71

1. $\sqrt[4]{x^3}$.　**3.** $\sqrt{3\,a}$.　**5.** $\sqrt{x}+\sqrt{y}$.　**7.** $\sqrt[6]{a^3b^2}$.　**9.** $\sqrt[6]{4\,a}$.
11. $x^{\frac{3}{5}}$.　**13.** $2\,a^{\frac{1}{2}}$.　**15.** $a^{\frac{5}{6}}b^{\frac{1}{2}}$.　**17.** $2\,x^{\frac{3}{4}}$.　**19.** $a^{\frac{1}{6}}$.　**21.** $5\sqrt{3}$.
23. $3\sqrt[3]{2}$.　**25.** $-2\sqrt[3]{5}$.　**27.** $\frac{1}{2}\sqrt[4]{14}$.　**29.** $-\frac{1}{2}\sqrt[3]{6}$.　**31.** 0.7.
33. $-a^2\sqrt[3]{2\,a}$.　**35.** $3\,b^2\sqrt[3]{3\,b}$.　**37.** $\sqrt{6\,a}/2\,b$.　**39.** $a\sqrt[6]{8\,a^4b^2}/2\,b$.
41. $\sqrt{2}$.　**43.** $\sqrt[3]{4}$.　**45.** $\sqrt{2}$.　**47.** $\sqrt[4]{4\,x}$.　**49.** $\sqrt[4]{2\,a^2}$.
51. $\sqrt[6]{27}$, $\sqrt[6]{25}$.　**53.** $\sqrt[12]{x^9}$, $\sqrt[12]{9\,x^{10}}$.　**55.** $\sqrt[12]{729}$, $\sqrt[12]{256}$, $\sqrt[12]{125}$.

Exercise 33, Page 72

1. $9\sqrt{2}$.　**3.** $\sqrt{6}$.　**5.** $\frac{1}{6}\sqrt[3]{4}$.　**7.** $2\sqrt{7}+6\sqrt{5}$.　**9.** 0.
11. $-11\sqrt{2}-2\sqrt[3]{5}$.　**13.** $\sqrt{3}+2\sqrt{15}$.　**15.** $\frac{3}{2}\sqrt[3]{4}$.
17. $(a-b+c)\sqrt{b}$.　**19.** $(a-b)\sqrt{a-b}$.　**21.** $(x+y-2)\sqrt{xy}/xy$.
23. $\sqrt[3]{xy}/x$.

Exercise 34, Page 73

1. 360.   **3.** 120.   **5.** $7\sqrt{66}$.   **7.** $\frac{7}{3}\sqrt{2}$.   **9.** $\frac{1}{16}\sqrt[3]{36}$.   **11.** $2\sqrt{2}$.
13. $10\sqrt{2} - 10\sqrt{5} + 15\sqrt{6}$.   **15.** $\frac{1}{3}\sqrt{3} + \sqrt{2} - \frac{2}{3}$.   **17.** $a\sqrt{b} + b\sqrt{a}$.
19. $12 - 11\sqrt{21}$.   **21.** $\frac{7}{30}\sqrt{10} - \frac{1}{45}\sqrt{15}$.   **23.** $\sqrt[3]{4} - 2\sqrt[3]{2}$.
25. $7 + 3\sqrt[3]{20} + 3\sqrt[3]{50}$.   **27.** $a + 9b - 6\sqrt{ab}$.   **29.** $4x - 3y + 4\sqrt{xy}$.
31. $x\sqrt[3]{a} - a\sqrt[3]{x}$.   **33.** 2.   **35.** $2a - 2\sqrt{a^2 - x^2}$.   **37.** $x - y$.
39. 0.   **41.** 0.

Exercise 35, Page 74

1. $\frac{1}{4}\sqrt{15}$.   **3.** $\frac{5}{3}\sqrt[3]{3}$.   **5.** $3\sqrt{6}$.   **7.** $\frac{1}{5}\sqrt[4]{8}$.   **9.** $\sqrt{xy}/y$.
11. $\sqrt[6]{x^3 y^2}$.   **13.** $\sqrt{2} - 3\sqrt{5} + 4\sqrt{7}$.   **15.** $\frac{1}{2}\sqrt{10} + \frac{1}{3}\sqrt{15} + \frac{1}{2}\sqrt{5}$.
17. $\sqrt{a} + \sqrt{b} + 1$.   **19.** $\sqrt{5} - 2\sqrt{2}$.   **21.** $2 + \sqrt{6}$.   **23.** $6 - \sqrt{35}$.
25. $\sqrt{x} - 3\sqrt{2}$.   **27.** $2a - 1 - 2\sqrt{a^2 - a}$.   **29.** $\sqrt{x + y} - \sqrt{x - y}$.
31. $-2 - \sqrt{2} + 2\sqrt{3}$.   **33.** $2\sqrt{10}$.   **35.** $6 + 2\sqrt{2}$.   **37.** $\sqrt{2}$.
39. $\sqrt{10}$.

Exercise 36, Page 77

1. $5i$.   **3.** $2i\sqrt{2}$.   **5.** $\frac{1}{3}i$.   **7.** $0.2i$.   **9.** $2x^2 i\sqrt{5}$.
11. $\frac{1}{3}xi\sqrt{6x}$.   **13.** $-i$.   **15.** i.   **17.** 1.   **19.** 1.   **21.** $-i$.
23. $8 - 2i$.   **25.** $-1 - 5i$.   **27.** $-72i$.   **29.** $23 + 2i$.
31. $-\sqrt{3} - \frac{3}{2}i$.   **33.** $1 - 4i$.   **35.** $-7 - 11i$.   **37.** $-9 - 46i$.
39. 0.   **41.** $\frac{3}{2}i$.   **43.** $3 + 39i$.   **45.** $-5 - 6i$.   **47.** $x = -\frac{2}{5} - \frac{1}{5}i$.
49. $x = -\frac{9}{5} - \frac{3}{5}i$.

Exercise 37, Page 78

1. $x = 14$.   **3.** No root.   **5.** $x = 4$.   **7.** $x = 5$.   **9.** $x = 4$.
11. $x = \frac{5}{2}$.   **13.** No root.   **15.** $x = 50$.   **17.** $x = 9$.   **19.** $x = 20$.
21. $x = -\frac{1}{3}$.   **23.** $x = 10$.

Exercise 38, Page 81

1. $x = \pm\frac{7}{3}$.   **3.** $x = \pm 2$.   **5.** $x = \pm 3$.   **7.** $x = \pm a$.
9. $x = \pm\frac{2}{3}\sqrt{3}$.   **11.** $x = \pm\sqrt{6}$.   **13.** $r = \pm\sqrt{3V/\pi h}$.
15. $d = \pm\sqrt{mM/F}$.   **17.** $x = 2, -4$.   **19.** $x = 5, \frac{1}{2}$.
21. $x = \frac{1}{2}, -3$.   **23.** $x = \frac{1}{3}, \frac{5}{2}$.   **25.** $x = \frac{1}{5}, -5$.
27. $x = 0.1, -0.3$.   **29.** $x = 8, -4$.   **31.** $x = 2n, 6n$.
33. $x = a, b - a$.   **35.** $x = p, 1/p$.

Exercise 39, Page 83

1. 4.   **3.** $\frac{9}{4}$.   **5.** $\frac{1}{25}$.   **7.** $\frac{4}{49}m^2$.   **11.** $x = 2, -4$.
13. $x = 3, -\frac{1}{2}$.   **15.** $x = \frac{1}{2}(1 \pm \sqrt{5})$.   **17.** $x = \frac{3}{2}, -\frac{1}{4}$.
19. $x = \frac{2}{5}(2 \pm i)$.   **21.** $x = \frac{3}{2}a, \frac{1}{2}a$.   **23.** $x = \frac{1}{3}(1 \pm \sqrt{10})a$.

25. $x = -2, -\frac{1}{2}$. **27.** $x = \frac{1}{3}(1 \pm \sqrt{22})$. **29.** $x = \frac{1}{20}(-1 \pm \sqrt{6})$.
31. $x = \frac{1}{12}(7 \pm \sqrt{13})$. **33.** $x = 5.32, -1.32$. **35.** $x = 1.64, -0.24$.
37. $x = 2.37, 0.63$. **39.** $x = 4\,ab, 5\,ab$. **41.** $x = 1, \frac{1}{6}(a - 4)$.
43. $x = a \pm \sqrt{a^2 + a}$. **45.** $y = x, 3 - x; x = y, 3 - y$.
47. $y = \frac{1}{2} \pm \frac{1}{2}\sqrt{16\,x^2 - 8\,x - 7}$; $x = \frac{1}{4} \pm \frac{1}{4}\sqrt{4\,y^2 - 4\,y + 9}$.
49. $y = -x \pm 3\sqrt{x}; x = \frac{1}{2}(9 - 2\,y \pm 3\sqrt{9 - 4\,y})$.

Exercise 40, Page 86

1. $x = 4, -10$. **3.** $x = 2, -1$. **5.** $x = 3, -2$. **7.** $x = 4$,
$-2 \pm 2\,i\sqrt{3}$. **9.** $x = 1, -\frac{7}{5}$. **11.** $x = \pm 2\,c$. **13.** $x = 5, -1$.
15. $x = 20, -8$. **17.** $x = 2, -\frac{1}{3}$. **19.** $x = 5, \frac{1}{26}$.
21. $x = 3\,d, -d$. **23.** $x = 6$. **25.** $x = 3, 7$. **27.** $x = 1$.
29. $x = 2\,b/a, 3\,b/a$. **31.** 11, 12, 13 or $-11, -12, -13$.
33. 30 pigs. **35.** 36 days and 45 days. **37.** 50 bars. **39.** 49.
41. 30 min. **43.** 5 ft. and 12 ft. **45.** \$5000 at 4%. **47.** $\frac{3}{7}$.
49. 12 days.

Exercise 41, Page 88

1. $x = \pm \frac{1}{2}, \pm \sqrt{2}$. **3.** $x = \pm 1, \pm \frac{1}{3}$. **5.** $x = -1, \frac{1}{2}$,
$\frac{1}{2}(1 \pm i\sqrt{3}), \frac{1}{4}(-1 \pm i\sqrt{3})$. **7.** $x = \pm 8, \pm 3\sqrt{3}$. **9.** $x = 2 \pm \sqrt{2}$.
11. $x = 1, -2, \frac{1}{2}(-1 \pm i\sqrt{19})$. **13.** $x = 1, -6, 2 \pm \sqrt{10}$.
15. $x = 1 \pm \sqrt{3}, \frac{1}{2}(1 \pm \sqrt{5})$. **17.** $x = -1, -5, \pm 2$. **19.** $x = \pm 1$,
$\pm 2, \pm i, \pm 2\,i$. **21.** $x = 32\frac{1}{2}$. **23.** $x = 1, -4$. **25.** $x = \frac{1}{2}, \frac{1}{3}$.
27. $x = \pm 2, \pm i\sqrt{3}$. **29.** $x = \pm 2, \pm \frac{1}{5}\,i\sqrt{30}$.

Exercise 42, Page 90

1. (a) Real, rational, and unequal; (b) $S = 7, P = 10$.
3. (a) Real and unequal; (b) $S = \frac{4}{3}, P = -3$. **5.** (a) Imaginary;
(b) $S = \frac{1}{4}, P = \frac{5}{32}$. **7.** (a) Real and unequal; (b) $S = \frac{32}{7}, P = -\frac{5}{14}$.
9. (a) Real and unequal; (b) $S = \frac{10}{3}, P = -\frac{5}{4}$. **11.** (a) Real and
unequal; (b) $S = -\sqrt{2}, P = -\frac{3}{2}$. **13.** $x^2 + x - 20 = 0$.
15. $x^2 - 9 = 0$. **17.** $49\,x^2 + 28\,x + 4 = 0$. **19.** $50\,x^2 + 25\,x - 7 = 0$.
21. $50\,x^2 + 75\,x + 13 = 0$. **23.** $16\,x^2 - 5 = 0$. **25.** $x^2 - 8\,x + 28 = 0$.
27. $4\,x^2 - 24\,x + 37 = 0$. **29.** $9\,x^2 + 6\,x + 2 = 0$. **31.** $k = 4$.
33. $k = 2$. **35.** $k = -1 \pm 2\sqrt{30}$. **37.** $k = -1$.
39. $k = -2, -10$. **41.** $k = -3$. **43.** $k = \frac{3}{2}$. **45.** $k = -\frac{3}{4}$.
47. $k = \frac{5}{2}$. **49.** $k = 9, 0$. **51.** $k = \pm \sqrt{6}$. **53.** $k = 2\,a \pm 2$.

Exercise 43, Page 92

1. $x = 1.6, -2.6$. **3.** $x = 0.6, 2.4$. **5.** $x = 1.6, -0.2$.
7. (a) $(1, 3)$; (b) $x = 1$. **9.** (a) $(2, 9)$; (b) $x = 2$.
11. (a) $(\frac{2}{3}, -\frac{4}{3})$; (b) $x = \frac{2}{3}$. **13.** (a) $(-\frac{1}{10}, \frac{61}{20})$; (b) $x = -\frac{1}{10}$.

15. (a) $(\frac{9}{4}, -\frac{121}{8})$; (b) $x = \frac{9}{4}$.   **17.** Max. $7\frac{1}{4}$.   **19.** Min. $-2\frac{17}{32}$.
21. Max. $1\frac{33}{70}$.   **23.** Min. $14\frac{27}{28}$.   **25.** 20 and 20.   **27.** $\frac{1}{2}$.
29. $6601\frac{9}{16}$ feet

Exercise 44, Page 97

1. Circle.   **3.** Hyperbola.   **5.** Parabola.   **7.** Parabola.
9. Parabola.   **11.** Ellipse.

Exercise 45, Page 98

1. $(6, 8), (-8, -6)$.   **3.** $(3, 2), (-4, -\frac{3}{2})$.   **5.** $(0, 2)$.
7. $(1, \pm 2)$.   **9.** $(-3, 0)$.   **11.** $(5, 4)$.   **13.** $(1.7, 2.9)$.
15. $(-4.4, \pm 2.3)$.   **17.** $(2.3, -2.6), (-1.3, 4.6)$.

Exercise 46, Page 100

1. $(3, 2), (-2, -3)$.   **3.** $(5, 7)$.   **5.** $(5, 2), (-4, -\frac{5}{2})$.
7. $(1, 2), (0, \frac{9}{4})$.   **9.** $(4, 3), (-4, -3)$.   **11.** $(4, -3)$.   **13.** $(\frac{1}{2}, \frac{1}{2})$.
15. $(3, 1), (7, 3)$.   **17.** $(1 + c, -1 + c), (1 - c, -1 - c)$.

Exercise 47, Page 101

1. $(2, 3), (2, -3), (-2, 3), (-2, -3)$.   **3.** $(3, 4), (-3, -4)$,
$(4, 3), (-4, -3)$.   **5.** $(3, 1), (3, -1), (-3, 1), (-3, -1)$.
7. $(2, 1), (2, -1), (-2, 1), (-2, -1)$.   **9.** $(4, 5), (4, -5)$,
$(-4, 5), (-4, -5)$.   **11.** $(\sqrt{2}, \sqrt{3}), (\sqrt{2}, -\sqrt{3}), (-\sqrt{2}, \sqrt{3})$,
$(-\sqrt{2}, -\sqrt{3})$.   **13.** $(1.41, -1.41), (-1.41, 1.41), (1.15, -1.73)$,
$(-1.15, 1.73)$.   **15.** $(1.20, 1.84), (1.20, -1.84), (-2, 1.73\,i)$,
$(-2, -1.73\,i)$.   **17.** $(2\,a, 2\,a), (-2\,a, -2\,a), (4\,a, a), (-4\,a, -a)$.

Exercise 48, Page 103

1. $(4, 3), (-4, -3), (0, -5), (-5, 0)$.   **3.** $(2, 3), (-2, -3)$,
$(\frac{1}{5}\sqrt{35}, -\frac{2}{15}\sqrt{35}), (-\frac{1}{5}\sqrt{35}, \frac{2}{15}\sqrt{35})$.   **5.** $(3, 3), (-3, -3)$,
$(i\sqrt{3}, -i\sqrt{3}), (-i\sqrt{3}, i\sqrt{3})$.   **7.** $(1, 1), (0, 2), (-1, -1), (0, -2)$.
9. $(0, 0), (1, -1), (3, 1)$.   **11.** $(2, 1), (-2, -1), (2\,i\sqrt{2}, -2\,i\sqrt{2})$,
$(-2\,i\sqrt{2}, 2\,i\sqrt{2})$.   **13.** $(4, 5), (-4, -5), (3\sqrt{3}, \sqrt{3})$,
$(-3\sqrt{3}, -\sqrt{3})$.   **15.** $(2, 1), (-2, -1)$.   **17.** $(2, -1), (-2, 1)$.
19. $(2, 5), (-2, -5), (4\sqrt{2}, 3\sqrt{2}), (-4\sqrt{2}, -3\sqrt{2})$.   **21.** $(-2, -1)$,
$(\frac{3}{2}, \frac{5}{2}), (-6, 5)$.   **23.** $(1, a), (-1, -a)$.

Exercise 49, Page 105

1. $(1, 4), (-4, -1), (4, -1), (1, -4)$.   **3.** $(2, 1), (1, 2)$,
$(-2 + i\sqrt{5}, -2 - i\sqrt{5}), (-2 - i\sqrt{5}, -2 + i\sqrt{5})$.   **5.** $(5, 3)$,

$(-5, -3)$. **7.** $(\frac{5}{2}, 2), (-2, -\frac{5}{2})$. **9.** $(1, 1), (-\frac{1}{2} + \frac{1}{2} i\sqrt{3},$
$-\frac{1}{2} - \frac{1}{2} i\sqrt{3}), (-\frac{1}{2} - \frac{1}{2} i\sqrt{3}, -\frac{1}{2} + \frac{1}{2} i\sqrt{3})$. **11.** $(-2, -2),$
$(6, \frac{2}{3}),$ $(-5 + i\sqrt{5}, \frac{5}{3} + \frac{1}{3} i\sqrt{5}),$ $(-5 - i\sqrt{5}, \frac{5}{3} - \frac{1}{3} i\sqrt{5})$.
13. $(2, 1), (2, \omega), (2, \omega^2), (2\omega, 1), (2\omega, \omega), (2\omega, \omega^2), (2\omega^2, 1), (2\omega^2, \omega),$
$(2\omega^2, \omega^2)$ where $\omega = -\frac{1}{2} + \frac{1}{2} i\sqrt{3}$. **15.** $(27, 1)$. **17.** $(4, -3),$
$(-3, 4)$. **19.** $(1, 3), (-5, -3), (\sqrt{5}, -2+\sqrt{5}), (-\sqrt{5}, -2-\sqrt{5})$.
21. $(1, 2, 3), (1, -3, -2)$.

Exercise 50, Page 105

1. 13 ft. by 17 ft. **3.** 5 ft. and 12 ft. **5.** 5 A.M. **7.** 36 or 63.
9. P, 30 m.p.h.; Q, 24 m.p.h. **11.** 9 ft. and 12 ft. **13.** $\frac{3}{2}$.
15. 20 students. **17.** 48 problems. **19.** A 6, B 8.

Exercise 51, Page 109

1. $5 : 8$. **3.** $1 : 5$. **5.** $b : a$. **7.** $3 : 5$. **9.** $1 : 8$. **11.** $38\frac{8}{9}$.
13. bc/a. **15.** $\frac{10}{9}$. **17.** b^2/a. **19.** $7\frac{1}{2}$. **21.** $\sqrt{ab}$. **23.** $x = 10$.
25. $x = 3$. **27.** $x = 2, y = -3$. **29.** $11 : 14$. **31.** 34, 85, and 119.
33. 132 and 231. **35.** $1 : 6 : 4 : 2$. **37.** $21 : 20$.

Exercise 52, Page 112

1. $P = kx^2/\sqrt{y}$. **3.** $R = 7 pq$. **7.** $p = 90$. **9.** $z = 15$.
11. $a = 8$. **13.** $m = 1.458$. **15.** $z = 63$. **17.** $R = 15$.
19. 432 lb. **21.** $79\frac{1}{81}$ lb. **23.** 540 lb. **25.** 108 H.P. **27.** 30¢.
29. 25 years and 16 years.

Exercise 53, Page 115

1. A. P. **3.** G. P. **5.** Neither. **7.** A. P. **9.** G. P. **11.** $x = 13$.
13. $x = 4$. **15.** $x = 5$. **17.** $x = -\frac{1}{3}$. **19.** $x = 3, -1$.
21. $x = 18$. **23.** $x = 3$. **25.** $x = 1$. **27.** $x = 3, 0$. **29.** $x = \pm\sqrt{2}$.

Exercise 54, Page 118

1. $l = 52, S = 476$. **3.** $l = -67, S = -171$. **5.** $l = 11\frac{1}{3},$
$S = 183\frac{1}{3}$. **7.** $l = 31\frac{2}{3}, S = 288\frac{1}{6}$. **9.** $l = 7.33, S = 34.28$.
11. 13, 17, 21, 25, 29. **13.** $3\frac{1}{3}, 4, 4\frac{2}{3}, 5\frac{1}{3}$. **15.** 6.5, 6.8, 7.1, 7.4,
7.7, 8. **17.** (a) 14, (b) $5\frac{2}{3}$. **19.** 31. **21.** 16. **23.** $147\frac{1}{2}$. **25.** 70.
27. $n = 17, S = 510$. **29.** $a = 38, S = 308$. **31.** $n = 13, d = \frac{3}{2}$.
33. $a = -5, l = 11$. **35.** $n = 11, a = 19$. **37.** $a = 3, n = 40$.
39. $3, 7\frac{1}{2}, 12, \cdots$. **41.** $4q - 3p$. **43.** $(1 - 2\sqrt{x})/(1 - x)$.
45. $S = \frac{1}{2} n(n + 1)$. **47.** $n = (l - a + d)/d$.
$S = (l - a + d)(l + a)/2d$.

Exercise 55, Page 122

1. $l = 96,\ S = 189.$ **3.** $l = -81,\ S = -60\frac{2}{3}.$ **5.** $l = \frac{64}{27}$,
$S = 17\frac{4}{27}.$ **7.** $l = 3125,\ S = 3906.24.$ **9.** $l = 8\sqrt{2},\ S = 14 + 15\sqrt{2}.$
11. $14,\ 28.$ **13.** $\pm\frac{9}{2},\ 9,\ \pm 18.$ **15.** $\pm\sqrt{2},\ 2,\ \pm 2\sqrt{2},\ 4,\ \pm 4\sqrt{2}.$
17. (a) $50,$ (b) $5.$ **19.** $\frac{5}{8},\ \frac{5}{4},\ \frac{5}{2}.$ **21.** $40\frac{1}{2}.$ **23.** Eleventh.
25. $r = \frac{3}{2},\ S = 166\frac{1}{4}.$ **27.** $n = 5,\ S = 17\frac{7}{12}.$ **29.** $r = 3,\ l = 63$ or
$r = -4,\ l = 112.$ **31.** $-21\frac{3}{8}.$ **33.** $1999.872.$ **35.** $63 + 31\sqrt{2}.$
37. (a) $a = S(1 - r)/(1 - r^n),$ (b) $a = lr^{1-n}.$
39. (a) $l = (a - S + Sr)/r,$ (b) $l = Sr^{n-1}(1 - r)/(1 - r^n).$ **41.** $7.$
43. $11.492.$ **45.** $q^4/p^3.$ **47.** $(x + \sqrt{x})/x.$

Exercise 56, Page 124

1. $27.$ **3.** $6.$ **5.** $2\frac{1}{7}.$ **7.** $\frac{5}{4}(5 + \sqrt{5}).$ **9.** $\frac{1}{2}(2 - \sqrt{2}).$ **11.** $\frac{5}{9}.$
13. $\frac{17}{111}.$ **15.** $\frac{357}{1100}.$ **17.** $\frac{1177}{360}.$ **19.** $\frac{1547}{3300}.$ **21.** $6\frac{2}{5}.$

Exercise 57, Page 125

1. $\frac{1}{22}.$ **3.** $\frac{3}{13}.$ **5.** $2,\ \frac{2}{5}.$ **7.** $\frac{15}{17},\ \frac{15}{14},\ \frac{15}{11},\ \frac{15}{8}.$ **9.** $x = 8.$
11. $pq/(2p - q),\ pq/(3p - 2q).$

Exercise 58, Page 126

1. $\$315.$ **3.** $\$41.99.$ **5.** $100.$ **7.** 9 months.   **9.** $\$38.25.$
11. $3,\ 4\frac{1}{2},\ 6,\ \cdots.$ **13.** $345.$ **15.** $1239.$ **17.** $V = \frac{25}{2}(n^2 - 9n + 420).$
19. 9 hrs., 36 mi.   **21.** $\$1932.61.$ **23.** $6,\ 15,\ 24$ and $6,\ 12,\ 24;$ or
$6,\ 3,\ 0$ and $6,\ 0,\ 0.$ **25.** $\$104.$ **27.** $4\frac{1}{2}$ and $6;$ or $\frac{1}{2}$ and $-2.$
29. 8 hours.   **31.** $(1 - \sqrt{2}),\ 1,\ (1 + \sqrt{2});$ or $1,\ 1,\ 1.$ **33.** $1633.$
37. $r = \frac{1}{2}\sqrt{2\sqrt{5} + 2}$ or $r = \frac{1}{2}\sqrt{2\sqrt{5} - 2}.$ **39.** $(b^2 - ac)/(a + c - 2b).$

Exercise 60, Page 135

1. $30.$ **3.** $\frac{3}{2}.$ **5.** $9900.$ **7.** $10403.$ **11.** $64x^6 - 192ax^5 +$
$240a^2x^4 - 160a^3x^3 + 60a^4x^2 - 12a^5x + a^6.$ **13.** $a^8x^8 - 8a^7bx^7 +$
$28a^6b^2x^6 - 56a^5b^3x^5 + 70a^4b^4x^4 - 56a^3b^5x^3 + 28a^2b^6x^2 - 8ab^7x + b^8.$
15. $x^{12} + 12x^{10} + 60x^8 + 160x^6 + 240x^4 + 192x^2 + 64.$ **17.** $y^8 -$
$8y^5 + 24y^2 - 32y^{-1} + 16y^{-4}.$ **19.** $x^{10} - 20x^9y + 180x^8y^2 - 960x^7y^3 + \cdots.$
21. $1 - 9x + 39x^2 - \frac{325}{3}x^3 + \cdots.$ **23.** $256x^8 + 1024x^6 +$
$1792x^4 + 1792x^2 + \cdots.$ **25.** $512x^{\frac{9}{2}} - 2304x^4y + 4608x^{\frac{7}{2}}y^2 -$
$5376x^3y^3 + \cdots.$ **27.** $x^{-10} - \frac{20}{3}x^{-\frac{17}{2}} + 20x^{-7} - \frac{320}{9}x^{-\frac{11}{2}} + \cdots.$
29. $1.030301.$ **31.** $7 + 5\sqrt{2}.$ **33.** $9\sqrt{3} - 11\sqrt{2}.$ **35.** $1.3728.$

Exercise 61, Page 138

1. $13440\,x^{12}y^{12}.$ **3.** $42240\,a^3x^4.$ **5.** $924\,x^{13}.$ **7.** $-\frac{99}{16}x^5.$
9. $-960\,y^{\frac{7}{2}}.$ **11.** $-1,464,320\,x^{11}.$ **13.** $1 + x + x^2 + x^3 + \cdots.$

15. $1 + 3x + 6x^2 + 10x^3 + \cdots$. **17.** $1 + \frac{1}{2}x + \frac{3}{8}x^2 + \frac{5}{16}x^3 + \cdots$.
19. $a + \frac{1}{3}a^{-2}x^3 - \frac{1}{9}a^{-5}x^6 + \frac{5}{81}a^{-8}x^9 + \cdots$. **21.** $16 - \frac{8}{3}z + \frac{1}{18}z^2 + \frac{1}{648}z^3 + \cdots$. **23.** $\frac{1}{2} + \frac{1}{16}x^2 + \frac{3}{256}x^4 + \frac{5}{2048}x^6 + \cdots$. **25.** 9.899.
27. 2.048. **29.** 0.6300. **31.** 0.6756.

Exercise 62, Page 143

1. $x < -4$. **3.** $x < 2$. **5.** $x < \frac{1}{2}$. **7.** $x > -3\frac{1}{2}$.
9. $x < -1$, or $x > \frac{1}{2}$. **11.** $x < -1$, or $x > \frac{5}{4}$. **13.** $x < 2$, or $x > 2\frac{1}{2}$. **15.** $x < -1$, or $x > 2$. **17.** All values of x.
19. $-2 < x < 1$, or $x > 5$. **21.** $-2 < x < 0$, or $x > 2$.
23. $-1 < x < 0$, or $0 < x < \frac{5}{3}$. **25.** $x < \frac{3}{2}$. **27.** $x < 1$, or $x > 2$.
29. $x < 0$, or $x > 1$. **31.** $x < -4$, or $1 < x < 2$.
33. $-2 < x < -1$, or $-\frac{1}{3} < x < \frac{1}{2}$. **35.** $0 < x < 2$, or $x > 2$.
37. $x \leqq -2$, or $x \geqq 2$. **39.** $-2 \leqq x \leqq 3$. **41.** $k \leqq -4$, or $k \geqq -1$. **43.** (a) $k = 1$, (b) $k < 1$, (c) $k > 1$. **45.** (a) $k = \pm 25$, (b) $-25 < x < 25$, (c) $x < -25$, or $x > 25$.

Exercise 64, Page 147

1. $2i$. **3.** $-5ci$. **5.** $ai - a$. **7.** $x = 2, y = -3$. **9.** $x = 7, y = 0$. **11.** $x = 2, y = -1$. **13.** $-4 + 7i$. **15.** $1 + 5i$.
17. $16 - i$. **19.** $\frac{1}{2}i$. **21.** $2 + 4i$. **23.** $-1 - 2i$. **25.** $-60i$.
27. $13i$. **29.** $7 - 6i\sqrt{2}$. **31.** $-3 + 2i$. **33.** $6 + i\sqrt{3}$.
35. $-\frac{5}{2} - 4i$. **37.** $-9 + 46i$. **39.** $-4 + 7i$. **41.** $-1 - \frac{3}{2}i$.
43. $32 + 24i$. **45.** $\frac{1}{2} - \frac{3}{2}i$. **47.** $2i$. **49.** $-\frac{7}{242} + \frac{3}{121}i\sqrt{2}$.
51. $-24i$. **53.** $\frac{8}{5}$. **55.** 0. **57.** $x = \frac{1}{2} - \frac{3}{2}i$. **59.** $x = 1 + i$.

Exercise 65, Page 151

1. 13. **3.** 5. **5.** 8. **13.** $5 + 3i$. **15.** $-2 + 7i$.
17. $-1 + 6i$. **19.** $-2 + 5i$. **21.** $3\sqrt{2}\operatorname{cis}45°$. **23.** $5\operatorname{cis}180°$.
25. $5\sqrt{2}\operatorname{cis}315°$. **27.** $5\operatorname{cis}306.9°$. **29.** $\sqrt{6}\operatorname{cis}35.3°$.
31. $6\operatorname{cis}270°$. **33.** $2\sqrt{2} + 2i\sqrt{2}$. **35.** $-\frac{5}{2}\sqrt{3} + \frac{5}{2}i$. **37.** $-2i$.
39. $3.214 + 0.383i$. **41.** $2\operatorname{cis}135°$. **43.** $\operatorname{cis}90°$.

Exercise 66, Page 156

1. $3\sqrt{2} + 3i\sqrt{2}$. **3.** $-9i$. **5.** $1 + i\sqrt{3}$. **7.** $-2\sqrt{2} + 2i\sqrt{2}$.
9. $4\operatorname{cis}180°$. **11.** $\frac{3}{2}\operatorname{cis}150°$. **13.** $12\sqrt{2}\operatorname{cis}45°$. **15.** $16\sqrt{3} + 16i$.
17. $\frac{1}{8}\operatorname{cis}174°$. **19.** $32i$. **21.** $64\sqrt{3} + 64i$. **23.** $\frac{1}{4} - \frac{1}{4}i$.
25. $-\frac{5}{2} + \frac{5}{2}i\sqrt{3}, \frac{5}{2} - \frac{5}{2}i\sqrt{3}$. **27.** $2\operatorname{cis}6°, 2\operatorname{cis}78°, -\sqrt{3} + i$, $2\operatorname{cis}222°, 2\operatorname{cis}294°$. **29.** $1 + i, \sqrt{2}\operatorname{cis}165°, \sqrt{2}\operatorname{cis}285°$.
31. $\frac{1}{2} + \frac{1}{2}i\sqrt{3}, \quad -\frac{1}{2}\sqrt{3} + \frac{1}{2}i, \quad -\frac{1}{2} - \frac{1}{2}i\sqrt{3}, \quad \frac{1}{2}\sqrt{3} - \frac{1}{2}i$.
33. $\sqrt{2}\operatorname{cis}63°, \quad -1 + i, \quad \sqrt{2}\operatorname{cis}207°, \quad \sqrt{2}\operatorname{cis}279°, \quad \sqrt{2}\operatorname{cis}351°$.

35. $x = -2, 1 \pm i\sqrt{3}$.   **37.** $x = \pm 3, \frac{3}{2} \pm \frac{3}{2} i\sqrt{3}, -\frac{3}{2} \pm \frac{3}{2} i\sqrt{3}$.
39. $x = -i, \pm \frac{1}{2}\sqrt{3} + \frac{1}{2} i$.   **41.** $\pm \frac{1}{2}\sqrt{2}(3 - i)$.   **43.** $\pm \frac{1}{2}\sqrt{2}(3 + 5 i)$.
45. $\pm \frac{1}{2}\sqrt{2}(1 + i)$.   **47.** $x = \frac{1}{2}(1 - i), \frac{1}{2}(1 - 3 i)$.   **49.** $x = i \pm 1$.

Exercise 67, Page 161

1. 19.   **3.** 3.   **5.** $m = 0$.   **7.** $m = -1$.   **9.** Yes.   **11.** Yes.
13. $m = -25$.   **15.** $m = -3$.   **17.** $x^2 - 2$; -1.
19. $x^4 - 2 x^3 + 6 x^2 - 12 x + 17$; -19.   **21.** $2 x^2 + 0.2 x - 1.7$;
-0.1.   **23.** $3 x^2 - 3 x - 2$; $\frac{4}{3}$.   **25.** $x^2 - 2 ax - 6 a^2$; $3 a^3$.
27. -5; -65.   **29.** -1; 305.   **31.** $-4\frac{1}{8}$; -5.672.
33. $-3 a^3$; $21 a^3$.   **35.** $m = \frac{1}{2}$.

Exercise 68, Page 164

9. $2.5, -0.7, -1.8$.   **11.** $2.7, 0.9, -0.5, -3.1$.

Exercise 69, Page 168

1. $x^3 - 2 x^2 - 5 x + 6 = 0$.   **3.** $2 x^4 + x^3 - 12 x^2 - 3 x + 18 = 0$.
5. $x^3 - 2 x^2 - 11 x + 52 = 0$.   **7.** $4 x^4 + 12 x^3 + x^2 - 12 x + 4 = 0$.
9. $x^5 - 2 x^3 - 8 x = 0$.   **11.** $x^5 - 12 x^4 + 57 x^3 - 134 x^2 + 156 x - 72 = 0$.
13. $x = 3, -4, -\frac{1}{2}$.   **15.** $x = 4, 1, -\frac{3}{2}$.   **17.** $x = \pm 2\sqrt{2}, 1 \pm i$.
19. $x^3 + x^2 - 3 x + 9 = 0$.   **21.** $8 x^3 - 28 x^2 + 46 x - 17 = 0$.
23. $x^4 - 5 x^2 + 6 = 0$.   **25.** $\frac{1}{2}(1 \pm i)$.   **27.** $-1, 3 + 2 i$.
29. $-i\sqrt{2}, \frac{1}{2}(3 \pm \sqrt{5})$.   **33.** $A = 10, B = -7$.

Exercise 70, Page 170

1. $x = -1, \pm 2$.   **3.** $x = 3, \frac{1}{2}(-1 \pm i\sqrt{3})$.   **5.** $x = 2, -1, -\frac{3}{2}$.
7. $x = \frac{2}{3}, \pm i\sqrt{5}$.   **9.** $x = 3, 2, -1, -4$.   **11.** $x = 2, -1, \pm 2 i$.
13. $x = -1, \frac{1}{2}, \pm \frac{1}{2} i\sqrt{2}$.   **15.** $x = \pm 2, \frac{1}{2}(-1 \pm \sqrt{3})$.   **17.** $x = 3$,
$2, 2, -1, -4$.   **19.** $x = 8, \frac{1}{2}(5 \pm i\sqrt{7})$.   **21.** $x = 1, \frac{1}{5}(-2 \pm i\sqrt{6})$.
23. $x = 2, -3$.   **25.** $(x - 3)(x + 1)^2$.   **27.** $(4 x - 1)(x^2 - 3 x - 1)$.
29. $(x + 3)(x - 2)(x^2 - x - 1)$.   **31.** $(1, 1), (2, 8), (-3, -27)$.
33. $(2, 1), (-1, 4), (\frac{1}{2} + \frac{1}{2} i\sqrt{7}, -\frac{3}{2} - \frac{1}{2} i\sqrt{7}), (\frac{1}{2} - \frac{1}{2} i\sqrt{7}, -\frac{3}{2} + \frac{1}{2} i\sqrt{7})$.   **35.** $\frac{5}{2}, \frac{3}{2}$.   **37.** 3, 4, and 5.   **39.** 5 ft. and 12 ft.

Exercise 71, Page 172

1. 1.70.   **3.** 0.54.   **5.** -0.40.   **7.** $1.46, -1.66$.
9. $-0.73, -1.93$.   **11.** $0.40, -2.20$.   **13.** 1.50.   **15.** 2.99.
17. 2.15.   **19.** 1.325.   **21.** 1.27 ft.   **23.** 1.10 in. or 2.63 in.

Exercise 72, Page 176

1. 3 pos.; 1 pos., 2 imag.   **3.** 1 pos., 2 neg.; 1 pos., 2 imag.
5. 1 pos., 2 imag.   **7.** 2 pos., 2 neg.; 2 pos., 2 imag.; 2 neg., 2 imag.;

4 imag. **9.** 3 pos., 1 neg.; 1 pos., 1 neg., 2 imag. **11.** 2 pos.,
3 neg.; 2 pos., 1 neg., 2 imag.; 3 neg., 2 imag.; 1 neg., 4 imag.
13. 1 pos., 2 neg., 4 imag.; 1 pos., 6 imag. **15.** 2. **17.** 4. **19.** 10.

Exercise 73, Page 177

1. $x^4 - (r_1 + r_2 + r_3 + r_4)x^3 + (r_1r_2 + r_1r_3 + r_1r_4 + r_2r_3 + r_2r_4 + r_3r_4)x^2$
$- (r_1r_2r_3 + r_1r_2r_4 + r_1r_3r_4 + r_2r_3r_4)x + r_1r_2r_3r_4.$ **3.** $x^3 - x^2 - 14x + 24 = 0.$
5. $x^3 - x^2 - 3x - 1 = 0.$ **7.** $x^4 - 2x^3 - 7x^2 + 20x - 12 = 0.$
9. $S_1 = -\frac{1}{2}, S_2 = -1, S_3 = \frac{5}{2}.$ **11.** $S_1 = 0, S_2 = -3, S_3 = 0,$
$S_4 = -4, S_5 = 7.$ **13.** $x = \frac{1}{2}, \pm i.$ **15.** $x = 1, 2, -\frac{3}{2}.$
17. $x = 0, 3, -\frac{1}{2}.$ **19.** $x = \frac{1}{2}, \frac{5}{2}, -2.$ **21.** $x = 2, \frac{1}{2}, -\frac{5}{2}.$
23. $x = 1, 1, 1, -3.$ **25.** $-2.$ **27.** $\frac{1}{2}.$

Exercise 74, Page 181

1. $y^3 - 9y^2 + 18y + 135 = 0.$ **3.** $8y^3 - 10y + 1 = 0.$
5. $y^4 - 12y^3 - 46 = 0.$ **7.** $y^3 - 3y^2 + 4y - 4 = 0.$
9. $y^3 - 3y + 4 = 0.$ **11.** $2y^3 - 4y^2 + y + 5 = 0.$
13. $y^5 + 2y^3 - 3y + 8 = 0.$ **15.** $y^3 + y^2 + 4y - 3 = 0.$
17. $3y^3 - 27y^2 + 76y - 63 = 0.$ **19.** $16y^4 - 64y^3 + 72y^2 + 48y - 67 = 0.$
21. $2y^3 - 0.2y^2 - 6.16y - 2.776 = 0.$ **23.** $y^5 + 5y^4 + 8y^3 +$
$2y^2 - 5y + 4 = 0.$ **25.** $y^3 - y - 5 = 0.$ **27.** $27y^3 + 45y - 70 = 0.$

Exercise 75, Page 184

1. 1.255. **3.** 0.811. **5.** $-1.676.$ **7.** 1.13, $-1.80.$
9. $-0.20, -1.11.$ **11.** 0.52, $-1.29.$ **13.** 1.913. **15.** 1.682.
17. 3.742, 5.742, 7.742.

Exercise 76, Page 188

3. $x = -3, \frac{1}{2}(3 \pm i\sqrt{3}).$ **5.** $x = 1 + \sqrt[3]{3} + \sqrt[3]{9},$
$\frac{1}{2}(2 - \sqrt[3]{3} - \sqrt[3]{9}) \pm \frac{1}{2}i\sqrt{3}(\sqrt[3]{3} - \sqrt[3]{9}).$ **7.** $x = 2\cos 20°, 2\cos 140°,$
$2\cos 260°.$ **9.** $x = 1 + 2\sqrt{2}\cos 45°, 1 + 2\sqrt{2}\cos 165°,$
$1 + 2\sqrt{2}\cos 285°.$ **11.** $x = \frac{3}{2}, -\frac{3}{2}, -\frac{3}{2}.$ **13.** $x = 2, -1 \pm 3i.$
15. $x = \sqrt[3]{2} - \sqrt[3]{4}, \frac{1}{2}(\sqrt[3]{4} - \sqrt[3]{2}) \pm \frac{1}{2}i\sqrt{3}(\sqrt[3]{4} + \sqrt[3]{2}).$

Exercise 77, Page 189

3. $x = \frac{1}{2}(3 \pm \sqrt{17}), \frac{1}{2}(-1 \pm i\sqrt{3}).$ **5.** $x = \pm\sqrt{2}, -2 \pm i.$
7. $x = 2 \pm \sqrt{2}, 2 \pm \sqrt{2}.$ **9.** $(x^2 - x - 1)(2x^2 - x + 6).$

Exercise 78, Page 191

1. $\log_3 9 = 2.$ **3.** $\log_2 16 = 4.$ **5.** $\log_4 \frac{1}{16} = -2.$ **7.** $\log_{32} 8 = \frac{3}{5}.$
9. $4^2 = 16.$ **11.** $10^2 = 100.$ **13.** $2^0 = 1.$ **15.** $5^1 = 5.$

17. $8^{-\frac{4}{3}} = \frac{1}{16}$.   **19.** 2, 1, 0, -1, -2.   **21.** 1, 10, 100000, $\frac{1}{10}$, $\frac{1}{1000}$, $\frac{1}{1000000}$.   **23.** $\frac{1}{3}$.   **25.** 6.   **27.** $\frac{1}{2}$.   **29.** -1.   **31.** $N = \frac{1}{3}$. **33.** $N = 625$.   **35.** $N = 1$.   **37.** $b = 3$.   **39.** $\frac{3}{2}$.   **41.** 1.

Exercise 79, Page 193

1. $\log a + \log b + \log c$.   **3.** $2 \log a - 3 \log b + \frac{1}{2} \log c$.
5. $3 \log a - \frac{2}{3} \log b - \frac{1}{3} \log c$.   **7.** $\frac{3}{4} \log a - \frac{1}{4} \log b + \frac{1}{8} \log c$.
9. $\frac{1}{2} \log a - \frac{1}{2} \log b - \frac{2}{3} \log$ c.   **11.** $\log a^2 b^{\frac{2}{3}}$.   **13.** $\log 55$.   **15.** $\log 4$.
17. $\log \frac{1}{2} \pi r^2$.   **19.** (a) 0.602, (b) 1.505, (c) -0.903, (d) 0.699.
21. 0.778.   **23.** 1.301.   **25.** 0.352.   **27.** 0.222.   **29.** -1.87.
31. 0.199.   **33.** 4.057.   **35.** -0.224.

Exercise 80, Page 197

1. 2; .8704.   **3.** 5; .7825.   **5.** 0; .9961.   **7.** -1; .6444.
9. -1; .9542.   **11.** -3; .6702.   **13.** -2; .4564.   **15.** -1; .1644.
17. 2.   **19.** -2.   **21.** -1.   **23.** 1.   **25.** 0.   **27.** 9.   **29.** -5.
31. -4.   **33.** $8.7356 - 10$.   **35.** $6.7356 - 10$.   **37.** 5.7356.
39. $7.7356 - 10$.   **41.** 0.04735.   **43.** 473,500.   **45.** 0.4735.
47. 0.004735.   **49.** 473.5.   **51.** 47,350.

Exercise 81, Page 199

1. 2.4594.   **3.** $9.0253 - 10$.   **5.** $7.2304 - 10$.   **7.** $8.5752 - 10$.
9. 5.4771.   **11.** 1.6075.   **13.** 1.92.   **15.** 11.   **17.** 500.   **19.** 39,000.
21. 129,000.   **23.** 8350.

Exercise 82, Page 200

1. 4.   **3.** 4.   **5.** 4.   **7.** 5.   **9.** 2.74×10^7.   **11.** 4.74×10^4.
13. 0.1995 and 0.2005.   **15.** 1.41565 and 1.41575.   **17.** 0.01234.
19. 23,460.   **21.** (a) 29.59, (b) 81.4.   **23.** (a) 2.95, (b) 0.0384.

Exercise 83, Page 202

1. 1.4208.   **3.** $9.9792 - 10$.   **5.** 2.6054.   **7.** 4.9066.   **9.** 1.1559.
11. 0.8754.   **13.** 0.3120.   **15.** 2.8632.   **17.** $7.4778 - 10$.
19. $9.5388 - 10$.   **21.** 414.4.   **23.** 22.43.   **25.** 0.07542.
27. 0.0004641.   **29.** 3199.   **31.** 0.6337.   **33.** 0.2266.   **35.** 31.48.
37. 1.328.   **39.** 1385.

Exercise 84, Page 204

1. 805.0.   **3.** 2.100.   **5.** 29.74.   **7.** 757.3.   **9.** 42.94.   **11.** 25.07.
13. 1.061.   **15.** -0.001517.   **17.** 3.295.   **19.** 0.5692.

Exercise 85, Page 205

1. 5,636,000.   **3.** 0.5781.   **5.** 2.229.   **7.** 2.615.   **9.** 157.8
11. 14.38.   **13.** 26.96.   **15.** 0.5514.   **17.** 4.839.   **19.** 1.737.

Exercise 86, Page 207

1. 4.5561. **3.** 1.2786. **5.** 1.653. **7.** 16.28. **9.** 3.176. **11.** 2.404.
13. (a) 7598, (b) 9.282. **15.** 2.150. **17.** (a) 1.906, (b) 5.369.
19. 0.75%.

Exercise 87, Page 208

1. $x = 5$. **3.** $x = 1.5$. **5.** -0.5. **7.** $x = 9$. **9.** $x = 0.09638$.
11. $x = 2.879$. **13.** $x = 1.029$. **15.** $x = 20.16$. **17.** $x = -11.15$.
19. $x = 3.796$. **21.** $y = 35.7$. **23.** $x = 63.1$.
25. $n = (\log l - \log a + \log r)/\log r$. **27.** $n = (\log A - \log P)/\log (1+r)$.

Exercise 88, Page 210

1. 1.431. **3.** 3.096. **5.** 0.3465. **7.** -0.8451. **9.** -4.6052.
11. 0.5581. **13.** $N = 37.15$. **15.** $N = 0.3437$. **17.** $N = 1.025$.

Exercise 90, Page 213

1. $5. **3.** $0.29. **5.** $480.77; $19.23. **7.** $247.86; $4.64.
9. $1216.15. **11.** (a) 6.38%, (b) 6.09%. **13.** 13.6%. **15.** $1045.

Exercise 91, Page 216

1. (a) $196.85, (b) $197.08, (c) $197.20. **3.** $794.05. **5.** $773.14.
7. (a) $384.66; $65.34, (b) $384.07; $65.93, (c) $383.77; $66.23.
9. $835.64; $164.36. **11.** $5000 now and $5000 in ten years.
13. (a) 8%, (b) 8.16%, (c) 8.24%. **15.** 4.94%. **17.** 6.76%.
19. 11.72 years.

Exercise 92, Page 220

1. $736.01; $1318.08. **3.** $6271.01; $11359.06. **5.** $1295.
7. $65.32. **9.** (a) 23.115, (b) 237.991. **11.** 5.88%.

Exercise 93, Page 223

1. $1123.15. **3.** (a) $1804.56, (b) $1125.51. **5.** $3138.66.
7. $24.44. **9.** $108.18. **11.** $954.25. **13.** $4668.23. **15.** $670.52.
17. $2921.45.

Exercise 94, Page 227

1. 24; *bac, bca, bad, bda, bcd, bdc.* **3.** 6720. **5.** 60. **7.** 70.
9. 360. **11.** 358,800. **13.** 48. **15.** 2880. **17.** 10,080. **19.** 48.

Exercise 95, Page 230

1. (a) 840, (b) 1,663,200, (c) 120. **3.** $n = 8$. **9.** 126. **11.** 720.
15. 720. **17.** 60. **19.** 36. **21.** 144. **23.** (a) 2520, (b) 1800,
(c) 60. **25.** 36. **27.** (a) 300, (b) 144, (c) 180. **29.** 3360; 180.

Exercise 96, Page 233

1. (a) 56, (b) 5005, (c) 12,650. **5.** 126. **7.** 635,013,559,600.
9. 31. **11.** 43,092,000. **13.** 792; 330; 462. **15.** 91. **17.** 511.
19. 163. **21.** (a) 350, (b) 546, (c) 596. **23.** (a) 200, (b) 381.

Exercise 97, Page 237

1. $\frac{4}{7}$. **3.** $\frac{1}{6}$. **5.** 5 to 3. **7.** $\frac{1}{4}$. **9.** $\frac{1}{6}$. **11.** 2 to 1. **13.** $\frac{1}{7}$.
15. \$7. **17.** 0.919. **19.** 0.011. **21.** 73. **23.** 6 to 1. **25.** \$3.50.
27. (a) $\frac{1}{10}$, (b) $\frac{1}{3}$. **29.** (a) $\frac{5}{11}$, (b) $\frac{2}{33}$.

Exercise 98, Page 241

1. $\frac{2}{3}$. **3.** (a) $\frac{1}{2}$, (b) $\frac{13}{30}$, (c) $\frac{1}{15}$. **5.** (a) $\frac{1}{2}$, (b) $\frac{5}{12}$. **7.** (a) $\frac{9}{35}$, (b) $\frac{8}{35}$.
9. (a) $\frac{11}{850}$, (b) $\frac{22}{425}$, (c) $\frac{13}{68}$. **11.** $\frac{65}{276}$. **13.** (a) $\frac{3}{4}$, (b) \$2. **15.** $\frac{14}{25}$.
17. (a) $\frac{12}{35}$, (b) $\frac{17}{35}$, (c) $\frac{18}{35}$. **19.** $\frac{11}{16}$. **21.** A $\frac{4}{7}$, B $\frac{3}{7}$. **23.** $\frac{6}{7}$.

Exercise 99, Page 244

1. (a) $\frac{3125}{7776}$, (b) $\frac{31031}{46656}$. **3.** $\frac{5}{16}$. **5.** (a) $\frac{7}{64}$, (b) $\frac{35}{128}$, (c) $\frac{163}{256}$.
7. $\frac{192}{243}$.

Exercise 100, Page 249

1. 4. **3.** 6. **5.** 7. **7.** 6. **9.** 7. **11.** 24; 120; 720.
13. (a) neg., (b) pos., (c) pos. **15.** (c) $a_2b_1c_4d_3$, $-a_2b_3c_4d_1$. **17.** II.
19. V and VII. **21.** VI and IV. **23.** VII, V, and IV.

Exercise 101, Page 255

1. -74. **3.** -787. **5.** 1865. **7.** -729. **9.** 731. **11.** 3542.
13. $x = 3, -2$. **15.** $x + y - 1 = 0$. **17.** $x - y - 1 = 0$.
19. $5x^2 + 5y^2 - 11x - 9y - 12 = 0$. **21.** $x^2 + y^2 - 3x - y - 6 = 0$.
23. $3x^2 + y^2 - 64 = 0$. **25.** $(x - y)(y - z)(z - x)(xy + yz + zx)$.
27. $(x - y)(x - z)(x - w)(y - z)(y - w)(z - w)$.

Exercise 102, Page 260

1. $x = \frac{25}{13}, y = -\frac{5}{13}, z = \frac{22}{13}$. **3.** $x = -2, y = 3, z = 1$.
5. $x = 3, y = -2, z = 2, w = -1$. **7.** $x = 1, y = 0, z = -3, w = 1$.
9. $x = -2, y = -1, z = 0, u = 1, v = 2$. **11.** $x = 9 - 7c$,
$y = c, z = 5c - 5$. **13.** $x = 2, y = -1$. **15.** $x = 3, y = -2, z = 4$.
17. $k = 1, -5$. **19.** $y = 2x^2 - 9x + 9$.

Exercise 103, Page 264

1. $\dfrac{1}{x} + \dfrac{2}{x + 2}$. **3.** $\dfrac{2}{2x - 1} - \dfrac{1}{x + 5}$. **5.** $\dfrac{2}{1 - x} - \dfrac{3}{1 + x}$.

7. $1 + \dfrac{1}{x} - \dfrac{3}{x + 2}$. **9.** $\dfrac{1}{x + 1} - \dfrac{2}{(x + 2)^2}$. **11.** $\dfrac{1}{x} - \dfrac{2}{x^2} + \dfrac{3}{2x - 1}$.

13. $\dfrac{1}{x+1} - \dfrac{2}{(x+1)^2} + \dfrac{3}{(x+1)^3}.$ **15.** $\dfrac{1}{x+1} - \dfrac{1}{x} + \dfrac{1}{(x-1)^2} + \dfrac{1}{x-1}.$

17. $\dfrac{3}{3x-a} - \dfrac{1}{x} + \dfrac{2a}{x^2}.$ **19.** $\dfrac{7}{x-2} - \dfrac{5}{(x-2)^2} + \dfrac{2}{x+3}.$

Exercise 104, Page 266

1. $\dfrac{1}{x+1} - \dfrac{x-2}{x^2+4}.$ **3.** $\dfrac{x+2}{x^2+x+1} - \dfrac{1}{x}.$ **5.** $2 - \dfrac{1}{x+1} - \dfrac{1}{x^2-x+1}.$

7. $\dfrac{2}{x^2+2} - \dfrac{4}{(x^2+2)^2}.$ **9.** $\dfrac{2}{x+2} + \dfrac{7}{(x+2)^2} - \dfrac{2x-1}{x^2-2x+4}.$

11. $\dfrac{x+1}{x^2+1} - \dfrac{x+1}{x^2+2}.$ **13.** $\dfrac{2x-1}{(x^2-x+2)^2} + \dfrac{x-1}{x^2-x+2} - \dfrac{1}{x}.$

15. $\dfrac{1}{x+1} + \dfrac{1}{x-1} - \dfrac{1}{x^2-x+1} + \dfrac{1}{x^2+x+1}.$ **17.** $\dfrac{x}{(x^2+1)^2} - \dfrac{x}{(x^2+1)^3}.$

19. $\dfrac{1}{a^2(x+a)} - \dfrac{x-a}{a^2(x^2+a^2)} - \dfrac{x+a}{(x^2+a^2)^2}.$

Exercise 105, Page 270

1. $1 + \dfrac{1}{\sqrt{3}} + \dfrac{1}{\sqrt{5}} + \cdots + \dfrac{1}{\sqrt{2n-1}} + \dfrac{1}{\sqrt{2n+1}} + \cdots.$

3. $1 + \dfrac{2}{3} + \dfrac{2}{3} + \cdots + \dfrac{2^n}{n(n+1)} + \dfrac{2^{n+1}}{(n+1)(n+2)} + \cdots.$

5. $1 - \dfrac{3}{8} + \dfrac{5}{27} - \cdots + (-1)^{n-1}\dfrac{2n-1}{n^3} + (-1)^n\dfrac{2n+1}{(n+1)^3} + \cdots.$

7. $\dfrac{1}{(2n)^2}.$ **9.** $\dfrac{1}{n^2}.$ **11.** $(-1)^{n-1}\dfrac{1}{n^2}.$ **13.** $\dfrac{2n+1}{n(n+1)}.$ **15.** $\dfrac{2}{3}.$ **17.** 0.

19. $\frac{1}{3}.$ **21.** (a) $\dfrac{1}{2n}$, (b) 0. **23.** (a) $\dfrac{2n-1}{n^2}$, (b) 0. **25.** (a) $\dfrac{n+1}{4n-1}$,

(b) $\frac{1}{4}.$ **27.** (a) $\dfrac{2n+1}{n(n+1)}$, (b) 0 **29.** (a) $\dfrac{(2n-1)(2n+1)}{2n(2n+2)}$, (b) 1.

Exercise 106, Page 277

7. Convergent. **9.** Convergent. **11.** Divergent. **13.** Convergent.
15. Convergent. **17.** Convergent. **19.** Convergent.

Exercise 107, Page 281

1. Abs. conv. **3.** Cond. conv. **5.** Abs. conv. **7.** Abs. conv.
9. Divergent. **11.** Abs. conv. **13.** Divergent. **15.** Abs. conv.
17. Divergent. **19.** Cond. conv.

Exercise 108, Page 283

1. $-1 \leqq x \leqq 1$. **3.** $-4 < x < 4$. **5.** $-3 < x \leqq 3$.
7. $-2 < x < 2$. **9.** $1 + \frac{1}{2} x^2 - \frac{1}{8} x^4 + \frac{1}{16} x^6 - \frac{5}{128} x^8 + \cdots$.
11. $-x - \frac{1}{2} x^2 - \frac{1}{3} x^3 - \frac{1}{4} x^4 - \cdots$. **13.** $x^2 - \frac{1}{2} x^4 + \frac{1}{3} x^6 - \frac{1}{4} x^8 + \cdots$.
15. 0.985. **17.** 1.221. **19.** 0.097. **21.** 0.309. **23.** 0.878.

Exercise 109, Page 288

1. 1.8. **3.** 10.6. **5.** $-\frac{33}{16}$. **7.** -7.2. **9.** $1^3 + 2^3 + 3^3 + 4^3$.
11. $(k - x_1) + (k - x_2) + (k - x_3) + (k - x_4)$. **13.** $2 \cdot 3^2 + 2 \cdot 4^2 +$
$2 \cdot 5^2 + 2 \cdot 6^2 + 2 \cdot 7^2$. **15.** $3 + 5 + 7 + 9 + 11$. **17.** $\sum_{i=1}^{m} a_i x_i$.
19. $\sum_{i=1}^{n} (x_i - 2)^2$. **25.** $\bar{x} = 2.6, \sigma = 0.417$. **27.** $\bar{x} = 500.33, \sigma = 6.90$.
29. $\bar{x} = -9.298, \sigma = 0.058$. **31.** Rain $\bar{x} = 43.46, \sigma = 5.92$;
snow $\bar{x} = 26.09, \sigma = 12.45$.

Exercise 110, Page 294

1. $y = -\frac{1}{3} x + \frac{10}{3}$. **3.** $y = -2 x^2 + 5 x + 5$.
5. $y = x^3 - x^2 - x + 1$. **7.** $91 y = 76 x - 232$.
9. $74 y = -211 x + 513$. **11.** $708 y = 151 x^2 - 625 x - 222$.
13. $1358 y = -689 x^2 - 1861 x + 10,066$. **15.** $165 y = 370 t + 1932$.
17. $165 y = 622 t + 4428$. **19.** $y = -2.13 t + 34.82$;
$y = -0.42 t + 19.54$; $y = 2.56 t + 45.64$, where $t = 0$ and $t = 1$
represent the years 1900 and 1910 respectively.

Exercise 111, Page 297

1. $S_y = 0.787, r = 0.924$. **3.** $S_y = 0.440, r = 0.995$. **5.** 0.812.
7. 0.491.

Index